Mathematics Curriculum

Table of Contents[1]

Descriptive Statistics

[1]Each lesson is ONE day, and ONE day is considered a 45-minute period.

EUREKA
MATH

Algebra I • Module 2

Descriptive Statistics

OVERVIEW

In this module, students reconnect with and deepen their understanding of statistics and probability concepts first introduced in Grades 6, 7, and 8. There is variability in data, and this variability often makes learning from data challenging. Students develop a set of tools for understanding and interpreting variability in data and begin to make more informed decisions from data. Students work with data distributions of various shapes, centers, and spreads. Measures of center and measures of spread are developed as ways of describing distributions. The choice of appropriate measures of center and spread is tied to distribution shape. Symmetric data distributions are summarized by the mean and mean absolute deviation, or standard deviation. The median and the interquartile range summarize data distributions that are skewed. Students calculate and interpret measures of center and spread and compare data distributions using numerical measures and visual representations.

Students build on their experience with bivariate quantitative data from Grade 8; they expand their understanding of linear relationships by connecting the data distribution to a model and informally assessing the selected model using residuals and residual plots. Students explore positive and negative linear relationships and use the correlation coefficient to describe the strength and direction of linear relationships. Students also analyze bivariate categorical data using two-way frequency tables and relative frequency tables. The possible association between two categorical variables is explored by using data summarized in a table to analyze differences in conditional relative frequencies.

This module sets the stage for more extensive work with sampling and inference in later grades.

Focus Standards

Summarize, represent, and interpret data on a single count or measurement variable.

S-ID.A.1 Represent data with plots on the real number line (dot plots, histograms, and box plots).★

S-ID.A.2 Use statistics appropriate to the shape of the data distribution to compare center (median, mean) and spread (interquartile range, standard deviation) of two or more different data sets.★

S-ID.A.3 Interpret differences in shape, center, and spread in the context of the data sets, accounting for possible effects of extreme data points (outliers).★

Summarize, represent, and interpret data on two categorical and quantitative variables.

S-ID.B.5 Summarize categorical data for two categories in two-way frequency tables. Interpret relative frequencies in the context of the data (including joint, marginal, and conditional relative frequencies). Recognize possible associations and trends in the data.★

S-ID.B.6 Represent data on two quantitative variables on a scatter plot, and describe how the variables are related.★

a. Fit a function to the data; use functions fitted to data to solve problems in the context of the data. Use given functions or choose a function suggested by the context. Emphasize linear, quadratic, and exponential models.

b. Informally assess the fit of a function by plotting and analyzing residuals.

c. Fit a linear function for a scatter plot that suggests a linear association.

Interpret linear models.

S-ID.C.7 Interpret the slope (rate of change) and the intercept (constant term) of a linear model in the context of the data.★

S-ID.C.8 Compute (using technology) and interpret the correlation coefficient of a linear fit.★

S-ID.C.9 Distinguish between correlation and causation.★

Foundational Standards

Develop understanding of statistical variability.

6.SP.A.1 Recognize a statistical question as one that anticipates variability in the data related to the question and accounts for it in the answers. *For example, "How old am I?" is not a statistical question, but "How old are the students in my school?" is a statistical question because one anticipates variability in students' ages.*

6.SP.A.2 Understand that a set of data collected to answer a statistical question has a distribution which can be described by its center, spread, and overall shape.

6.SP.A.3 Recognize that a measure of center for a numerical data set summarizes all of its values with a single number, while a measure of variation describes how its values vary with a single number.

Summarize and describe distributions.

6.SP.B.4 Display numerical data in plots on a number line, including dot plots, histograms, and box plots.

6.SP.B.5 Summarize numerical data sets in relation to their context, such as by:

a. Reporting the number of observations.

b. Describing the nature of the attribute under investigation, including how it was measured and its units of measurement.

c. Giving quantitative measures of center (median and/or mean) and variability (interquartile range and/or mean absolute deviation), as well as describing any overall pattern and any striking deviations from the overall pattern with reference to the context in which the data were gathered.

d. Relating the choice of measures of center and variability to the shape of the data distribution and the context in which the data were gathered.

Investigate patterns of association in bivariate data.

8.SP.A.1 Construct and interpret scatter plots for bivariate measurement data to investigate patterns of association between two quantities. Describe patterns such as clustering, outliers, positive or negative association, linear association, and nonlinear association.

8.SP.A.2 Know that straight lines are widely used to model relationships between two quantitative variables. For scatter plots that suggest a linear association, informally fit a straight line, and informally assess the model fit by judging the closeness of the data points to the line.

8.SP.A.3 Use the equation of a linear model to solve problems in the context of bivariate measurement data, interpreting the slope and intercept. *For example, in a linear model for a biology experiment, interpret a slope of* 1.5 cm/hr *as meaning that an additional hour of sunlight each day is associated with an additional* 1.5 cm *in mature plant height.*

8.SP.A.4 Understand that patterns of association can also be seen in bivariate categorical data by displaying frequencies and relative frequencies in a two-way table. Construct and interpret a two-way table summarizing data on two categorical variables collected from the same subjects. Use relative frequencies calculated for rows or columns to describe possible association between the two variables. *For example, collect data from students in your class on whether or not they have a curfew on school nights and whether or not they have assigned chores at home. Is there evidence that those who have a curfew also tend to have chores?*

Focus Standards for Mathematical Practice

MP.1 **Make sense of problems and persevere in solving them.** Students choose an appropriate method of analysis based on problem context. They consider how the data were collected and how data can be summarized to answer statistical questions. Students select a graphical display appropriate to the problem context. They select numerical summaries appropriate to the shape of the data distribution. Students use multiple representations and numerical summaries and then determine the most appropriate representation and summary for a given data distribution.

MP.2 **Reason abstractly and quantitatively.** Students pose statistical questions and reason about how to collect and interpret data in order to answer these questions. Students form summaries of data using graphs, two-way tables, and other representations that are appropriate for a given context and the statistical question they are trying to answer. Students reason about whether two variables are associated by considering conditional relative frequencies.

MP.3 **Construct viable arguments and critique the reasoning of others.** Students examine the shape, center, and variability of a data distribution and use characteristics of the data distribution to communicate the answer to a statistical question in the form of a poster presentation. Students also have an opportunity to critique poster presentations made by other students.

MP.4 **Model with mathematics.** Students construct and interpret two-way tables to summarize bivariate categorical data. Students graph bivariate numerical data using a scatterplot and propose a linear, exponential, quadratic, or other model to describe the relationship between two numerical variables. Students use residuals and residual plots to assess if a linear model is an appropriate way to summarize the relationship between two numerical variables.

MP.5 **Use appropriate tools strategically.** Students visualize data distributions and relationships between numerical variables using graphing software. They select and analyze models that are fit, using appropriate technology to determine whether or not the model is appropriate. Students use visual representations of data distributions from technology to answer statistical questions.

MP.6 **Attend to precision.** Students interpret and communicate conclusions in context based on graphical and numerical data summaries. Students use statistical terminology appropriately.

Terminology

New or Recently Introduced Terms

- **Association** (A *statistical association* is any relationship between measures of two types of quantities so that one is statistically dependent on the other.)
- **Conditional Relative Frequency** (A *conditional relative frequency* compares a frequency count to the marginal total that represents the condition of interest.)
- **Correlation Coefficient** (The *correlation coefficient*, often denoted by r, is a number between -1 and $+1$, inclusively, that measures the strength and direction of a linear relationship between the two types of quantities. If $r = 1$ or $r = -1$, then the graph of data points of the bivariate data set lie on a line of positive or negative slope.)
- **Interquartile Range** (The *interquartile range* (or IQR) is the distance between the first quartile and the second quartile: $IQR = Q3 - Q1$. The IQR describes variability by identifying the length of the interval that contains the middle 50% of the data values.)

- **Outlier** (An *outlier* of a finite numerical data set is a value that is greater than $Q3$ by a distance of $1.5 \cdot IQR$, or a value that is less than $Q1$ by a distance of $1.5 \cdot IQR$. Outliers are usually identified by an "*" or a "•" in a box plot.)
- **Residual** (The *residual of the data point* (x_i, y_i) is the (actual y_i-value) $-$ (predicted y-value) for the given x_i.)
- **Residual Plot** (Given a bivariate data set and linear equation used to model the data set, a *residual plot* is the graph of all ordered pairs determined as follows: For each data point (x_i, y_i) in the data set, the first entry of the ordered pair is the x-value of the data point, and the second entry is the residual of the data point.)
- **Sample Standard Deviation** (The *sample variance* for a numerical sample data set of n-values is the sum of the squared distances the values are from the mean divided by $(n-1)$. The *sample standard deviation* is the principle (positive) square root of the sample variance.)
- **Skewed Data Distribution** (A data distribution is said to be *skewed* if the distribution is not symmetric with respect to its mean. Left-skewed or skewed to the left is indicated by the data spreading out longer (like a tail) on the left side. Right-skewed or skewed to the right is indicated by the data spreading out longer (like a tail) on the right side.)

Familiar Terms and Symbols[2]

- Box Plot
- Data Distribution
- Mean
- Mean Absolute Deviation
- Median
- Quartile
- Variability

Suggested Tools and Representations

- Graphing Calculator
- Spreadsheet Software
- Dot Plot
- Box Plot
- Histogram
- Residual Plot

[2]These are terms and symbols students have seen previously.

Assessment Summary

Assessment Type	Administered	Format	Standards Addressed
Mid-Module Assessment Task	After Topic B	Constructed response with rubric	S-ID.A.1, S-ID.A.2, S-ID.A.3
End-of-Module Assessment Task	After Topic D	Constructed response with rubric	S-ID.A.2, S-ID.A.3, S-ID.B.5, S-ID.B.6, S-ID.C.7, S-ID.C.8, S-ID.C.9

Topic A

Shapes and Centers of Distributions

S-ID.A.1, S-ID.A.2, S-ID.A.3

Focus Standards:	S-ID.A.1	Represent data with plots on the real number line (dot plots, histograms, and box plots).★
	S-ID.A.2	Use statistics appropriate to the shape of the data distribution to compare center (median, mean) and spread (interquartile range, standard deviation) of two or more different data sets.★
	S-ID.A.3	Interpret differences in shape, center, and spread in the context of the data sets, accounting for possible effects of extreme data points (outliers).★
Instructional Days:	3	
Lesson 1:	Distributions and Their Shapes (P)[1]	
Lesson 2:	Describing the Center of a Distribution (E)	
Lesson 3:	Estimating Centers and Interpreting the Mean as a Balance Point (P)	

In Topic A, students observe and describe data distributions. They reconnect with their earlier study of distributions in Grade 6 by calculating measures of center and describing overall patterns or shapes. Students deepen their understanding of data distributions, recognizing that the value of the mean and median are different for skewed distributions and similar for symmetrical distributions. Students select a measure of center based on the distribution shape to appropriately describe a typical value for the data distribution. Topic A moves from the general descriptions used in Grade 6 to more specific descriptions of the shape and the center of a data distribution.

[1]Lesson Structure Key: **P**-Problem Set Lesson, **M**-Modeling Cycle Lesson, **E**-Exploration Lesson, **S**-Socratic Lesson

Lesson 1: Distributions and Their Shapes

Student Outcomes

- Students use informal language to describe the shape, center, and variability of a distribution based on a dot plot, histogram, or box plot.
- Students recognize that a first step in interpreting data is making sense of the context.
- Students make meaningful conjectures to connect data distributions to their contexts and the questions that could be answered by studying the distributions.

Lesson Notes

Students began their study of data in Grade 6 with dot plots, histograms, and box plots. In Grade 6, they learned how to construct a graph and how to summarize a distribution by its center and variability. This lesson looks back at the graphs students previously studied as an introduction to this module. Students are also asked to interpret what a graph communicates. They are reminded that a graph is not only a representation of data but also a summary of a data story. Each of the graphs presented in the exercises are encountered in the lessons that follow in this module. This lesson asks students to start thinking about what the data indicate, how they might have been collected, and what they tell us.

Classwork

Statistics is all about data. Without data to talk about or to analyze or to question, statistics would not exist. There is a story to be uncovered behind all data—a story that has characters, plots, and problems. The questions or problems addressed by the data and their story can be disappointing, exciting, or just plain ordinary. This module is about stories that begin with data.

Example (5 minutes): Graphs

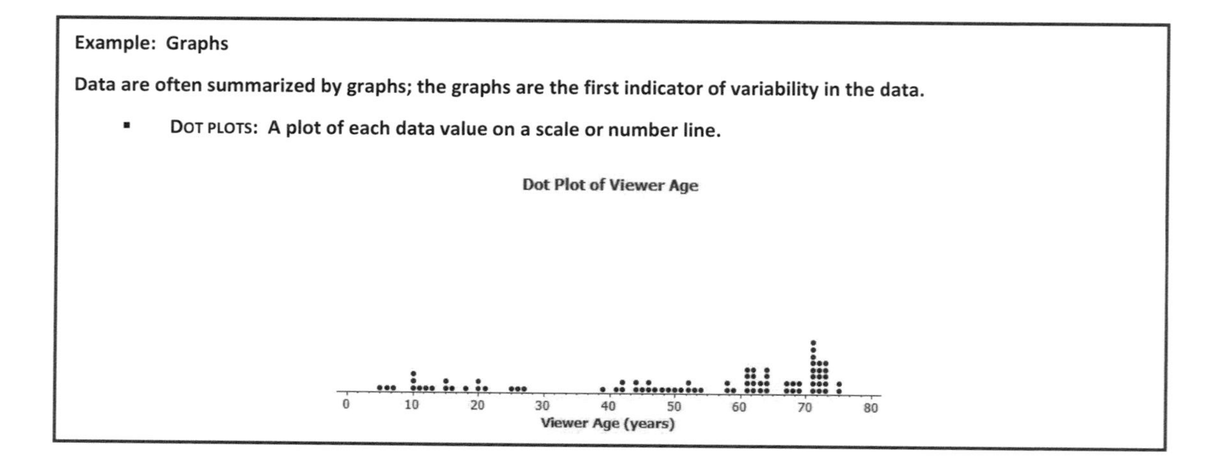

Example: Graphs

Data are often summarized by graphs; the graphs are the first indicator of variability in the data.

- **DOT PLOTS: A plot of each data value on a scale or number line.**

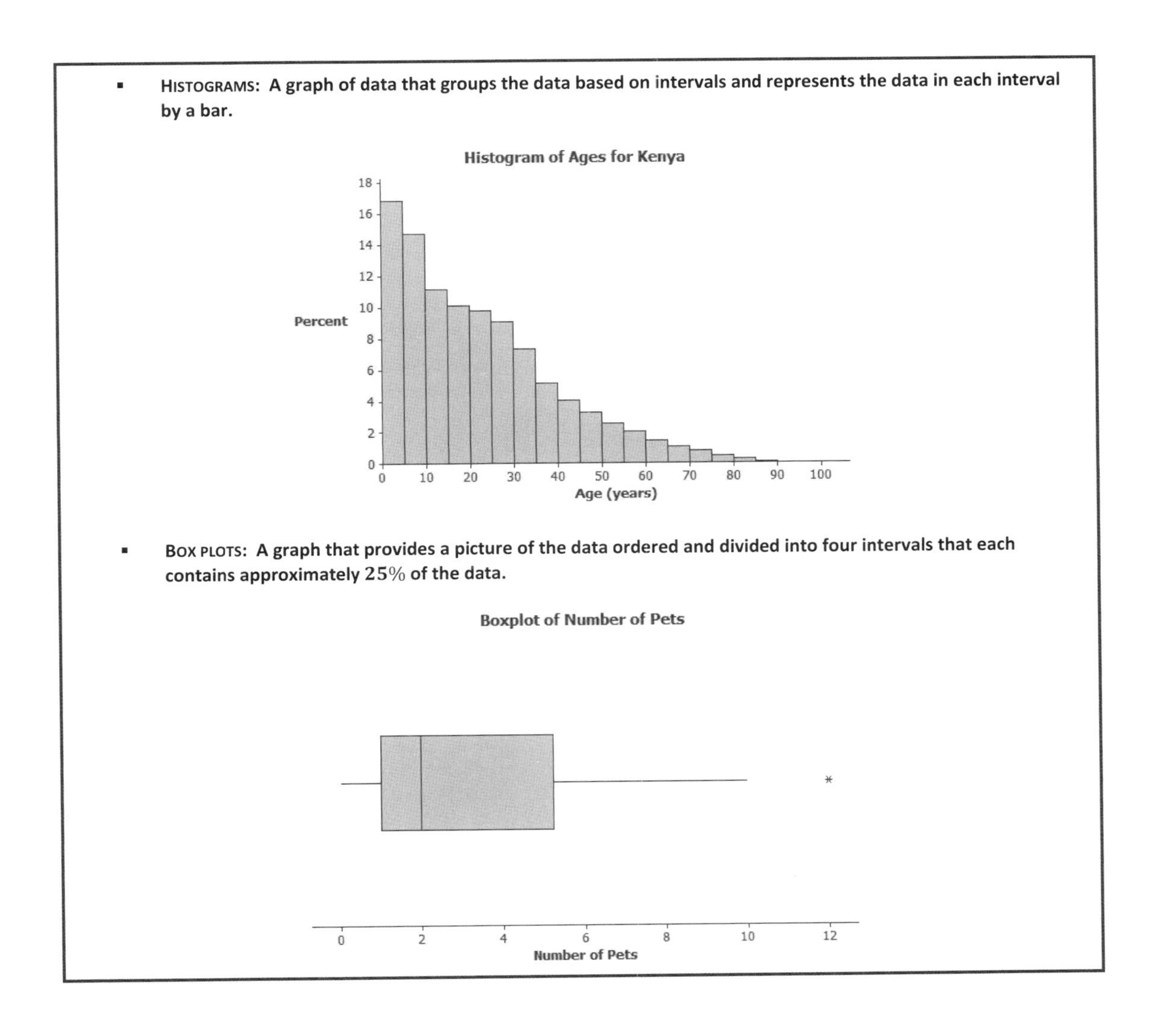

Review the different types of graphs that students have previously studied (dot plots, box plots, and histograms). Convey the following:

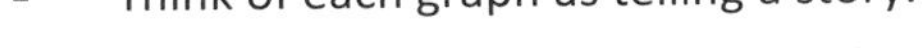

- Think of each graph as telling a story.
- **MP.2** Graphs of distributions are often the starting point in understanding the variability in the data.
- The graphs in the following exercises are analyzed in more detail in the lessons that follow.

Exercises (25 minutes)

Spend a few minutes with students reading the opening paragraph. Discuss with them the graphs presented in the example. Ask them if they remember these graphs from their previous work with data and what they recall about these graphs. Allow time for students to read the exercises. Then, provide time for students to discuss the questions individually or in small groups for each set of graphs. Conduct a brief discussion with students after they have developed answers for the questions. The graphs and the questions are summarized in the teacher notes along with possible responses and discussion items that students might address.

In most cases, the questions do not have exact answers. For this lesson, encourage students to make summaries based on what information the graphs convey about the data presented. More formal analysis of the data is developed in the next set of lessons of this module.

Exercises

Answer the questions that accompany each graph to begin your understanding of the story behind the data.

Transportation officials collect data on flight delays (the number of minutes past the scheduled departure time that a flight takes off).

Consider the dot plot of the delay times for sixty BigAir flights during December 2012.

Dot Plot of December Delay Times

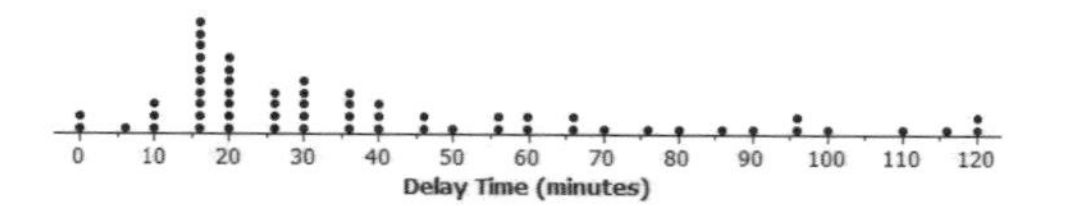

1. **What do you think this graph is telling us about the flight delays for these sixty flights?**

   Most flights are delayed for 15 minutes; some are delayed for a longer time.

2. **Can you think of a reason why the data presented by this graph provide important information? Who might be interested in this data distribution?**

   If flights are late, travelers would not select this airline.

   BigAir and travelers using this airline would be interested in this information.

3. **Based on your previous work with dot plots, would you describe this dot plot as representing a symmetric or a skewed data distribution? (Recall that a skewed data distribution is not mound shaped.) Explain your answer.**

   Skewed; it has a tail to the right. (Students are introduced to this in Grade 6.)

A random sample of eighty viewers of a television show was selected. The dot plot below shows the distribution of the ages (in years) of these eighty viewers.

Dot Plot of Viewer Age

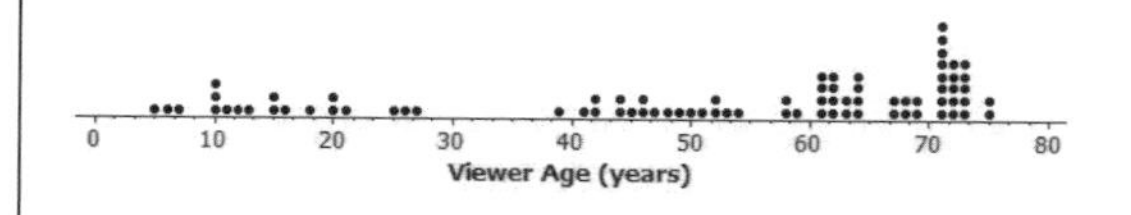

4. **What do you think this graph is telling us about the ages of the eighty viewers in this sample?**

   The typical age of viewers is between 60 and 70 years old; the show appeals to a wide range of ages.

5. **Can you think of a reason why the data presented by this graph provide important information? Who might be interested in this data distribution?**

   These data are important in understanding the audience of the show. If the show is paid for by commercials, then the distribution is important for sponsors.

6. **Based on your previous work with dot plots, would you describe this dot plot as representing a symmetric or a skewed data distribution? Explain your answer.**

   Skewed; it has a tail to the left.

The following histogram represents the age distribution of the population of Kenya in 2010.

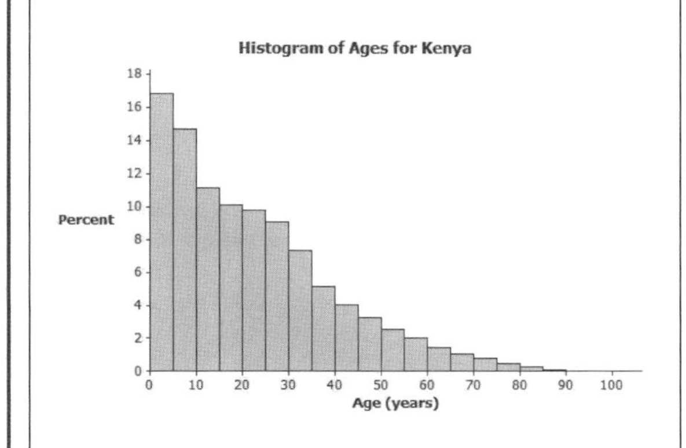

7. **What do you think this graph is telling us about the population of Kenya?**

   A large percentage of the people in Kenya are ages 10 *or younger.*

8. **Why might we want to study the data represented by this graph?**

   It tells us about Kenya and its challenges based on its population and demographics. It is important to understand the data because it may lead to finding the reason(s) as to why these data are occurring—which could lead to solutions.

9. **Based on your previous work with histograms, would you describe this histogram as representing a symmetrical or a skewed distribution? Explain your answer.**

   Skewed; it has a tail to the right.

The following histogram represents the age distribution of the population of the United States in 2010.

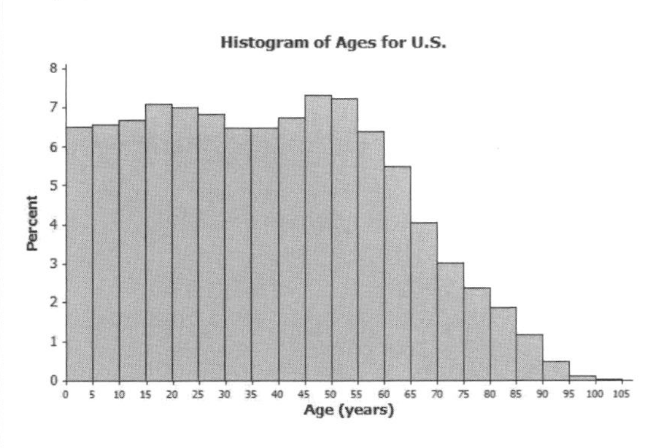

10. **What do you think this graph is telling us about the population of the United States?**

    The percentage of the population is about the same in each interval until the age range of 60 *to* 65 *years old. Then, the percentages decline.*

11. **Why might we want to study the data represented by this graph?**

    Population data are used to determine health-care challenges (for 65 *years and older) or education challenges (for* 0 *to* 20 *years old). Businesses (such as insurance companies) use this type of data.*

Thirty students from River City High School were asked how many pets they owned. The following box plot was prepared from their answers.

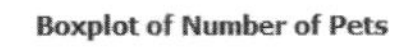

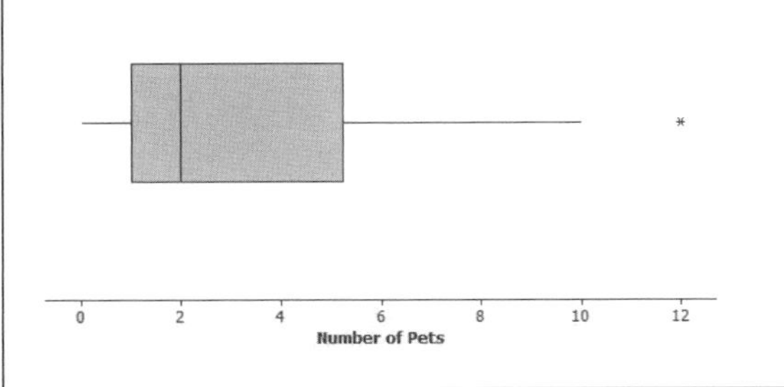

12. **What does the box plot tell us about the number of pets owned by the thirty students at River City High School?**

    50% *of students own between* 1 *and* 5 *pets.*

13. **Why might understanding the data behind this graph be important?**

    Understanding the data is important for planning special events involving pets and understanding interests of a group of people.

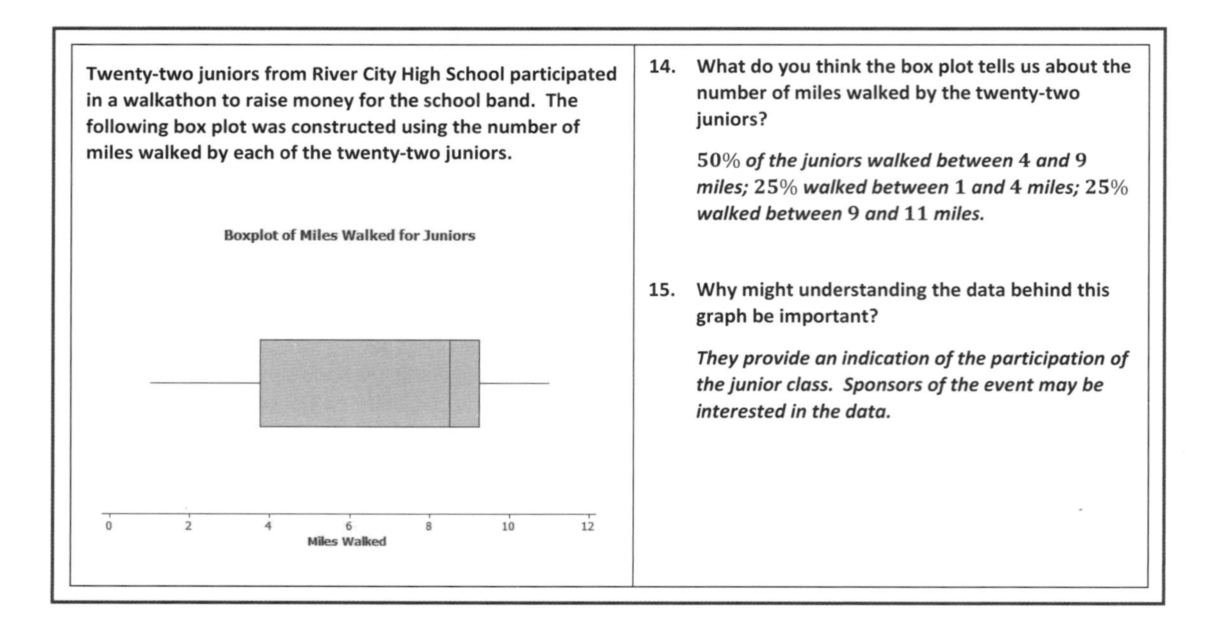

Twenty-two juniors from River City High School participated in a walkathon to raise money for the school band. The following box plot was constructed using the number of miles walked by each of the twenty-two juniors.

14. **What do you think the box plot tells us about the number of miles walked by the twenty-two juniors?**

    50% of the juniors walked between 4 and 9 miles; 25% walked between 1 and 4 miles; 25% walked between 9 and 11 miles.

15. **Why might understanding the data behind this graph be important?**

    They provide an indication of the participation of the junior class. Sponsors of the event may be interested in the data.

Closing (5 minutes)

Pose at least two of the following questions; allow a few student responses for each.

- What are reasons that a scheduled airline flight might be delayed?
- What are some of the favorite television shows of the students in your class? List some of the most memorable commercials that are shown during those shows. In your opinion, do the commercials connect with the viewers?
- You walk into a store. You estimate that most of the customers are between fifty and sixty years old. What kind of store do you think it is?
- If you asked students in your class how many pets they owned, what do you think would be a typical value?
- You are selected to take a trip to Kenya. Do you think you will meet several people ninety or older? Why or why not?

Lesson Summary

Statistics is about data. Graphs provide a representation of the data distribution and are used to understand the data and to answer questions about the distribution.

Exit Ticket (10 minutes)

Name ______________________________ Date ______________

Lesson 1: Distributions and Their Shapes

Exit Ticket

1. Sam said that a typical flight delay for the sixty BigAir flights was approximately one hour. Do you agree? Why or why not?

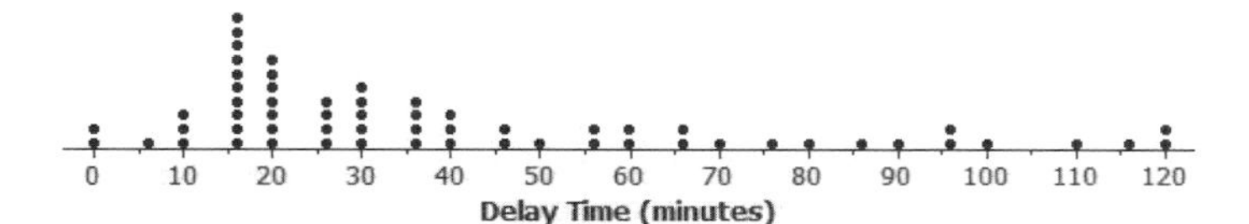

2. Sam said that 50% of the twenty-two juniors at River City High School who participated in the walkathon walked at least ten miles. Do you agree? Why or why not?

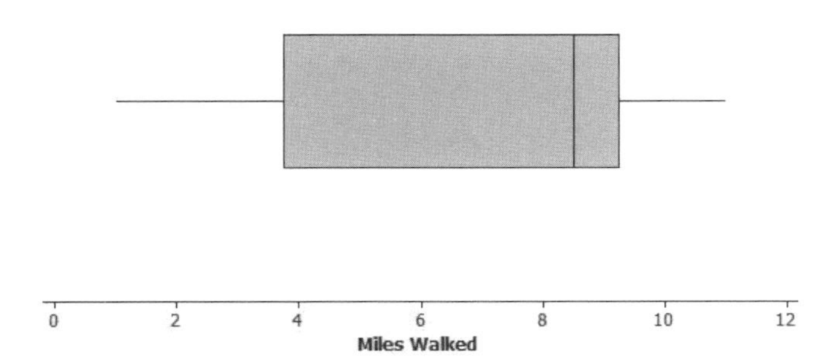

3. Sam said that young people from the ages of 0 to 10 years old make up nearly one-third of the Kenyan population. Do you agree? Why or why not?

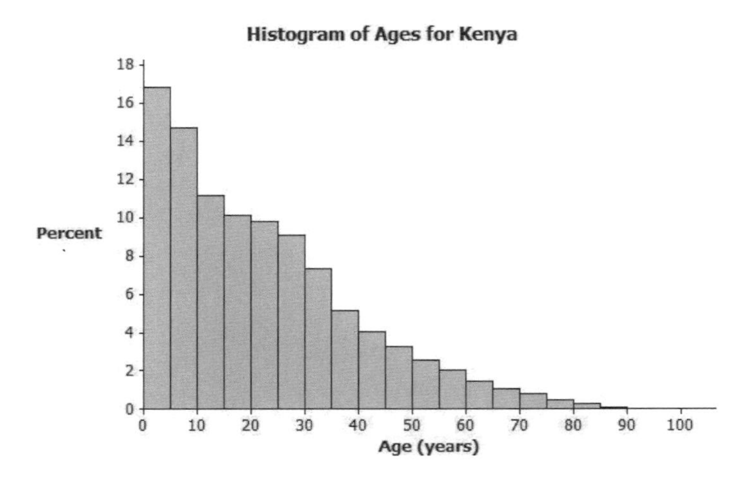

Exit Ticket Sample Solutions

1. **Sam said that a typical flight delay for the sixty BigAir flights was approximately one hour. Do you agree? Why or why not?**

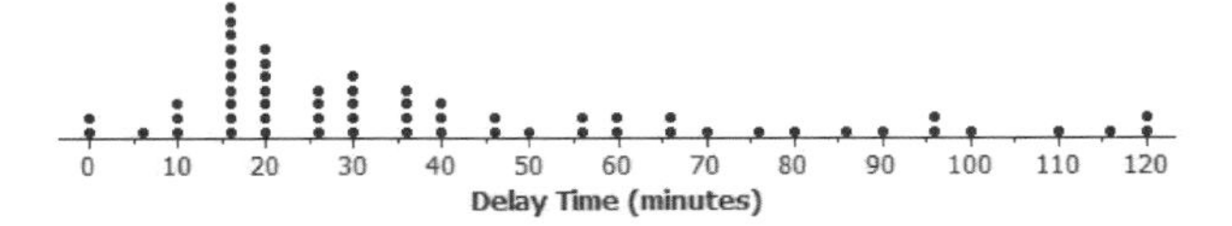

Most of the flight delays are less than 60 minutes; therefore, 60 minutes is not a typical description of how many minutes a flight is delayed.

2. **Sam said that 50% of the twenty-two juniors at River City High School who participated in the walkathon walked at least ten miles. Do you agree? Why or why not?**

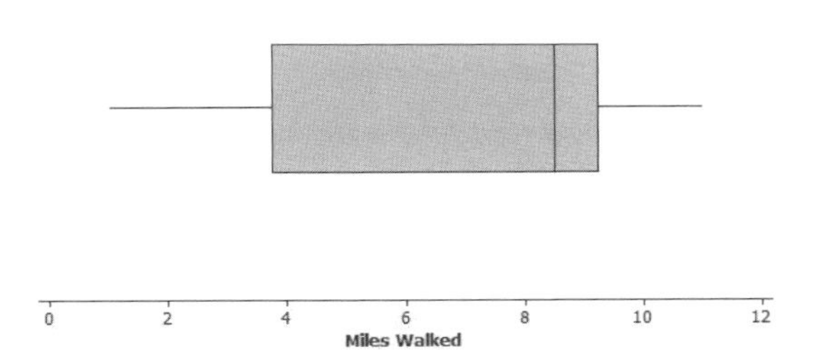

It would not be accurate to indicate that 50% walked 10 or more miles. The upper quartile indicates that 25% of the 22 students walked 9 or more miles.

3. **Sam said that young people from the ages of 0 to 10 years old make up nearly one-third of the Kenyan population. Do you agree? Why or why not?**

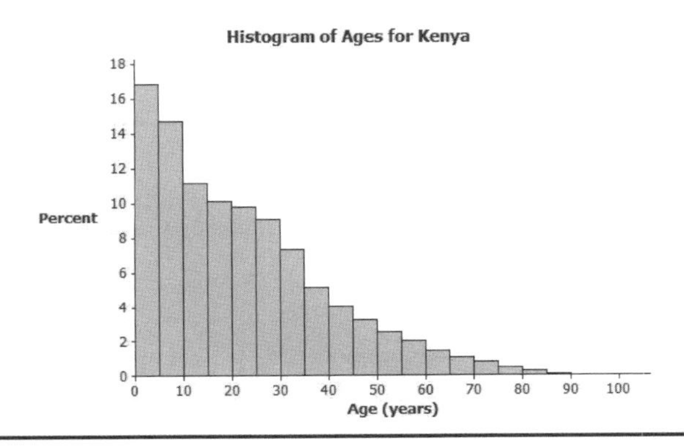

I do agree with Sam. The first two bars of the Kenya graph represent people between 0 and 10 years old. The first bar represents approximately 17% of the population (0–5 year olds), and the second bar represents approximately 15% of the population (5–10 year olds). Therefore, approximately 32%, or nearly one-third of the Kenyan population, is between 0 and 10 years old.

Problem Set Sample Solutions

1. **Twenty-five people were attending an event. The ages of the people are as follows:**

$$3, 3, 4, 4, 4, 4, 5, 6, 6, 6, 6, 6, 6, 6, 7, 7, 7, 7, 7, 7, 16, 17, 22, 22, 25.$$

   a. **Create a histogram of the ages using the provided axes.**

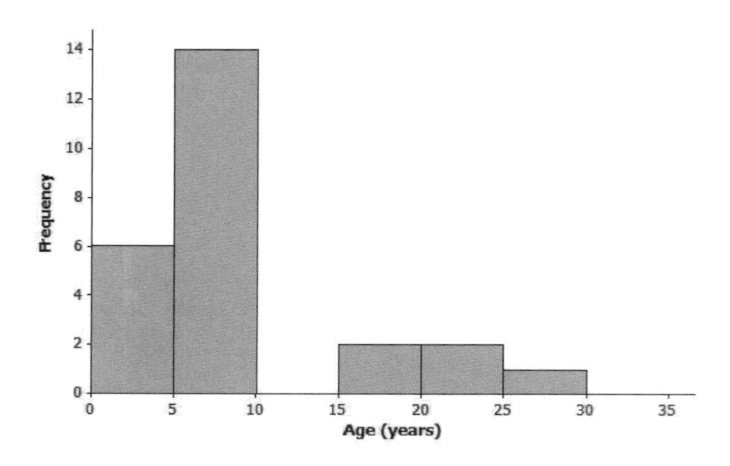

   b. **Would you describe your graph as symmetrical or skewed? Explain your choice.**

   This graph is skewed with a tail to the right. Most of the ages are in the younger intervals.

   c. **Identify a typical age of the twenty-five people.**

   A typical age could be any age in the interval of 5 *to* 10*, such as* 6 *or* 7 *years old.*

   d. **What event do you think the twenty-five people were attending? Use your histogram to justify your conjecture.**

   The 22 *ages were obtained from a story-time hour at a library. Most of the ages were the children attending the event. The older ages represent some of the caretakers and the storytellers. Discuss any conjectures in which the younger age intervals would likely represent most of the people attending the event, with some older people to help out with the event.*

2. A different forty people were also attending an event. The ages of the people are as follows:

$$6, 13, 24, 27, 28, 32, 32, 34, 38, 42, 42, 43, 48, 49, 49, 49, 51, 52, 52, 53,$$
$$53, 53, 54, 55, 56, 57, 57, 60, 61, 61, 62, 66, 66, 66, 68, 70, 72, 78, 83, 97.$$

a. Create a histogram of the ages using the provided axes.

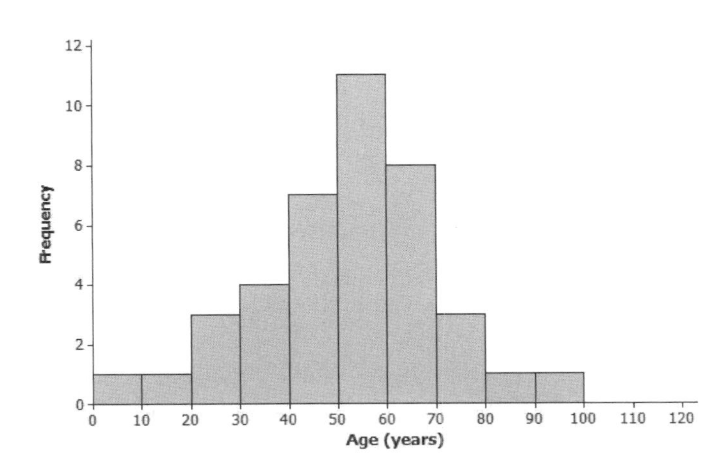

b. Would you describe your graph of ages as symmetrical or skewed? Explain your choice.

This histogram is nearly symmetrical.

c. Identify a typical age of the forty people.

A typical age is approximately 55 *years old.*

d. What event do you think the forty people were attending? Use your histogram to justify your conjecture.

The ages were obtained from people attending a family reunion. This is obviously not necessarily what you would expect from all family reunions. Discuss any conjectures in which a nearly symmetrical data distribution of ages could be a possibility.

e. How would you describe the differences in the two histograms?

The two age distributions differ primarily in shape (skewed and symmetrical) and in center (typical age).

Lesson 2: Describing the Center of a Distribution

Student Outcomes

- Students construct a dot plot from a data set.
- Students calculate the mean of a data set and the median of a data set.
- Students observe and describe that measures of center (mean and median) are nearly the same for distributions that are nearly symmetrical.
- Students observe and explain why the mean and median are different for distributions that are skewed.
- Students select the mean as an appropriate description of center for a symmetrical distribution and the median as a better description of center for a distribution that is skewed.

Lesson Notes

In Grade 6, students were introduced to center as a description of a typical value in a data set. In Grades 6 and 7, students used the mean or the median as a description of a typical value of data distribution, looking at the shape of the distribution to determine whether the median or the mean was a better description of a typical value. This lesson continues to expand their understanding and interpretation of the center of a distribution.

MP.1

Students are provided three data sets and asked to construct dot plots for each in order to study the distributions. A symmetrical or a nearly symmetrical distribution emerges from the first data set. Students determine that the mean and median are nearly the same in this distribution. In the second and third data sets, a nonsymmetrical distribution is given. Students determine that the mean and the median are not the same. They are asked to explain why the two measures of center are not equal.

In closing, students are asked to generalize what shape of distribution would have a median that is less than the mean and what shape of distribution would have a median that is greater than the mean.

Solving the problems in the exercises provides an opportunity to address the modeling cycle outlined in the conceptual category of modeling of the high school Common Core State Standards. The following graphic from the Common Core State Standards for high school mathematics summarizes the modeling cycle. As students work through the exercise, observe and point out to them how to *formulate* a summary of the data by constructing a dot plot. Students observe that the dot plot identifies a center that is appropriate for the data distribution. Students *compute* a measure of center, *interpret* the center given the context of the data set, and then *validate* that the center provides a description of a typical value by reexamining the data distribution. In some cases, students are expected to revisit their decision, select a new measure of center, interpret the value of the new center, and validate that it provides a description of a typical value. Students should be made familiar with the modeling cycle as it is designed to guide their thinking not only in this module but in all of their mathematics course work. If time permits at the end of this lesson, ask students to reflect on this cycle and how solving the questions in the exercise connect to this cycle.

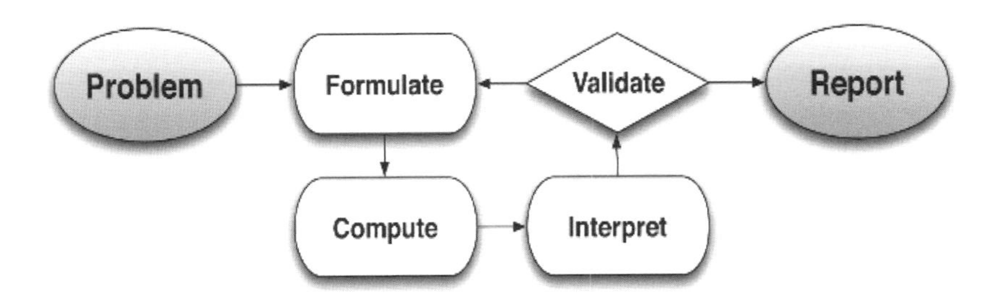

Classwork

> In previous work with data distributions, you learned how to derive the mean and the median of a data distribution. This lesson builds on your previous work with a center.

Exploratory Challenge/Exercises 1–9 (25 minutes)

Introduce each data set by discussing the data. Discuss the following questions before students complete the problems in the exercise to help them understand the context of the problems. Direct students to examine the data sets presented in the exercise of the lesson.

> **Exploratory Challenge/Exercises 1–9**
>
> **Consider the following three sets of data.**
>
> ***Data Set 1: Pet owners***
>
> **Students from River City High School were randomly selected and asked, "How many pets do you currently own?" The results are recorded below.**

0	0	0	0	1	1	1	1	1	1	1	1	1	1	2
2	2	2	3	3	4	5	5	6	6	7	8	9	10	12

- Can we assume that all students interpret the question "How many pets do you currently own?" in the same way?

> ***Data Set 2: Length of the east hallway at River City High School***
>
> **Twenty students were selected to measure the length of the east hallway. Two marks were made on the hallway's floor: one at the front of the hallway and one at the end of the hallway. Each student was given a meter stick and asked to use the meter stick to determine the length between the marks to the nearest tenth of a meter. The results are recorded below.**

8.2	8.3	8.3	8.4	8.4	8.5	8.5	8.5	8.5	8.5
8.6	8.6	8.6	8.6	8.7	8.7	8.8	8.8	8.9	8.9

- Why would the same hallway have different reported measures of length?
- What measures of the length of the hallway do you think are the most accurate from the data set?

Data Set 3: Age of cars

Twenty-five car owners were asked the age of their cars in years. The results are recorded below.

0	1	2	2	3	4	5	5	6	6	6	7	7
7	7	7	7	8	8	8	8	8	8	8	8	

- What number would you use to describe the typical age of cars in years by the car owners in this group?

Students now work through Exercises 1–9 of their lesson. Students determine for each distribution if the mean and the median are different or similar and how those characteristics relate to the distribution. Students relate their answers in the context of the data set.

Several of the questions within the exercises can be posed verbally as part of a discussion with students. Other questions may require written responses. Review the questions, and decide what format is best for your students.

1. **Make a dot plot of each of the data sets. Use the following scales.**

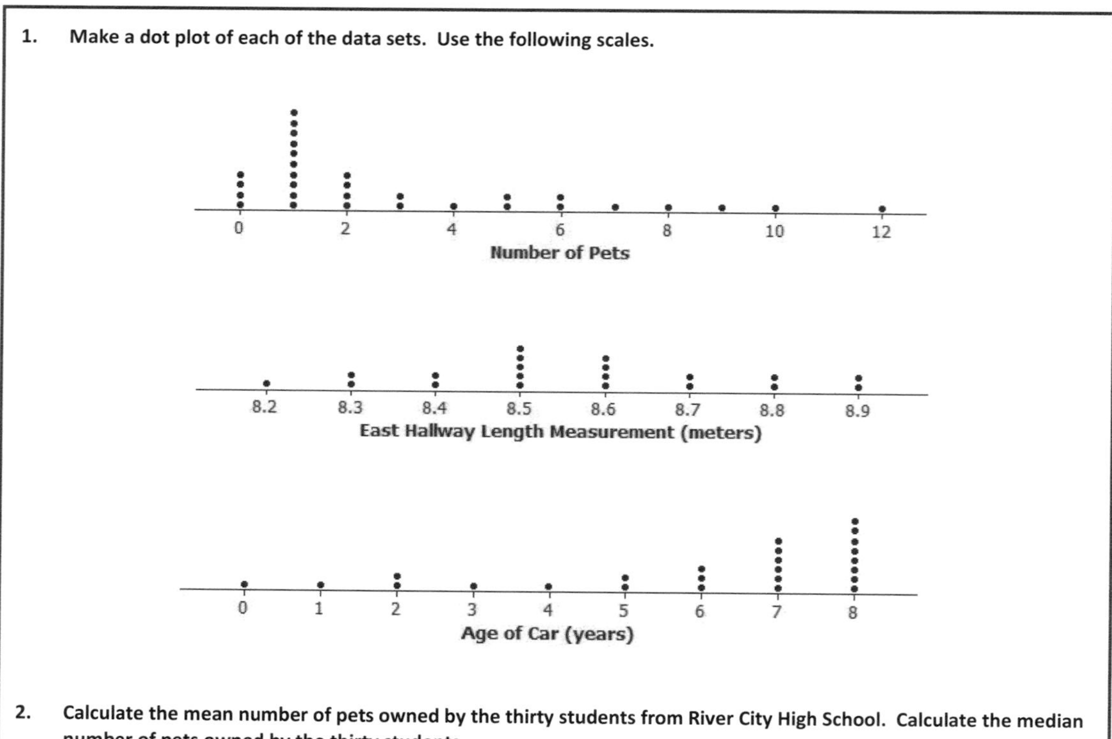

2. **Calculate the mean number of pets owned by the thirty students from River City High School. Calculate the median number of pets owned by the thirty students.**

   The mean number of pets owned is 3.2.

   The median number of pets owned is 2.

3. **What do you think is a typical number of pets for students from River City High School? Explain how you made your estimate.**

   The median is a better description of a typical value. The median is less than the mean because more of the data are located on the left side of the scale. The value of the mean is "pulled up" by the larger values in the data set.

4. **Why do you think that different students got different results when they measured the same distance of the east hallway?**

   Measurement errors occurred as a result of the placement of the meter stick at the starting point, the alignment of the meter stick after each length was made, and the different interpretation made by the person making the measurement.

5. **What is the mean length of the east hallway data set? What is the median length?**

   The mean length is approximately 8.57 ***meters.***

   The median length is approximately 8.55 ***meters.***

   They are approximately the same.

6. **A construction company will be installing a handrail along a wall from the beginning point to the ending point of the east hallway. The company asks you how long the handrail should be. What would you tell the company? Explain your answer.**

   It should be approximately 8.6 ***meters. Since the distribution is nearly symmetric, the mean should be used as a measure of center.***

7. **Describe the distribution of the age of cars.**

   The distribution is not symmetric. It is skewed to the left. Most of the data are on the right-hand side with a long tail to the left.

8. **What is the mean age of the twenty-five cars? What is the median age? Why are the mean and the median different?**

   The mean age is approximately 5.84 ***years old, and the median age is*** 7 ***years old. They are different. The mean is smaller because of the small values in the tail of the data distribution.***

9. **What number would you use as an estimate of the typical age of a car for the twenty-five car owners? Explain your answer.**

   The median is a better description of a typical age because the distribution is skewed.

Closing (10 minutes)

Ask the following of students:

- How is the choice made between mean and median to describe the typical value related to the shape of the data distribution?
- Sketch a dot plot in which the median is greater than the mean. Could you think of a context that might result in data where you think that would happen?

> **Lesson Summary**
>
> - **A dot plot provides a graphical representation of a data distribution, helping us to visualize the distribution.**
> - **The mean and the median of the distribution are numerical summaries of the center of a data distribution.**
> - **When the distribution is nearly symmetrical, the mean and the median of the distribution are approximately equal. When the distribution is not symmetrical (often described as skewed), the mean and the median are not the same.**
> - **For symmetrical distributions, the mean is an appropriate choice for describing a typical value for the distribution. For skewed data distributions, the median is a better description of a typical value.**

Exit Ticket (10 minutes)

Name ______________________________ Date ______________

Lesson 2: Describing the Center of a Distribution

Exit Ticket

Each person in a random sample of ten ninth graders was asked two questions:

- How many hours did you spend watching TV last night?
- What is the total value of the coins you have with you today?

Here are the data for these ten students:

Student	Hours of TV	Total Value of Coins (in dollars)
1	2	0.00
2	1	0.89
3	0	2.19
4	3	0.15
5	4	1.37
6	1	0.36
7	2	0.25
8	2	0.00
9	4	0.54
10	3	0.10

1. Construct a dot plot of the data on Hours of TV. Would you describe this data distribution as approximately symmetric or as skewed?

2. If you wanted to describe a typical number of hours of TV watched for these ten students, would you use the mean or the median? Calculate the value of the measure you selected.

3. Here is a dot plot of the data on Total Value of Coins.

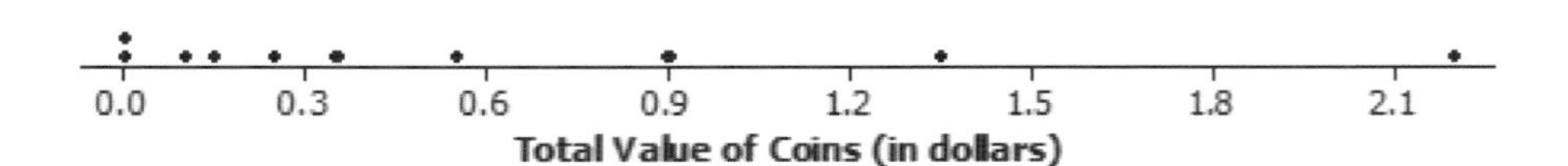

Calculate the values of the mean and the median for this data set.

4. Why are the values of the mean and the median that you calculated in Problem 3 so different? Which of the mean and the median would you use to describe a typical value of coins for these ten students?

Exit Ticket Sample Solutions

Each person in a random sample of ten ninth graders was asked two questions:

- How many hours did you spend watching TV last night?
- What is the total value of the coins you have with you today?

Here are the data for these ten students:

Student	Hours of TV	Total Value of Coins (in dollars)
1	2	0.00
2	1	0.89
3	0	2.19
4	3	0.15
5	4	1.37
6	1	0.36
7	2	0.25
8	2	0.00
9	4	0.54
10	3	0.10

1. Construct a dot plot of the data on Hours of TV. Would you describe this data distribution as approximately symmetric or as skewed?

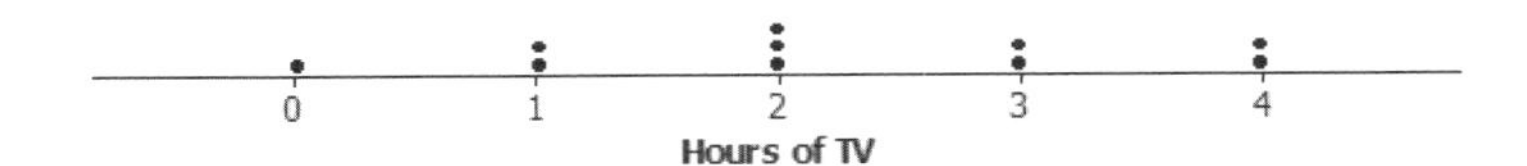

This distribution is approximately symmetric.

2. If you wanted to describe a typical number of hours of TV watched for these ten students, would you use the mean or the median? Calculate the value of the measure you selected.

Because the distribution is approximately symmetric, I would use the mean. The value of the mean is $\frac{22}{10}$ *or* 2.2 *hours.*

3. Here is a dot plot of the data on Total Value of Coins.

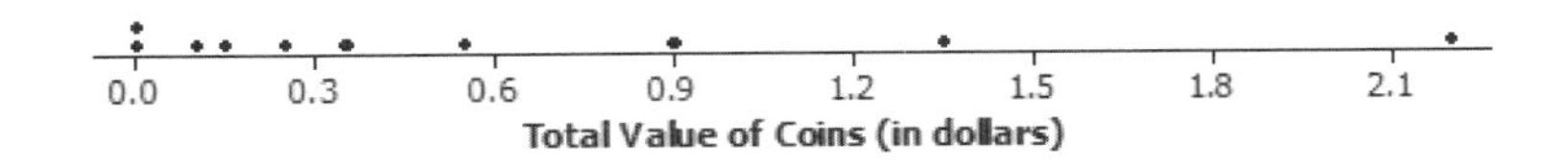

Calculate the values of the mean and the median for this data set.

Mean $= \frac{5.85}{10} = 0.585$, *or about* 59 *cents. Arranging the data in order from smallest to largest, you get*

$0.00 \quad 0.00 \quad 0.10 \quad 0.15 \quad 0.25 \quad 0.36 \quad 0.54 \quad 0.89 \quad 1.37 \quad 2.19$

The median is the average of the two middle numbers, $\frac{0.25+0.36}{2} = 0.305$, *or about* 31 *cents.*

4. **Why are the values of the mean and the median that you calculated in Problem 3 so different? Which of the mean and the median would you use to describe a typical value of coins for these ten students?**

   The values of the mean and median are different because the data distribution is skewed, and the mean is pulled up by the large values in the data set. Because the data distribution is skewed, the median would be a better choice for describing a typical value.

Problem Set Sample Solutions

Consider the following scenario. The company that created a popular video game "Leaders" plans to release a significant upgrade of the game. Users earn or lose points for making decisions as the leader of an imaginary country. In most cases, repeated playing of the game improves a user's ability to make decisions. The company will launch an online advertising campaign, but at the moment, they are not sure how to focus the advertising. Your goal is to help the company decide how the advertising campaign should be focused. Five videos have been proposed for the following target audiences:

Video 1: Target females with beginning level scores

Video 2: Target males with advanced level scores

Video 3: Target all users with middle range level scores

Video 4: Target males with beginning level scores

Video 5: Target females with advanced level scores

1. **Why might the company be interested in developing different videos based on user score?**

   Answers may vary.

2. **Thirty female users and twenty-five male users were selected at random from a database of people who play the game regularly. Each of them agreed to be part of a research study and report their scores. A leadership score is based on a player's answers to leadership questions. A score of 1 to 40 is considered a beginning level leadership score, a score of 41 to 60 is considered a middle level leadership score, and a score of greater than 60 is considered an advanced level leadership score.**

   Use the following data to make a dot plot of the female scores, a dot plot of the male scores, and a dot plot of the scores for the combined group of males and females.

   Female scores:

10	20	20	20	30	30	30	40	40	40
50	50	55	65	65	65	65	65	70	70
70	70	76	76	76	76	76	76	76	76

   Male scores:

15	20	20	25	25	25	25	30	30	30
30	30	30	35	35	35	35	35	40	40
40	45	45	45	50					

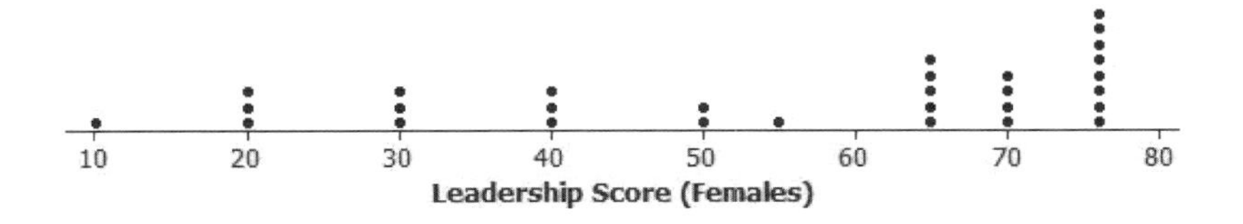

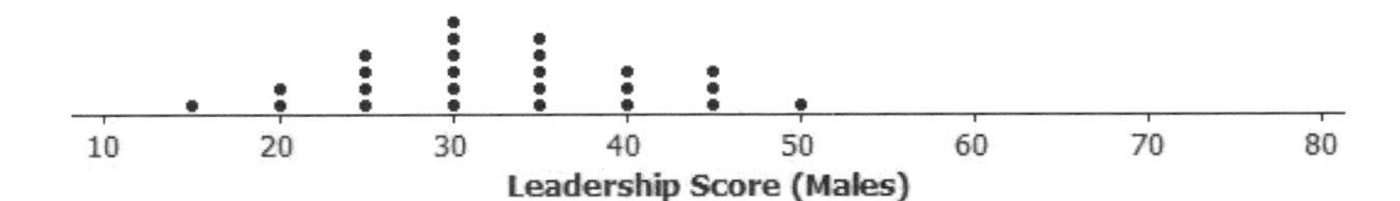

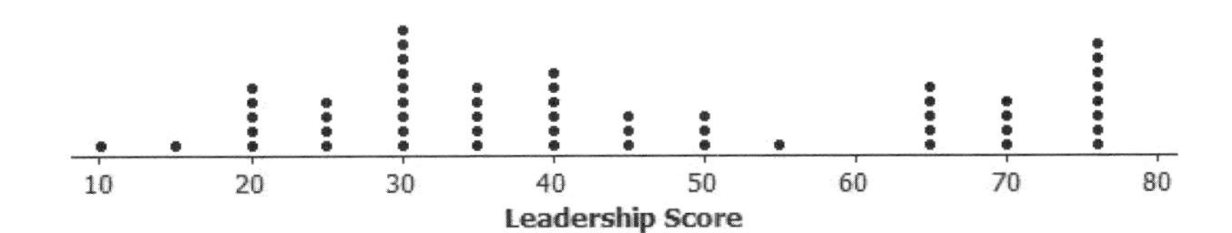

3. **What do you think is a typical score for a female user? What do you think is a typical score for a male user? Explain how you determined these typical scores.**

   The mean score for the female users is approximately 54.9*, and the median score is* 65*. The median is a better description of a typical score for females. Students may note that the mean score describes a female user at the middle level of leadership, and the median score describes a female user at the advanced level. The median is a better description of a typical score for females.*

   The mean score for the male users is approximately 32.6*, and the median score is* 30*. This has an approximate symmetrical distribution, and this is why the mean and the median are nearly equal. The mean is a good description of a typical score for males. Students may further indicate that this describes males at the beginning level of this game.*

4. **Why is it more difficult to report a typical score for the overall group that includes both the males and females?**

   The overall distribution is difficult to summarize in terms of shape. It obviously combines the symmetrical shape from the male users and the skewed shape from the female users. The mean score of all users is approximately 44.8*. The median score is* 40*. The mean and the median are not the same, but the values are relatively close. The mean is often interpreted as a balance point for this type of distribution. This interpretation of a mean is developed in the next lesson; however, it is also discussed in the Grade 6 standards and could be introduced again with this Problem Set.*

5. **Production costs will only allow for two video advertisements to be developed. Which two videos would you recommend for development? Explain your recommendations.**

   In recommending which videos to produce based on the dot plots and measure of center, students will generally select Video 4 (males with beginning level scores) and Video 5 (females with advanced level scores).

Lesson 3: Estimating Centers and Interpreting the Mean as a Balance Point

Student Outcomes

- Students estimate the mean and median of a distribution represented by a dot plot or a histogram.
- Students indicate that the mean is a reasonable description of a typical value for a distribution that is symmetrical, but the median is a better description of a typical value for a distribution that is skewed.
- Students interpret the mean as a balance point of a distribution.
- Students indicate that for a distribution in which neither the mean nor the median is a good description of a typical value, the mean still provides a description of the center of a distribution in terms of the balance point.

Lesson Notes

This lesson continues the work started in Lesson 2 by presenting nearly symmetrical data distributions in which the mean is a reasonable description of a typical value and skewed data distributions in which the median is a reasonable description.

MP.4

This lesson reviews and deepens understanding of the mean as a balance point as was introduced in Grade 6 (**6.SP.A.3**, **6.SP.B.5b**). The concept of balance is developed by using a dot plot and a representation of the data as equal weights along a number line. Balance would be a position on the number line in which the sum of the distances on the right and the sum of the distances on the left are equal. Students model with mathematics as they verify this position.

Students estimate a balance point for a data distribution and then compare their estimate to the actual mean. The visual of a balance point helps students understand how a mean provides a reasonable description of a typical value for a distribution that is symmetrical. The balance point for a skewed data distribution, however, does not describe a typical value as well as it did for a symmetrical data distribution. Students should recognize that the median of the data set is a better description of a typical value based on the visual representation of a skewed data distribution.

In the next set of lessons (Lessons 4, 5, and 6), students use this balance point position to develop a measure of the variability in a data distribution, ultimately leading to the standard deviation.

Classwork

Example (3 minutes)

Example

Your previous work in mathematics involved estimating a balance point of a data distribution. Let's review what we learned about the balance point of a distribution. A 12-inch ruler has several quarters taped to positions along the ruler. The broad side of a pencil is placed underneath the ruler to determine an approximate balance point of the ruler with the quarters.

Demonstrate balancing a ruler with quarters taped on it to the class. Tape quarters to the positions 1 inch and 11 inches on a ruler. Demonstrate that the ruler balances on the tip of a pencil at the position 6 inches.

Be aware, however, that the model may not necessarily balance at the mean, as factors due to the physical weight of the ruler, variation in the weights of the quarters, and precision of the placement of the quarters all affect the resulting balance point. It is best to use a lightweight ruler to minimize the effect of the weight of the ruler on the balance point.

Exercises 1–7 (15 minutes)

The questions in this exercise can be part of a class discussion or a small group discussion. You may also direct students to write out answers for several of these questions. Consider a format that works best for your students.

Encourage students to make a visual estimate of the balance point before they make any calculations. If needed, prompt students to understand that the balance point is a position that balances the sum of the distances to the right of the balance point with the sum of the distances to the left of the balance point.

Students are directed in the questions to calculate the mean and median. They observe that the mean is either equal to their estimate of the balance point or close to their estimate.

MP.2

Ask the following questions as students develop their responses to the exercises:

- How do you think the quarter located at the 1-inch position affects the balance point? If that quarter were moved to the position of 3 inches, what would happen to the balance point?
  - *If the quarter moved to 3 inches, then the balance point would have to shift to the right in order to balance the sum of the distances.*
- Is there any arrangement of the three quarters that you could make in which the balance point would be located at the position of 6 inches? Explain your arrangement and why you think it might work.
  - *One option is to place quarters at 1, 8, and 9 inches. The distance to the left of the mean is 5, and the sum of the distances to the right of the balance point is also 5.*
- How are the mean and the balance point related?
  - *The mean is the balance point in which the sum of the distances to the left of the balance point is the same as the sum of the distances to the right of the balance point.*

Exercises 1–7

Consider the following example of quarters taped to a lightweight ruler.

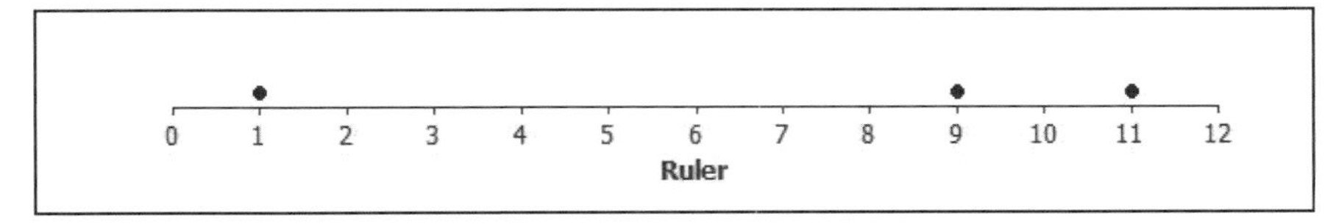

1. **Sam taped 3 quarters to his ruler. The quarters were taped to the positions 1 inch, 9 inches, and 11 inches. If the pencil was placed under the position 5 inches, do you think the ruler would balance? Why or why not?**

   5 would not be the position of balance. The quarters at 9 and 11 pull the balance point toward that side.

2. **If the ruler did not balance, would you move the pencil to the left or to the right of 5 inches to balance the ruler? Explain your answer.**

   I would move the position to the right because the quarters at position 9 and 11 pull the balance point to that side.

3. **Estimate a balance point for the ruler. Complete the following based on the position you selected.**

   Answers will vary. Allow students to describe distance as a signed number. The following table is based upon a balance point of 6 inches.

Position of Quarter	Distance from Quarter to Your Estimate of the Balance Point
1	5
9	3
11	5

4. **What is the sum of the distances to the right of your estimate of the balance point?**

   Answers will vary. Using a balance point of 6 inches, the sum to the right is 8 units.

5. **What is the sum of the distances to the left of your estimate of the balance point?**

   Using a balance point of 6 inches, the sum to the left is 5 units.

6. **Do you need to adjust the position of your balance point? If yes, explain how.**

   Using a balance point of 6 inches, an adjustment is needed. The balance point is found by increasing the distances to the left and decreasing the distances to the right.

7. **Calculate the mean and the median of the position of the quarters. Does the mean or the median of the positions provide a better estimate of the balance point for the position of the 3 quarters taped to this ruler? Explain why you made this selection.**

   The mean of the positions is 7 inches, and the median is 9 inches. The mean provides a better estimate of the balance point. If the mean position of 7 was selected, then the distance of the quarter to the left of 7 would be 6, and the sum of the distances of the two quarters to the right of 7 would be $2 + 4$, or 6. The balance point is the position in which the sum of the distances to the right and to the left are equal. If the median position of 9 was selected, then the distance to the left would be 8, and the distance to the right would be 2. Clearly, that would not balance the 3 quarters on the ruler.

Exercises 8–20 (20 minutes)

Before students answer questions, have a discussion of this exercise by prompting students to make connections between the dot plot and the context of the problem. For example, highlight a specific point on one of the dot plots, and ask students to explain what the point represents.

Direct students to work individually or in small groups to complete this exercise. Use the following sample responses (which represent possible answers or comments) to develop student outcomes.

Exercises 8–20

Twenty-two students from the junior class and twenty-six students from the senior class at River City High School participated in a walkathon to raise money for the school's band. Dot plots indicating the distances in miles students from each class walked are as follows.

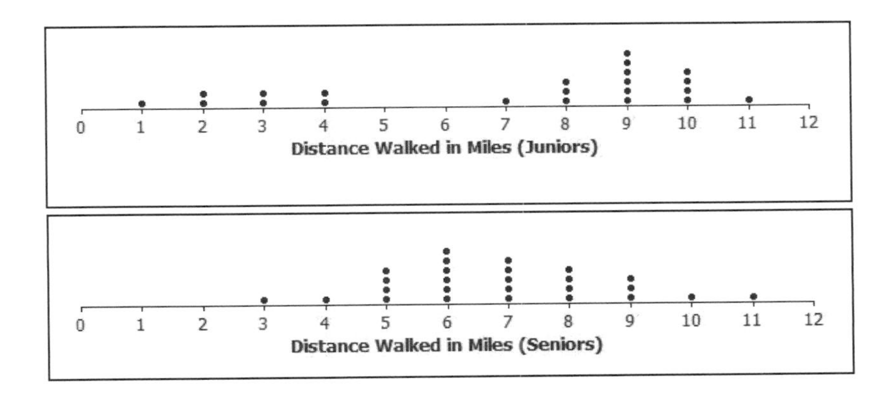

8. Estimate the mean number of miles walked by a junior, and mark it with an X on the junior class dot plot. How did you estimate this position?

   Answers will vary. Some students may take into account the skewed shape of the distribution. Others may put the mean in the middle of the number line. Listen to students as they make their estimates.

9. What is the median of the junior data distribution?

   The median is 8.5*. (It is halfway between the eleventh and twelfth person.)*

10. Is the mean number of miles walked by a junior less than, approximately equal to, or greater than the median number of miles? If they are different, explain why. If they are approximately the same, explain why.

    The mean is less than the median. The small cluster of data values to the left pulls the mean in that direction. The median is not affected by the values of those points.

11. How would you describe the typical number of miles walked by a junior in this walkathon?

    The mean appears to underestimate the distance walked by a junior. Only eight students walked less than the mean, while fourteen students walked more. (Answers may vary. Since students are estimating, they may say seven students walked less than the mean.) The median is a better description of a typical value.

12. Estimate the mean number of miles walked by a senior, and mark it with an X on the senior class dot plot. How did you estimate this position?

    The distribution appears to be symmetric, around 6 *or* 7*. The balance point should be in the middle of the distribution.*

13. What is the median of the senior data distribution?

    The median is 7 *miles.*

14. **Estimate the mean and the median of the miles walked by the seniors. Is your estimate of the mean number of miles less than, approximately equal to, or greater than the median number of miles walked by a senior? If they are different, explain why. If they are approximately the same, explain why.**

    Since the distribution is symmetric, the mean and median are approximately equal. A good estimate for both is around 7 *miles.*

15. **How would you describe the typical number of miles walked by a senior in this walkathon?**

    A typical number of miles walked by a senior would be around 7 *miles.*

16. **A junior from River City High School indicated that the number of miles walked by a typical junior was better than the number of miles walked by a typical senior. Do you agree? Explain your answer.**

    Yes. The median is a better indicator of a typical value for the junior class. The median of the junior class is more than the median of the senior class.

Finally, the twenty-five sophomores who participated in the walkathon reported their results. A dot plot is shown below.

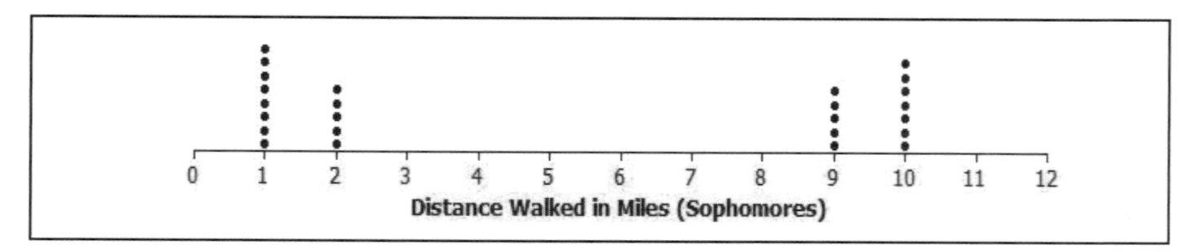

17. **What is different about the sophomore data distribution compared to the data distributions for juniors and seniors?**

    It is a U-shaped distribution. Half of the sophomores walk on the low end and half on the high end. The juniors had a skewed distribution, and the seniors had a symmetric distribution.

18. **Estimate the balance point of the sophomore data distribution.**

    An estimate of the mean is 5.

19. **What is the median number of miles walked by a sophomore?**

    Since there are 25 *values, the median is the thirteenth value from the right or left. The median is* 2.

20. **How would you describe the sophomore data distribution?**

    It is a U-shaped distribution. The values are either small or large. The mean and median are not good indicators of a typical distance for sophomores.

Scaffolding:

Some students may not remember seeing a U-shaped distribution, as demonstrated by the sophomore data distribution. In this U-shaped distribution, neither the mean nor the median is a good description of a typical value of the number of miles walked by a sophomore. However, the mean, as a balance point, remains a description of center for this data distribution.

Closing (2 minutes)

After students have answered the questions in this exercise, ask the following questions:

MP.2

- How does the dot plot for the juniors differ from the dot plot for the seniors? What might explain the difference between the dot plots for juniors and seniors?
- How would you describe the typical number of miles walked by a junior?

> **Lesson Summary**
>
> **The mean of a data distribution represents a balance point for the distribution. The sum of the distances to the right of the mean is equal to the sum of the distances to the left of the mean.**

Exit Ticket (5 minutes)

Name ______________________________ Date______________

Lesson 3: Estimating Centers and Interpreting the Mean as a Balance Point

Exit Ticket

1. Draw a dot plot of a data distribution representing the ages of twenty people for which the median and the mean would be approximately the same.

2. Draw a dot plot of a data distribution representing the ages of twenty people for which the median is noticeably less than the mean.

3. An estimate of the balance point for a distribution of ages represented on a number line resulted in a greater sum of the distances to the right than the sum of the distances to the left. In which direction should you move your estimate of the balance point? Explain.

Exit Ticket Sample Solutions

1. **Draw a dot plot of a data distribution representing the ages of twenty people for which the median and the mean would be approximately the same.**

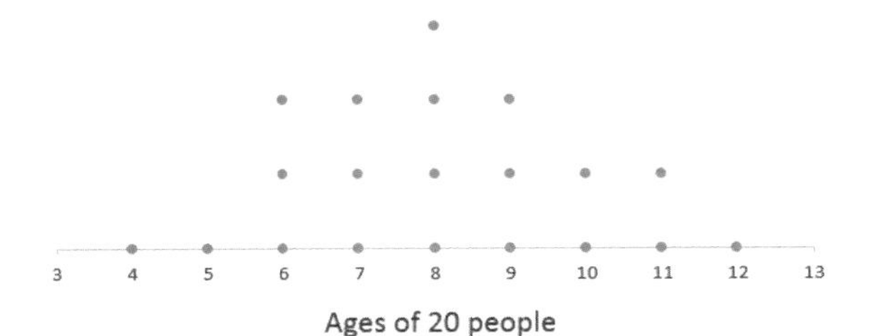

A dot plot representing a symmetrical distribution is an example in which the mean and median are approximately the same.

2. **Draw a dot plot of a data distribution representing the ages of twenty people for which the median is noticeably less than the mean.**

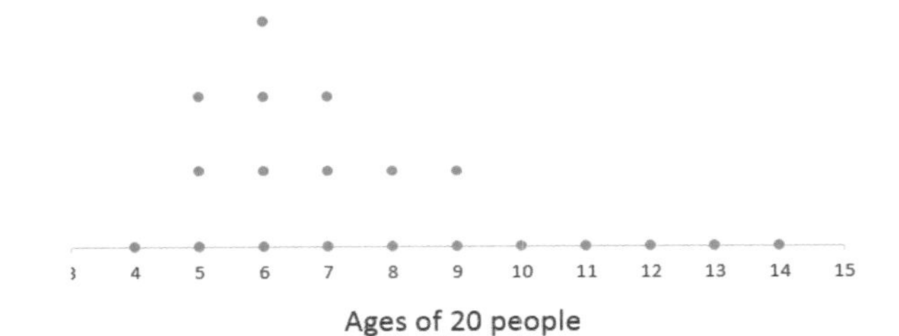

A dot plot representing a skewed data distribution in which most of the values are located farther to the left results in a median value less than the mean.

3. **An estimate of the balance point for a distribution of ages represented on a number line resulted in a greater sum of the distances to the right than the sum of the distances to the left. In which direction should you move your estimate of the balance point? Explain.**

Moving the position to the right would result in decreasing the sum of the distances to the right and increasing the sum of the distances to the left. The position where they are equal is the mean.

Problem Set Sample Solutions

Consider another example of balance. Mr. Jackson is a mathematics teacher at Waldo High School. Students in his class are frequently given quizzes or exams. He indicated to his students that an exam is worth 4 quizzes when calculating an overall weighted average to determine their final grade. During one grading period, Scott got an 80% on one exam, a 90% on a second exam, a 60% on one quiz, and a 70% on another quiz.

How could we represent Scott's test scores? Consider the following number line.

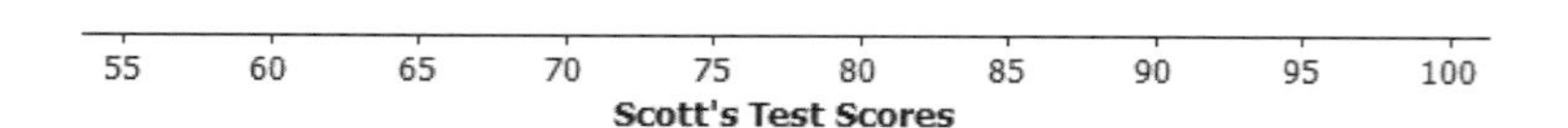

1. What values are represented by the number line?

   The values represented along the number line are percents.

2. If one "•" symbol is used to represent a quiz score, how might you represent an exam score?

   Since an exam is worth 4 quizzes, students could use a stack of 4 of the "•" symbols to represent an exam score.

3. Represent Scott's exams and quizzes on this number line using "•" symbols.

   The following dot plot could be used to represent Scott's scores:

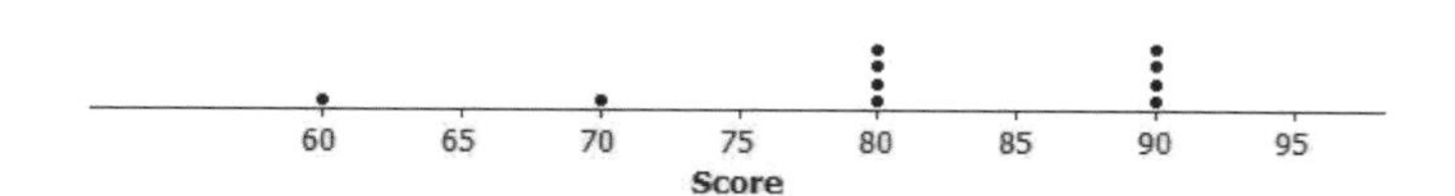

4. Mr. Jackson indicated that students should set an 85% overall weighted average as a goal. Do you think Scott met that goal? Explain your answer.

   Students' responses may vary. The overall weighted average could be represented by the balance point for the dot plot. The balance point is approximately 81% and is less than the goal set by Mr. Jackson.

5. Place an X on the number line at a position that you think locates the balance point of all of the "•" symbols. Determine the sum of the distances from the X to each "•" on the right side of the X.

   Answers depend on a student's estimate of the balance point. If students placed their estimate close to the mean, the sum of the distances on the right side of their estimate would be approximately the same as the sum of the distances on the left side.

6. Determine the sum of the distances from the X to each "•" on the left side of the X.

   Answers depend on a student's estimate of the balance point. If students placed their estimate close to the mean, the sum of the distances on the right side of their estimate would be approximately the same as the sum of the distances on the left side.

7. **Do the total distances to the right of the X equal the total distances to the left of the X?**

   Answers depend on students' estimates.

8. **Based on your answer to Problem 7, would you change your estimate of the balance point? If yes, where would you place your adjusted balance point? How does using this adjusted estimate change the total distances to the right of your estimate and the total distances to the left?**

   Changes in the position would be based on whether or not the sum of the distances on the right equals the sum of the distances on the left. Students would adjust their estimate by moving the position of their balance point to equalize the sums of the distances.

9. **Scott's weighted average is 81. Recall that each exam score is equal to 4 times a quiz score. Show the calculations that lead to this weighted average.**

   A weighted average of 81 would be based on multiplying each exam score by 4 (representing that an exam score is worth 4 times a quiz score). For this problem, the weighted average is

$$\frac{(60 + 70 + (4 \cdot 80) + (4 \cdot 90))}{10} = 81.$$

10. **How does the calculated mean score compare with your estimated balance point?**

    Answers may vary. This question asks students to compare their estimates to the weighted average.

11. **Compute the total distances to the right of the mean and the total distances to the left of the mean. What do you observe?**

    The weighted average, like the mean discussed earlier, is a balance point. After each exam is represented by 4 "•" symbols (where each "•" represents the same weight), the result is 10 "•" symbols, which determines the mean or weighted average of Scott's test scores. The sum of the distances to the right of the balance point is equal to the sum of the distances to the left of the balance point. If a student estimated 81% as the balance point, then:

    The sum of the distances to the right:

$$4 \cdot |90 - 81| = 4 \cdot |9| = 36$$

    The sum of the distances to the left:

$$|60 - 81| + |70 - 81| + 4 \cdot |80 - 81| = 21 + 11 + 4 = 36$$

    Therefore, for estimates of a balance point that is less than or greater than 81%, the distances are not equal.

12. **Did Scott achieve the goal set by Mr. Jackson of an 85% average? Explain your answer.**

    Scott did not achieve Mr. Jackson's goal since his average is 81%.

Topic B

Describing Variability and Comparing Distributions

S-ID.A.1, S-ID.A.2, S-ID.A.3

Focus Standards:	S-ID.A.1	Represent data with plots on the real number line (dot plots, histograms, and box plots).★
	S-ID.A.2	Use statistics appropriate to the shape of the data distribution to compare center (median, mean) and spread (interquartile range, standard deviation) of two or more different data sets.★
	S-ID.A.3	Interpret differences in shape, center, and spread in the context of the data sets, accounting for possible effects of extreme data points (outliers).★
Instructional Days:	5	
Lesson 4:	Summarizing Deviations from the Mean (P)[1]	
Lesson 5:	Measuring Variability for Symmetrical Distributions (P)	
Lesson 6:	Interpreting the Standard Deviation (E)	
Lesson 7:	Measuring Variability for Skewed Distributions (Interquartile Range) (E)	
Lesson 8:	Comparing Distributions (E)	

In Topic B, students reconnect with methods for describing variability that they first used in Grade 6. Topic B deepens students' understanding of measures of variability by connecting a measure of the center of a data distribution to an appropriate measure of variability. The mean is used as a measure of center when the distribution is more symmetrical. Students calculate and interpret the mean absolute deviation and the standard deviation to describe variability for data distributions that are approximately symmetric. The median is used as a measure of center for distributions that are more skewed, and students interpret the interquartile range as a measure of variability for data distributions that are not symmetric. Students match histograms to box plots for various distributions based on an understanding of center and variability. Students describe data distributions in terms of shape, a measure of center, and a measure of variability from the center.

[1]Lesson Structure Key: **P**-Problem Set Lesson, **M**-Modeling Cycle Lesson, **E**-Exploration Lesson, **S**-Socratic Lesson

Lesson 4: Summarizing Deviations from the Mean

Student Outcomes

- Students calculate the deviations from the mean for two symmetrical data sets that have the same means.
- Students interpret deviations that are generally larger because they have a greater spread or variability than a distribution in which the deviations are generally smaller.

Lesson Notes

The lesson prepares students for a future understanding of the standard deviation of a data set, focusing on the role of the deviations from the mean. Students practice calculating deviations from the mean and generalize their calculations by relating them to the expression $x - \bar{x}$. Students reflect on the relationship between the sizes of the deviations from the mean and the spread (variability) of the distribution.

Classwork

Exercises 1–4 (15 minutes)

Discuss Exercises 1–4 as a class.

Exercises 1–4

A consumers' organization is planning a study of the various brands of batteries that are available. As part of its planning, it measures lifetime (i.e., how long a battery can be used before it must be replaced) for each of six batteries of Brand A and eight batteries of Brand B. Dot plots showing the battery lives for each brand are shown below.

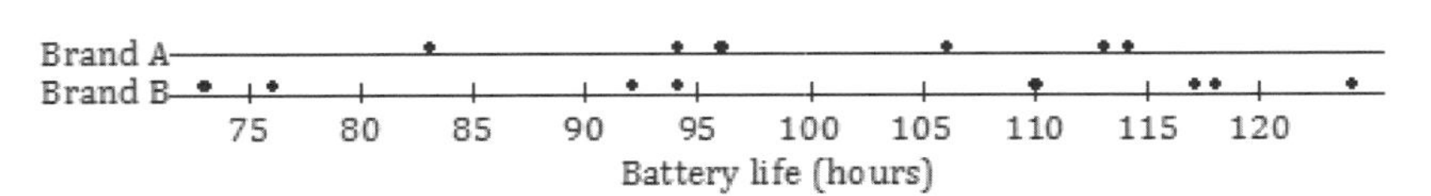

1. **Does one brand of battery tend to last longer, or are they roughly the same? What calculations could you do in order to compare the battery lives of the two brands?**

   It should be clear from the dot plot that the two brands are roughly the same in terms of expected battery life. One way of making this comparison would be to calculate the means for the two brands. The means are 101 hours for Brand A and 100.5 hours for Brand B, so there is very little difference between the two.

2. **Do the battery lives tend to differ more from battery to battery for Brand A or for Brand B?**

   The dot plot shows that the variability in battery life is greater for Brand B than for Brand A.

3. **Would you prefer a battery brand that has battery lives that do not vary much from battery to battery? Why or why not?**

   We prefer a brand with small variability in lifespan because these batteries will be more consistent and more predictable.

- What would I mean by "variability" in the set of battery lives? How could I measure it?

MP.1 Allow students to discuss ideas. Perhaps some come up with a general idea of the differences between the mean and the values. Perhaps some students notice the term *deviation from the mean* in the table that follows the questions just completed. If not:

- Notice that in the next table in your packet (Brand A), the second row says "Deviation from the Mean." How do you suppose you might fill in this row of the table?

The table below shows the lives (in hours) of the Brand A batteries.

Life (Hours)	83	94	96	106	113	114
Deviation from the Mean	-18	-7	-5	$+5$	$+12$	$+13$

4. Calculate the deviations from the mean for the remaining values, and write your answers in the appropriate places in the table.

The table below shows the battery lives and the deviations from the mean for Brand B.

Life (Hours)	73	76	92	94	110	117	118	124
Deviation from the Mean	-27.5	-24.5	-8.5	-6.5	9.5	16.5	17.5	23.5

Guide students to conclude the following, and work a couple of examples as a group:

- To calculate the deviations from the mean, we take each data value, x, and subtract the mean, $\bar{x}$, from that data value. The mean for Brand A is 101 hours.
- The deviation from the mean for the battery whose life was 114 is $x - \bar{x} = 114 - 101 = 13$.
- For the battery whose life was 83 hours, the deviation from the mean is $83 - 101 = -18$.

Students finish filling in the table independently (Exercise 4) and confirm answers with a neighbor.

- What do you notice about the values you came up with?
  - *The values that are greater than the mean have positive deviations from the mean, and the values that are less than the mean have negative deviations from the mean.*
- Notice the next table showing deviations from the mean for Brand B.
- Ignoring the sign of the deviation, which data set tends to have larger deviations from the mean—A or B?
- Why do you think that is?

Encourage students to summarize that the greater the *variability (spread) of the distribution, the greater the deviations from the mean*.

- What do the deviations from the mean look like on the dot plot?

You could draw or project the dot plot for the Brand A batteries on the board, and students might volunteer to come to the front of the room, locate the mean on the dot plot, and show on the dot plot the distances of the points from the mean. This is an important step toward a full understanding of deviations from the mean.

After seeing the deviations from the mean for Brand B, students see that this second brand has deviations from the mean that are generally larger than those for Brand A. This comes about as a result of the fact that the distribution for Brand B has a greater spread than the distribution for Brand A.

Exercises 5–10 (10 minutes)

Allow students to work Exercises 5–10 independently and then compare their answers with a neighbor. Frame discussions around any disagreements between students.

Exercises 5–10

The lives of five batteries of a third brand, Brand C, were determined. The dot plot below shows the lives of the Brand A and Brand C batteries.

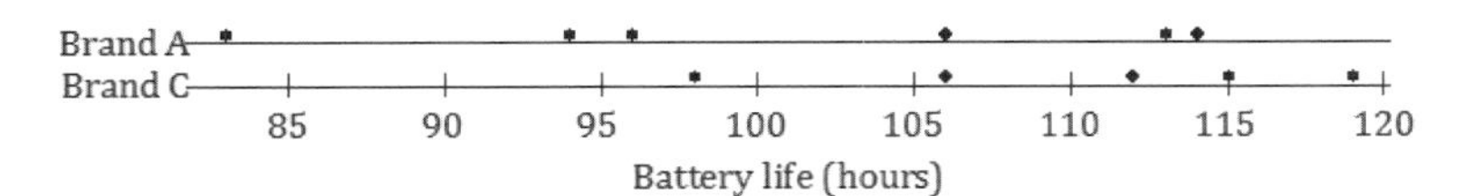

5. **Which brand has the greater mean battery life? (You should be able to answer this question without doing any calculations.)**

   Brand C has a greater mean battery life.

6. **Which brand shows greater variability?**

   Brand A shows greater variability.

7. **Which brand would you expect to have the greater deviations from the mean (ignoring the signs of the deviations)?**

   Brand A would have greater deviations from the mean.

The table below shows the lives for the Brand C batteries.

Life (Hours)	115	119	112	98	106
Deviation from the Mean	5	9	2	−12	−4

8. **Calculate the mean battery life for Brand C. (Be sure to include a unit in your answer.)**

   The mean battery life for Brand C is 110 hours.

9. **Write the deviations from the mean in the empty cells of the table for Brand C.**

   See table above.

10. **Ignoring the signs, are the deviations from the mean generally larger for Brand A or for Brand C? Does your answer agree with your answer to Exercise 7?**

    The deviations from the mean are generally larger for Brand A. Yes, my answer agrees with my answer to Exercise 7.

Exercises 11–15 (10 minutes)

Allow students to work Exercises 11–15 independently and then compare their answers with a neighbor. Frame discussions around any disagreements between students.

Exercises 11–15

The lives of 100 batteries of Brand D and 100 batteries of Brand E were determined. The results are summarized in the histograms below.

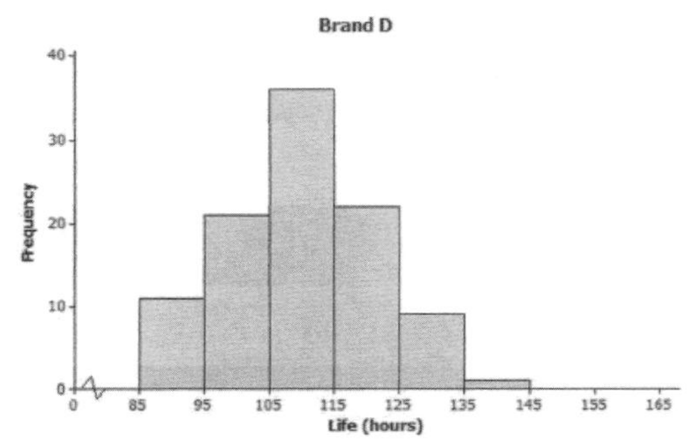

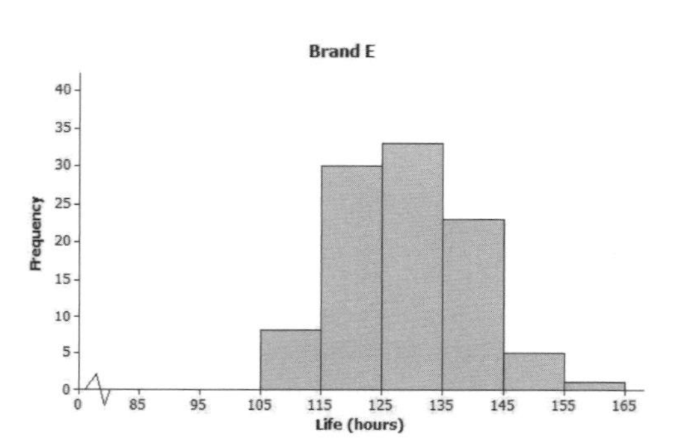

11. **Estimate the mean battery life for Brand D. (Do not do any calculations.)**

    The mean battery life is approximately 110 ***hours.***

12. **Estimate the mean battery life for Brand E. (Do not do any calculations.)**

    The mean battery life is approximately 130 ***hours.***

13. **Which of Brands D and E shows the greater variability in battery lives? Do you think the two brands are roughly the same in this regard?**

    The two brands are roughly the same in terms of variability.

14. **Estimate the largest deviation from the mean for Brand D.**

    The estimate for the largest value is 143 ***hours. So, the largest deviation is*** 143 ***hours*** $-$ 110 ***hours, or*** 33 ***hours.***

15. **What would you consider a typical deviation from the mean for Brand D?**

    Answers will vary. Sensible answers would be between 5 ***and*** 16 ***hours.***

If there is time available, it would be useful to show students how to *calculate* an estimate of the mean for Brand E. See below for a histogram with the frequencies shown in parentheses.

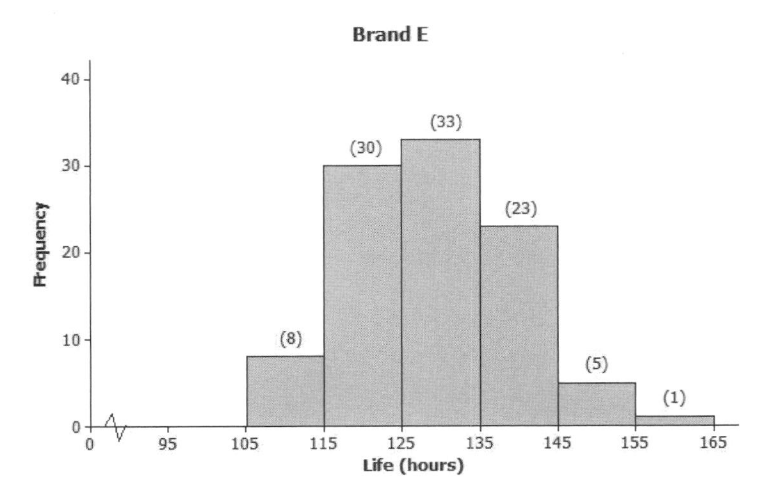

The actual lives of the batteries cannot be determined from the histogram, so we have to assume that the lives of all the batteries represented by the first block were 110 hours, the lives of all the batteries represented by the second block were 120 hours, and so on.

Making this assumption, adding up all of the battery lives gives us:

$$8 \cdot 110 + 30 \cdot 120 + 33 \cdot 130 + 23 \cdot 140 + 5 \cdot 150 + 1 \cdot 160 = 12900.$$

The total number of batteries in the study is

$$8 + 30 + 33 + 23 + 5 + 1 = 100.$$

So, our estimate of the mean battery life is $\frac{12900 \text{ hours}}{100} = 129$ hours.

It would be beneficial to ask students this focus question: When adding up the battery lives above, why did we multiply 110 by 8, 120 by 30, and so on?

Closing (2 minutes)

> **Lesson Summary**
>
> - **For any given value in a data set, the deviation from the mean is the value minus the mean. Written algebraically, this is $x - \bar{x}$.**
> - **The greater the variability (spread) of the distribution, the greater the deviations from the mean (ignoring the signs of the deviations).**

Exit Ticket (8 minutes)

Name ______________________________ Date ______________

Lesson 4: Summarizing Deviations from the Mean

Exit Ticket

Five people were asked approximately how many hours of TV they watched per week. Their responses were as follows.

$$6 \quad 4 \quad 6 \quad 7 \quad 8$$

1. Find the mean number of hours of TV watched for these five people.

2. Find the deviations from the mean for these five data values.

3. Write a new set of five values that has roughly the same mean as the data set above but that has, generally speaking, greater deviations from the mean.

Exit Ticket Sample Solutions

Five people were asked approximately how many hours of TV they watched per week. Their responses were as follows.

$$6 \quad 4 \quad 6 \quad 7 \quad 8$$

1. Find the mean number of hours of TV watched for these five people.

   Mean $= \dfrac{6+4+6+7+8}{5} = 6.2$

2. Find the deviations from the mean for these five data values.

   The deviations from the mean are -0.2, -2.2, -0.2, 0.8, *and* 1.8.

3. Write a new set of five values that has roughly the same mean as the data set above but that has, generally speaking, greater deviations from the mean.

   There are many correct answers to this question. Check that students' answers contain five numbers, that the mean is around 6.2, *and that the spread of the numbers is obviously greater than that of the original set of five values. Here is one example:* $0, 0, 0, 15, 16$.

Problem Set Sample Solutions

1. Ten members of a high school girls' basketball team were asked how many hours they studied in a typical week. Their responses (in hours) were $20, 13, 10, 6, 13, 10, 13, 11, 11, 10$.

   a. Using the axis given below, draw a dot plot of these values. (Remember, when there are repeated values, stack the dots with one above the other.)

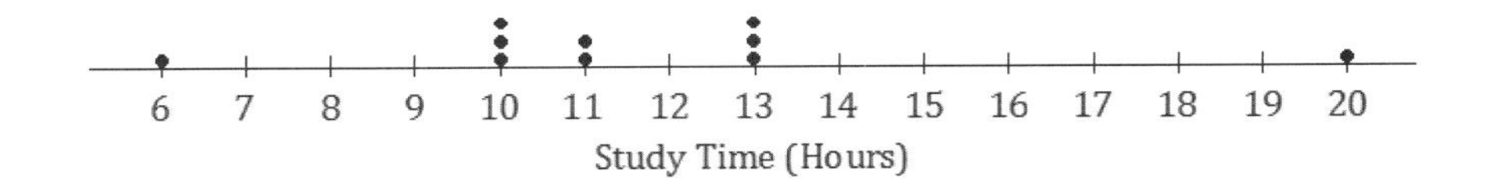

   b. Calculate the mean study time for these students.

   Mean $= 11.7$

   c. Calculate the deviations from the mean for these study times, and write your answers in the appropriate places in the table below.

Number of Hours Studied	20	13	10	6	13	10	13	11	11	10
Deviation from the Mean	8.3	1.3	-1.7	-5.7	1.3	-1.7	1.3	-0.7	-0.7	-1.7

d. The study times for fourteen girls from the soccer team at the same school as the one above are shown in the dot plot below.

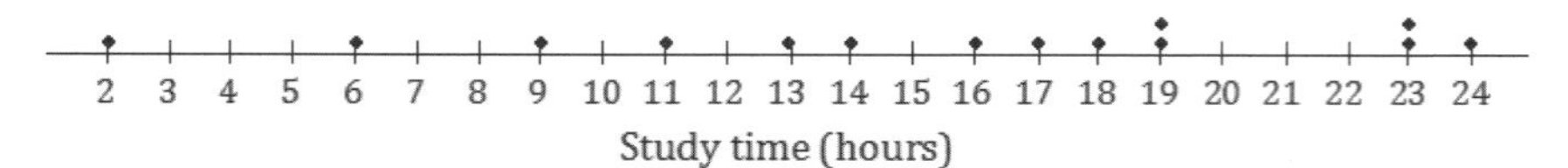

Based on the data, would the deviations from the mean (ignoring the sign of the deviations) be greater or less for the soccer players than for the basketball players?

The spread of the distribution of study times for the soccer players is greater than that for the basketball players. So, the deviations from the mean would be greater for the soccer players than for the basketball players.

2. All the members of a high school softball team were asked how many hours they studied in a typical week. The results are shown in the histogram below.

(The data set in this question comes from NCTM Core Math Tools, http://www.nctm.org/Classroom-Resources/Core-Math-Tools/Data-Sets/)

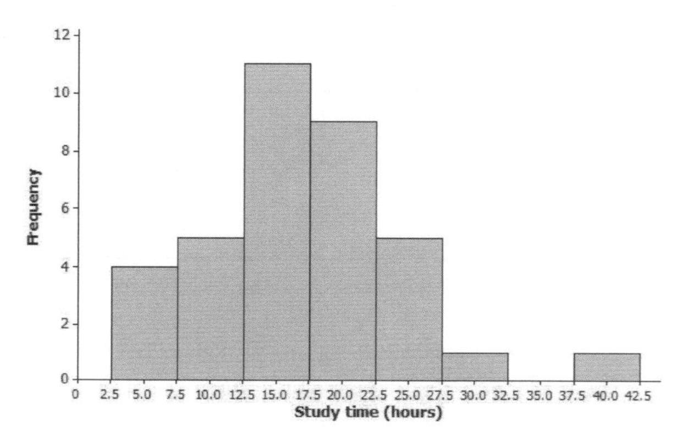

a. We can see from the histogram that four students studied around 5 hours per week. How many students studied around 15 hours per week?

Eleven students studied around 15 hours per week.

b. How many students were there in total?

Number of students $= 4 + 5 + 11 + 9 + 5 + 1 + 0 + 1 = 36$

c. Suppose that the four students represented by the histogram bar centered at 5 had all studied exactly 5 hours, the five students represented by the next histogram bar had all studied exactly 10 hours, and so on. If you were to add up the study times for all of the students, what result would you get?

$(4 \cdot 5) + (5 \cdot 10) + (11 \cdot 15) + (9 \cdot 20) + (5 \cdot 25) + (1 \cdot 30) + (0 \cdot 35) + (1 \cdot 40) = 610$

d. What is the mean study time for these students?

Mean $= \frac{610}{36} = 16.94$

e. What would you consider to be a typical deviation from the mean for this data set?

Answers will vary. A correct answer would be something between 4 and 10 hours. (The mean absolute deviation from the mean for the original data set was 5.2, and the standard deviation was 7.1.)

Lesson 5: Measuring Variability for Symmetrical Distributions

Student Outcomes

- Students calculate the standard deviation for a set of data.
- Students interpret the standard deviation as a typical distance from the mean.

Lesson Notes

In this lesson, students calculate standard deviation for the first time and examine the process for its calculation more closely. Through questioning and discussion, students link each step in the process to its meaning in the context of the problem and explore the many questions about the rationale behind the development of the formula. Guiding questions and responses to facilitate this discussion are provided as the closing discussion for this lesson. However, it is recommended that the discussion be allowed to occur at any point in the lesson when students are asking questions about the calculation of standard deviation.

Classwork

Example 1 (12 minutes): Calculating the Standard Deviation

Discuss the following points with students using the dot plot and students' previous results in Lesson 4.

- In Lesson 4, we looked at what might be a typical deviation from the mean. We will now develop a way to use the deviations from the mean to calculate a measure of variability called the *standard deviation*.
- Let's return to the battery lifetimes of Brand A from Lesson 4. Look at the dot plot of the lives of the Brand A batteries.

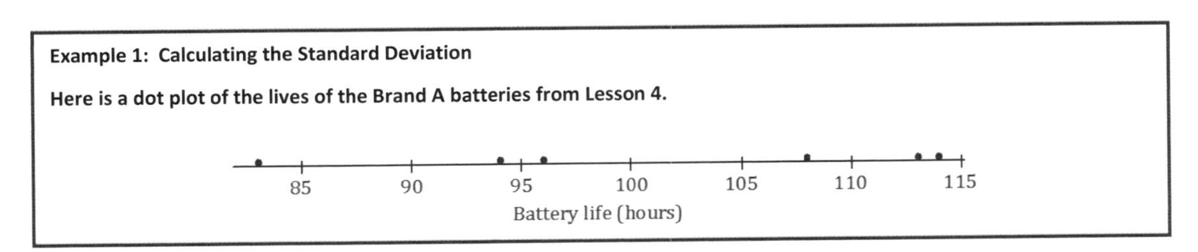

- The mean was 101 hours. Mark the location of the mean on the dot plot above.
- What is a typical distance or deviation from the mean for these Brand A batteries?
  - *A typical deviation is around* 10 *hours.*
- Now let's explore a more common measure of deviation from the mean—the standard deviation.

Walk students through the steps in their lesson resources for Example 1.

How do you measure variability of this data set? One way is by calculating standard deviation.

- **First, find each deviation from the mean.**
- **Then, square the deviations from the mean. For example, when the deviation from the mean is -18, the squared deviation from the mean is $(-18)^2 = 324$.**

Life (Hours)	83	94	96	106	113	114
Deviation from the Mean	-18	-7	-5	5	12	13
Squared Deviations from the Mean	324	49	25	25	144	169

- **Add up the squared deviations:**

  $324 + 49 + 25 + 25 + 144 + 169 = 736.$

  This result is the *sum* of the squared deviations.

The number of values in the data set is denoted by n. In this example, n is 6.

- **You divide the sum of the squared deviations by $n - 1$, which here is $6 - 1$, or 5.**

$$\frac{736}{5} = 147.2$$

- **Finally, you take the square root of 147.2, which to the nearest hundredth is 12.13.**

That is the standard deviation! It seems like a very complicated process at first, but you will soon get used to it.

We conclude that a typical deviation of a Brand A battery lifetime from the mean battery lifetime for Brand A is 12.13 hours. The unit of standard deviation is always the same as the unit of the original data set. So, the standard deviation to the nearest hundredth, with the unit, is 12.13 hours. How close is the answer to the typical deviation that you estimated at the beginning of the lesson?

- How close is the answer to the typical deviation that you estimated at the beginning of the lesson?
  - *It is fairly close to the typical deviation of around* 10 *hours.*

The value of 12.13 could be considered to be reasonably close to the earlier estimate of 10. The fact that the standard deviation is a little larger than the earlier estimate could be attributed to the effect of the point at 83. The standard deviation is affected more by values with comparatively large deviations from the mean than, for example, is the mean absolute deviation that students learned about in Grade 6.

This is a good time to mention precision when calculating the standard deviation. Encourage students, when calculating the standard deviation, to use several decimal places in the value that they use for the mean. Explain that students might get somewhat varying answers for the standard deviation depending on how far they round the value of the mean.

Exercises 1–5 (8 minutes)

Have students work independently and confirm answers with a neighbor or the group. Discuss any conflicting answers as needed.

Exercises 1–5

Now you can calculate the standard deviation of the lifetimes for the eight Brand B batteries. The mean was 100.5. We already have the deviations from the mean.

Life (Hours)	73	76	92	94	110	117	118	124
Deviation from the Mean	-27.5	-24.5	-8.5	-6.5	9.5	16.5	17.5	23.5
Squared Deviation from the Mean	756.25	600.25	72.25	42.25	90.25	272.25	306.25	552.25

1. **Write the squared deviations in the table.**

   See table above.

2. **Add up the squared deviations. What result do you get?**

   The sum is $2,692$.

3. **What is the value of n for this data set? Divide the sum of the squared deviations by $n-1$, and write your answer below. Round your answer to the nearest thousandth.**

   $n = 8; \frac{2692}{7} \approx 384.571$

4. **Take the square root to find the standard deviation. Record your answer to the nearest hundredth.**

   $\sqrt{384.571} \approx 19.61$

5. **How would you interpret the standard deviation that you found in Exercise 4? (Remember to give your answer in the context of this question. Interpret your answer to the nearest hundredth.)**

   The standard deviation, 19.61 ***hours, is a typical deviation of a Brand B battery lifetime from the mean battery lifetime for Brand B.***

- So, now we have computed the standard deviation of the data on Brand A and of the data on Brand B. Compare the two, and describe what you notice in the context of the problem.
  - *The fact that the standard deviation for Brand B is greater than the standard deviation for Brand A tells us that the battery life of Brand B had a greater spread (or variability) than the battery life of Brand A. This means that the Brand B battery lifetimes tended to vary more from one battery to another than the battery lifetimes for Brand A.*

Exercises 6–7 (8 minutes)

Have students work independently and confirm answers with a neighbor or the group. Discuss any conflicting answers as needed.

> **Exercises 6–7**
>
> **Jenna has bought a new hybrid car. Each week for a period of seven weeks, she has noted the fuel efficiency (in miles per gallon) of her car. The results are shown below.**
>
> $$45 \quad 44 \quad 43 \quad 44 \quad 45 \quad 44 \quad 43$$
>
> 6. **Calculate the standard deviation of these results to the nearest hundredth. Be sure to show your work.**
>
>   *The mean is* 44.
>
>   *The deviations from the mean are* $1,\ 0,\ -1,\ 0,\ 1,\ 0,\ -1$.
>
>   *The squared deviations from the mean are* $1,\ 0,\ 1,\ 0,\ 1,\ 0,\ 1$.
>
>   *The sum of the squared deviations is* 4.
>
> $n = 7;\ \frac{4}{6} \approx 0.667$
>
>   *The standard deviation is* $\sqrt{0.667}$ *which is approximately* 0.82 *miles per gallon.*
>
> 7. **What is the meaning of the standard deviation you found in Exercise 6?**
>
>   *The standard deviation,* 0.82 *miles per gallon, is a typical deviation of a weekly fuel efficiency value from the mean weekly fuel efficiency.*

Closing (7 minutes)

- What result would we get if we just added the deviations from the mean?
  - *Zero. This value highlights the fact that the mean is the balance point for the original distribution.*
- Why do you suppose that we square each deviation?
  - *This is one way to avoid the numbers adding to zero. By squaring the deviations, we make sure that all the numbers are positive.*

Students might also ask why we square the deviations and then take the square root at the end. Why not just find the average of the absolute values of the deviations from the mean? The answer is that the two approaches give different answers. (The square root of an average of squares of positive numbers is different from the average of the original set of numbers.) However, this idea of finding the mean of the absolute values of the deviations is a perfectly valid measure of the variability of a data set. This measure of spread is known as the mean absolute deviation (MAD), and students used this measure in previous years. The reason that variance and standard deviation are used more commonly than the mean absolute deviation is that the variance (and, therefore, the standard deviation) turns out to behave very nicely, mathematically, and is useful for developing relatively straightforward techniques of statistical analysis.

- Why do we take the square root?
  - *Before taking the square root, we have a typical squared deviation from the mean. It is easier to interpret a typical deviation from the mean than a typical squared deviation from the mean because a typical deviation has the same units as the original data. For example, the typical deviation from the mean for the battery life data is expressed in hours rather than hours^2.*
- Why did we divide by $n-1$ instead of n?
  - *We only use $n-1$ when we are calculating the standard deviation using sample data. Careful study has shown that using $n-1$ gives the best estimate of the standard deviation for the entire population. If we have data from an entire population, we would divide by n instead of $n-1$. (See note below for a detailed explanation.)*

NOTE: This topic is addressed throughout a study of statistics:

More information on why to divide by $n-1$ and not n:

It is helpful to first explore the variance. The variance of a set of values is the square of the standard deviation. So, to calculate the variance, the same process is used, but the square root is not taken at the end.

Suppose, for a start, that there is a very large population of values, for example, the heights of all the people in a country. One can think of the variance of this population as being calculated using a division by n (although, since the population is very large, the difference between using n or $n-1$ for the population is extremely small).

Imagine now taking a random sample from the population, such as taking a random sample of people from the country and measuring their heights. Use the variance of the sample as an estimate of the variance of the population. If division by n is used in calculating the variance of the sample, the result tends to be a little too small as an estimate of the population variance. (To be a little more precise about this, the sample variance would sometimes be smaller and sometimes larger than the population variance. But, on average, over all possible samples, the sample variance is a little too small.)

So, something has to be done about the formula for the sample variance in order to fix this problem of its tendency to be too small as an estimate of the population variance. It turns out, mathematically, that replacing the n with $n-1$ has exactly the desired effect. Now, when dividing by $n-1$, rather than n, even though the sample variance is sometimes greater and sometimes less than the population variance, on average, the sample variance is correct as an estimator of the population variance.

- What does standard deviation measure? How can we summarize what we are attempting to compute?
  - *The value of the standard deviation is close to the average distance of observations from the mean. It can be interpreted as a typical deviation from the mean.*
- How does the spread of the distribution relate to the value of the standard deviation?
  - *The larger the spread of the distribution, the larger the standard deviation.*
- Who can write a formula for standard deviation, s?
  - *Encourage students to attempt to write the formula without assistance, perhaps comparing their results with their peers.*

$$s=\sqrt{\frac{\sum(x-\bar{x})^2}{n-1}}$$

In this formula,

- x is a value from the original data set;
- $x - \bar{x}$ is a deviation of the value, x, from the mean, $\bar{x}$;
- $(x - \bar{x})^2$ is a squared deviation from the mean;
- $\sum(x - \bar{x})^2$ is the sum of the squared deviations;
- $\frac{\sum(x-\bar{x})^2}{n-1}$ is the result of dividing the sum of the squared deviations by $n - 1$;
- So, $\sqrt{\frac{\sum(x-\bar{x})^2}{n-1}}$ is the standard deviation.

Lesson Summary

- **The standard deviation measures a typical deviation from the mean.**
- **To calculate the standard deviation,**
  1. **Find the mean of the data set;**
  2. **Calculate the deviations from the mean;**
  3. **Square the deviations from the mean;**
  4. **Add up the squared deviations;**
  5. **Divide by $n - 1$ (if working with data from a sample, which is the most common case);**
  6. **Take the square root.**
- **The unit of the standard deviation is always the same as the unit of the original data set.**
- **The larger the standard deviation, the greater the spread (variability) of the data set.**

Exit Ticket (10 minutes)

Name ____________________________________ Date ____________________

Lesson 5: Measuring Variability for Symmetrical Distributions

Exit Ticket

1. Look at the dot plot below.

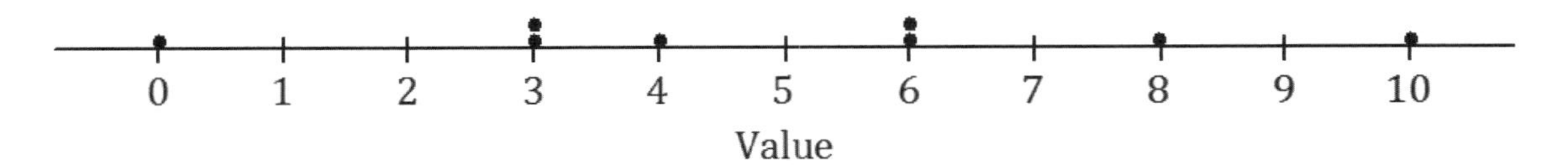

a. *Estimate* the mean of this data set.

b. Remember that the standard deviation measures a typical deviation from the mean. The standard deviation of this data set is either 3.2, 6.2, or 9.2. Which of these values is correct for the standard deviation?

2. Three data sets are shown in the dot plots below.

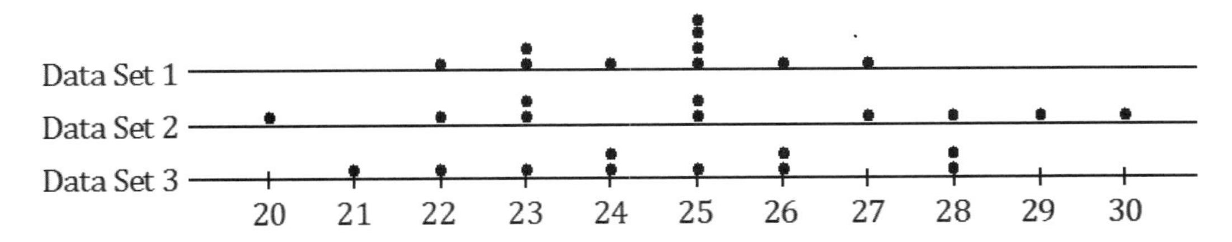

a. Which data set has the smallest standard deviation of the three? Justify your answer.

b. Which data set has the largest standard deviation of the three? Justify your answer.

Exit Ticket Sample Solutions

1. Look at the dot plot below.

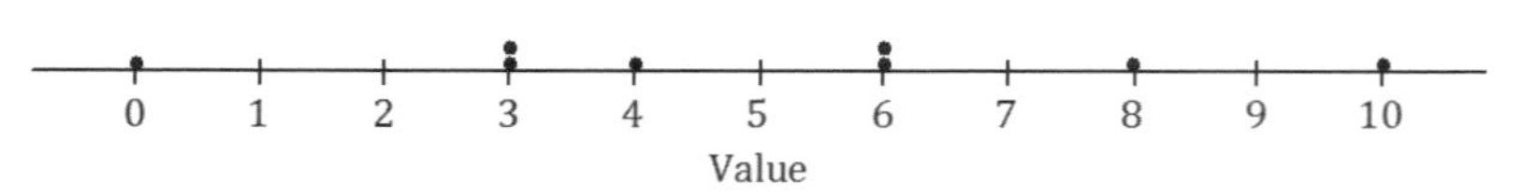

   a. *Estimate* the mean of this data set.

   The mean of the data set is 5, so any number above 4 and below 6 would be acceptable as an estimate of the mean.

   b. Remember that the standard deviation measures a typical deviation from the mean. The standard deviation of this data set is either 3.2, 6.2, or 9.2. Which of these values is correct for the standard deviation?

   The greatest deviation from the mean is 5 (found by calculating $10 - 5$ or $0 - 5$), and a typical deviation from the mean must be less than 5. So, 3.2 must be chosen as the standard deviation.

2. Three data sets are shown in the dot plots below.

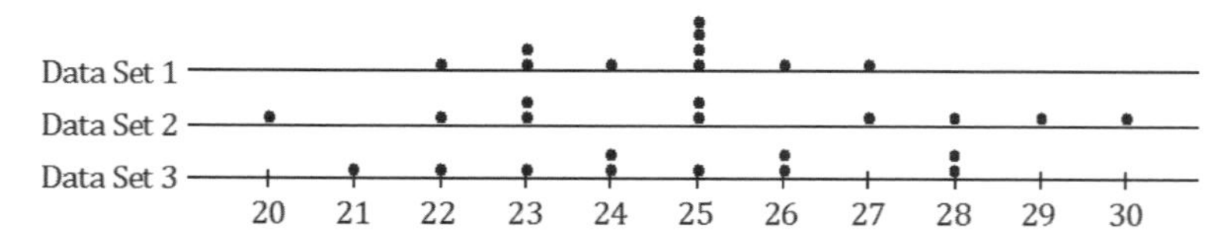

   a. Which data set has the smallest standard deviation of the three? Justify your answer.

   Data Set 1

   The points are clustered more closely together in Data Set 1. The deviations or the distances of the points to the left and to the right of the mean position would be smaller for this data set. As a result, the sum of the squares of the distances would also be smaller; thus, the standard deviation would be smaller.

   b. Which data set has the largest standard deviation of the three? Justify your answer.

   Data Set 2

   The points of this data set are the most spread out. The deviations or the distances of the points to the left and to the right of the mean position would be larger for this data set. The sum of the squares of the distances would also be larger. As a result, the standard deviation would be larger.

Problem Set Sample Solutions

1. A small car dealership tests the fuel efficiency of sedans on its lot. It chooses 12 sedans for the test. The fuel efficiency (mpg) values of the cars are given in the table below. Complete the table as directed below.

Fuel Efficiency (miles per gallon)	29	35	24	25	21	21	18	28	31	26	26	22
Deviation from the Mean	3.5	9.5	-1.5	-0.5	-4.5	-4.5	-7.5	2.5	5.5	0.5	0.5	-3.5
Squared Deviation from the Mean	12.25	90.25	2.25	0.25	20.25	20.25	56.25	6.25	30.25	0.25	0.25	12.25

a. Calculate the mean fuel efficiency for these cars.

Mean $= 25.5$

b. Calculate the deviations from the mean, and write your answers in the second row of the table.

See table above.

c. Square the deviations from the mean, and write the squared deviations in the third row of the table.

See table above.

d. Find the sum of the squared deviations.

The sum of the squared deviations is 251.

e. What is the value of n for this data set? Divide the sum of the squared deviations by $n - 1$.

$n = 12$

$\frac{251}{11} = 22.818$, *to the nearest thousandth.*

f. Take the square root of your answer to part (e) to find the standard deviation of the fuel efficiencies of these cars. Round your answer to the nearest hundredth.

$\sqrt{22.818} = 4.78$

The standard deviation of the fuel efficiencies of these cars is 4.78 *miles per gallon.*

2. **The same dealership decides to test fuel efficiency of SUVs. It selects six SUVs on its lot for the test. The fuel efficiencies (in miles per gallon) of these cars are shown below.**

$$21 \quad 21 \quad 21 \quad 30 \quad 28 \quad 24$$

Calculate the mean and the standard deviation of these values. Be sure to show your work, and include a unit in your answer.

Mean $= 24.17$ *miles per gallon; standard deviation* $= 3.97$ *miles per gallon*

Note: Students might get somewhat varying answers for the standard deviation depending on how far they round the value of the mean. Encourage students, when calculating the standard deviation, to use several decimal places in the value that they use for the mean.

3. **Consider the following questions regarding the cars described in Problems 1 and 2.**

   a. **What is the standard deviation of the fuel efficiencies of the cars in Problem 1? Explain what this value tells you.**

   The standard deviation for the cars in Problem 1 is 4.78 *miles per gallon. This is a typical deviation from the mean for the fuel efficiencies of the cars in Problem 1.*

   b. **You also calculated the standard deviation of the fuel efficiencies for the cars in Problem 2. Which of the two data sets (Problem 1 or Problem 2) has the larger standard deviation? What does this tell you about the two types of cars (sedans and SUVs)?**

   The standard deviation is greater for the cars in Problem 1. This tells us that there is greater variability in the fuel efficiencies of the cars in Problem 1 (the sedans) than in the fuel efficiencies of the cars in Problem 2 (the SUVs). This means that the fuel efficiency varies more from car to car for sedans than for SUVs.

Lesson 6: Interpreting the Standard Deviation

Student Outcomes

- Students calculate the standard deviation of a sample with the aid of a calculator.
- Students compare the relative variability of distributions using standard deviations.

Lesson Notes

Students use a calculator to compute the mean and the standard deviation of a data set and compare the variability of data sets where the differences in variability are less obvious than in previous lessons. Additionally, students continue to refine their knowledge of standard deviation and how it measures a typical deviation from the mean.

Classwork

Example 1 (10 minutes)

Use a calculator to find the mean and standard deviation.

> **Example 1**
>
> **Your teacher will show you how to use a calculator to find the mean and standard deviation for the following set of data.**
>
> **A set of eight men have heights (in inches) as shown below.**
>
> $67.0 \quad 70.9 \quad 67.6 \quad 69.8 \quad 69.7 \quad 70.9 \quad 68.7 \quad 67.2$
>
> **Indicate the mean and standard deviation you obtained from your calculator to the nearest hundredth.**
>
> **Mean:** 68.98 *inches*
>
> **Standard Deviation:** 1.59 *inches*

Show students the steps to calculate the mean and the standard deviation of a data set using a calculator or statistical software. The following instructions outline the steps of the statistical features for the TI-83 or TI-84 calculators (one of several calculators used by high school students):

1. From the home screen, press STAT, ENTER to access the stat editor.
2. If there are already numbers in L1, clear the data from L1 by moving the cursor to L1 and pressing CLEAR, ENTER.
3. Move the cursor to the first element of L1, type the first data value, and press ENTER. Continue entering the remaining data values to L1 in the same way.
4. Press 2ND, QUIT to return to the home screen.
5. Press STAT, select CALC, select 1-Var Stats, and press ENTER.
6. The screen should now show summary statistics for your data set. The mean is the $\bar{x}$ value, and the standard deviation for a sample is the s_x value.

Note: Instructions may vary based on the type of calculator or software used. The instructions above are based on using data stored in L1. If data are stored in another list, they need to be referred to after selecting 1-Var Stats in step 5. For example, if data were entered in L2:

5. Press STAT, select CALC, select 1-Var Stats, and then refer to L2. This is done by pressing 2ND, L2 (i.e., 2ND and then the 2 key). The screen will display 1-Var Stats L2. Then, press ENTER.

Exercise 1 (5 minutes)

Students should practice finding the mean and standard deviation on their own.

Exercise 1

1. **The heights (in inches) of nine women are as shown below.**

   $68.4 \quad 70.9 \quad 67.4 \quad 67.7 \quad 67.1 \quad 69.2 \quad 66.0 \quad 70.3 \quad 67.6$

   Use the statistical features of your calculator or computer software to find the mean and the standard deviation of these heights to the nearest hundredth.

   Mean: 68.29 *inches*

   Standard Deviation: 1.58 *inches*

Exploratory Challenge/Exercises 2–5

Exercise 2 (5 minutes)

Be sure that students understand how the numbers that are entered relate to the dot plot given in the example as they enter the data into a calculator.

Ask students the following question to determine if they understand the dot plot:

- What is the meaning of the single dot at 4?
  - *Only one person answered all four questions.*

A common misconception is that a student answered Question 4 of the survey and not that a person answered four questions.

Allow students to attempt the problem independently. Sample responses are listed on the next page. If needed, scaffold with the following:

- The dot plot tells us that one person answered 0 questions, two people answered 1 question, four people answered 2 questions, two people answered 3 questions, and one person answered 4 questions.
- We can find the mean and the standard deviation of these results by entering these numbers into a calculator:

  $0 \quad 1 \quad 1 \quad 2 \quad 2 \quad 2 \quad 2 \quad 3 \quad 3 \quad 4$

Exploratory Challenge/Exercises 2–5

2. **A group of people attended a talk at a conference. At the end of the talk, ten of the attendees were given a questionnaire that consisted of four questions. The questions were optional, so it was possible that some attendees might answer none of the questions, while others might answer 1, 2, 3, or all 4 of the questions (so, the possible numbers of questions answered are 0, 1, 2, 3, and 4).**

   Suppose that the numbers of questions answered by each of the ten people were as shown in the dot plot below.

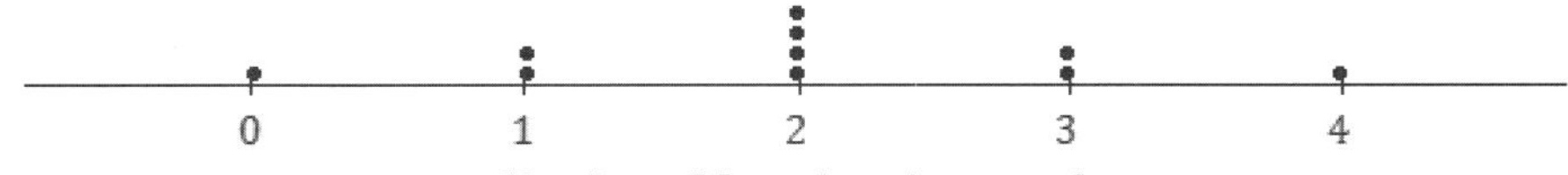

   Use the statistical features of your calculator to find the mean and the standard deviation of the data set.

   Mean: _2 questions_

   Standard Deviation: _1.15 questions_

Exercise 3 (5 minutes)

Students should practice finding the standard deviation on their own. The data are uniformly distributed in this problem, and its standard deviation is compared to Exercise 2.

3. **Suppose the dot plot looked like this:**

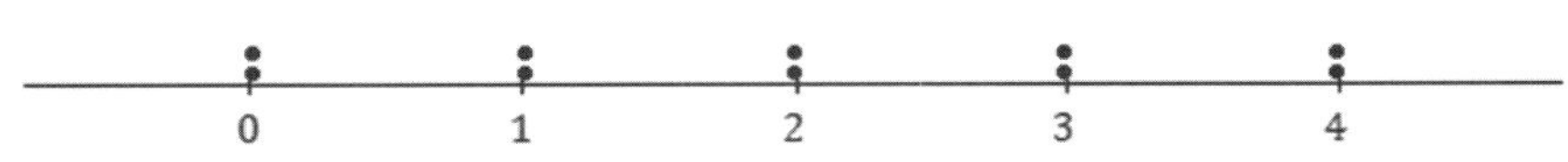

   a. **Use your calculator to find the mean and the standard deviation of this distribution.**

      Mean: *2 questions*

      Standard Deviation: *1.49 questions*

   b. **Remember that the size of the standard deviation is related to the size of the deviations from the mean. Explain why the standard deviation of this distribution is greater than the standard deviation in Exercise 2.**

      The points in Exercise 3 are generally farther from the mean than the points in Exercise 2, so the standard deviation is larger. Notice there is greater clustering of the points around the central value and less variability in Exercise 2.

Optionally, draw the following on the board, and compare the diagrams to reinforce the idea.

Mound Shaped:

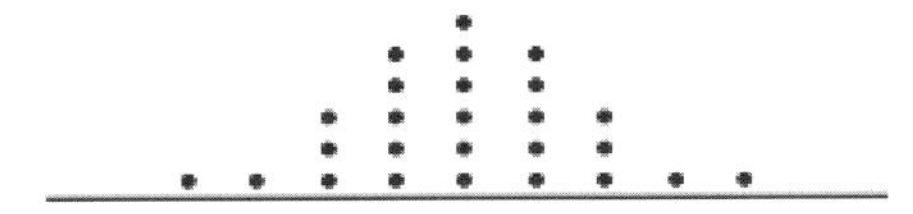

Uniform:

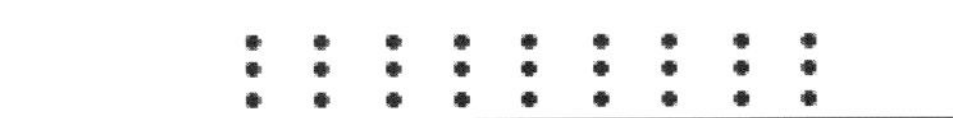

Exercise 4 (5 minutes)

Students work on this question individually and then compare notes with a neighbor. Students construct the plot and evaluate (without calculating) the mean and standard deviation of the data set where there is no variability.

4. Suppose that all ten people questioned answered all four questions on the questionnaire.

a. What would the dot plot look like?

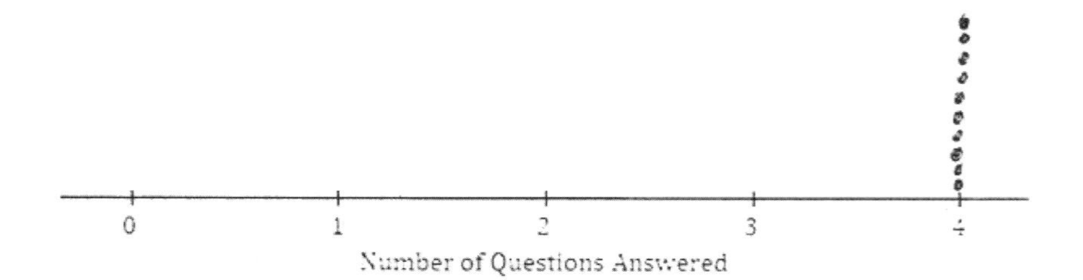

b. What is the mean number of questions answered? (You should be able to answer without doing any calculations!)

Mean: 4 questions

c. What is the standard deviation? (Again, don't do any calculations!)

The standard deviation is 0 because all deviations from the mean are 0. There is no variation in the data.

Exercise 5 (7 minutes)

Again, it would be a good idea for students to think about this themselves and then to discuss the problem with a neighbor.

5. Continue to think about the situation previously described where the numbers of questions answered by each of ten people was recorded.

a. Draw the dot plot of the distribution of possible data values that has the largest possible standard deviation. (There were ten people at the talk, so there should be ten dots in your dot plot.) Use the scale given below.

Place the data points as far from the mean as possible.

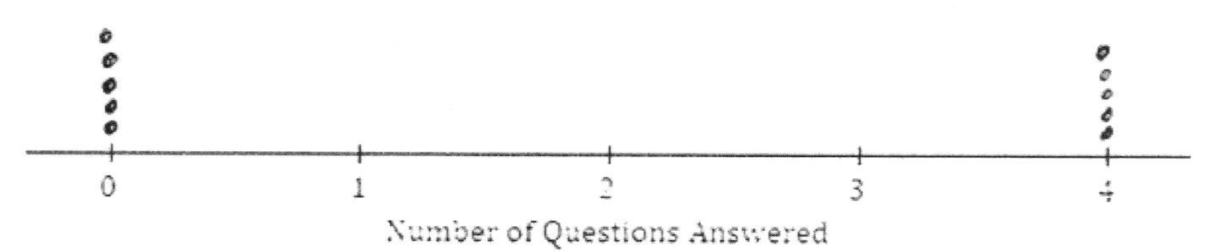

b. Explain why the distribution you have drawn has a larger standard deviation than the distribution in Exercise 4.

The standard deviation of this distribution is larger than that of the one in Exercise 4 because the deviations from the mean here are all greater than or equal to the deviations from the mean in Exercise 4.

Note for Exercise 5(a): The answer to this question is not necessarily obvious, but one way to think of it is that by moving one of the dots from 0 to 4, we are clustering more of the points together; the points at zero are isolated from those at 4, but by moving one dot from 0 to 4, there are now fewer dots suffering this degree of isolation than there were previously.

Closing (3 minutes)

> Lesson Summary
>
> - **The mean and the standard deviation of a data set can be found directly using the statistical features of a calculator.**
> - **The size of the standard deviation is related to the sizes of the deviations from the mean. Therefore, the standard deviation is minimized when all the numbers in the data set are the same and is maximized when the deviations from the mean are made as large as possible.**

Exit Ticket (5 minutes)

Name ______________________________ Date ______________

Lesson 6: Interpreting the Standard Deviation

Exit Ticket

1. Use the statistical features of your calculator to find the mean and the standard deviation to the nearest tenth of a data set of the miles per gallon from a sample of five cars.

$$24.9 \quad 24.7 \quad 24.7 \quad 23.4 \quad 27.9$$

2. Suppose that a teacher plans to give four students a quiz. The minimum possible score on the quiz is 0, and the maximum possible score is 10.

   a. What is the smallest possible standard deviation of the students' scores? Give an example of a possible set of four student scores that would have this standard deviation.

   b. What is the set of four student scores that would make the standard deviation as large as it could possibly be? Use your calculator to find this largest possible standard deviation.

Exit Ticket Sample Solutions

1. **Use the statistical features of your calculator to find the mean and the standard deviation to the nearest tenth of a data set of the miles per gallon from a sample of five cars.**

$$24.9 \quad 24.7 \quad 24.7 \quad 23.4 \quad 27.9$$

Mean: 25.1 *miles per gallon, to the nearest tenth*

Standard Deviation: 1.7 *miles per gallon, to the nearest tenth*

2. **Suppose that a teacher plans to give four students a quiz. The minimum possible score on the quiz is 0, and the maximum possible score is 10.**

   a. **What is the smallest possible standard deviation of the students' scores? Give an example of a possible set of four student scores that would have this standard deviation.**

   The minimum possible standard deviation is 0*. This will come about if all the students receive the same score (e.g., if every student scores an* 8 *on the quiz).*

   b. **What is the set of four student scores that would make the standard deviation as large as it could possibly be? Use your calculator to find this largest possible standard deviation.**

   $0, 0, 10, 10$

   Standard Deviation: 5.77*, to the nearest hundredth*

Problem Set Sample Solutions

Students must have access to a graphing calculator to complete the Problem Set.

1. **At a track meet, there are three men's 100 m races. The times for eight of the sprinters are recorded to the nearest $\frac{1}{10}$ of a second. The results of the three races for these eight sprinters are shown in the dot plots below.**

Race 1

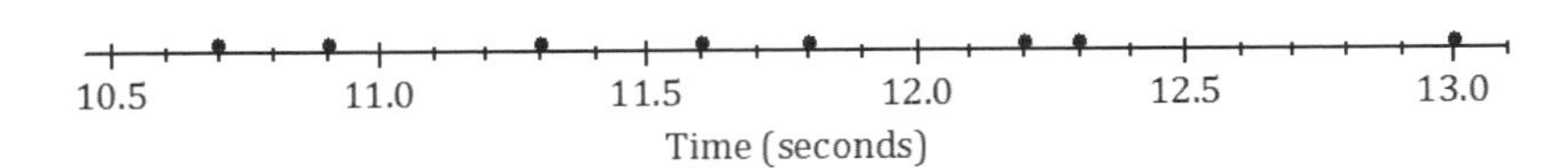

Race 2

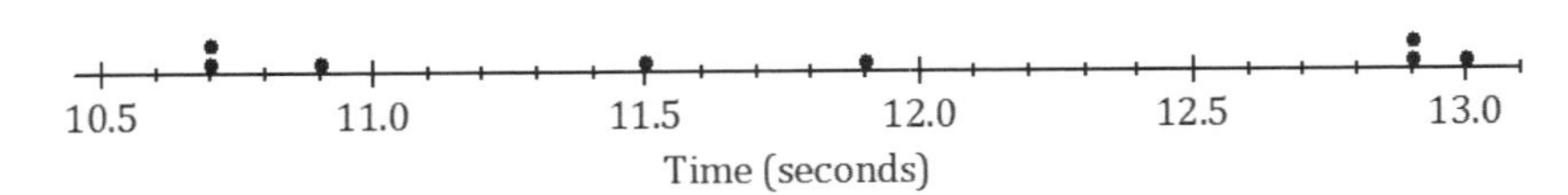

Race 3

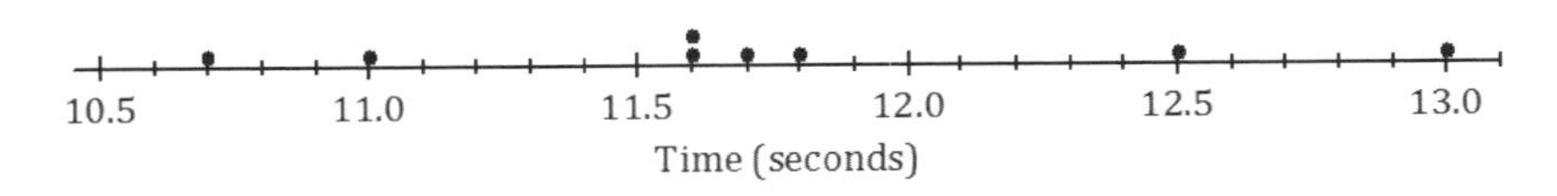

a. **Remember that the size of the standard deviation is related to the sizes of the deviations from the mean. Without doing any calculations, indicate which of the three races has the smallest standard deviation of times. Justify your answer.**

Race 3 has the smallest standard deviation because several race times are clustered around the mean.

b. **Which race had the largest standard deviation of times? (Again, don't do any calculations!) Justify your answer.**

Race 2 has the largest standard deviation because the race times are spread out from the mean.

c. **Roughly what would be the standard deviation in Race 1? (Remember that the standard deviation is a typical deviation from the mean. So, here you are looking for a typical deviation from the mean, in seconds, for Race 1.)**

Around 0.5–1.0 *second would be a sensible answer.*

d. **Use your calculator to find the mean and the standard deviation for each of the three races. Write your answers in the table below to the nearest thousandth.**

	Mean	Standard Deviation
Race 1	11.725	0.767
Race 2	11.813	1.013
Race 3	11.738	0.741

e. **How close were your answers for parts (a)–(c) to the actual values?**

Answers will vary based on students' responses.

2. **A large city, which we will call City A, holds a marathon. Suppose that the ages of the participants in the marathon that took place in City A were summarized in the histogram below.**

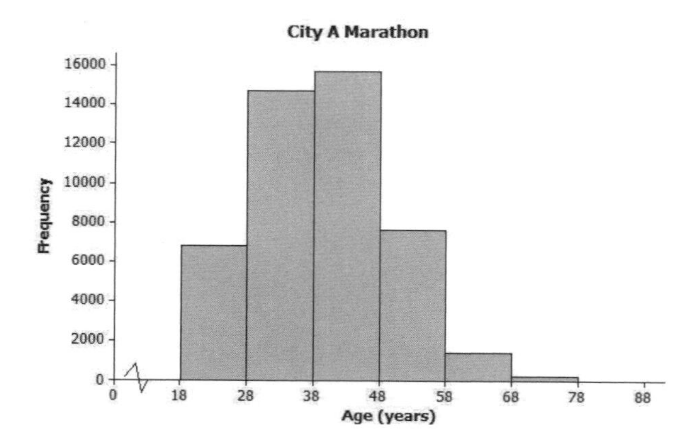

a. **Make an estimate of the mean age of the participants in the City A marathon.**

Around 40 *years would be a sensible estimate.*

b. Make an *estimate* of the standard deviation of the ages of the participants in the City A marathon.

Between 8 and 15 years would be a sensible estimate.

A smaller city, City B, also held a marathon. However, City B restricts the number of people of each age category who can take part to 100. The ages of the participants are summarized in the histogram below.

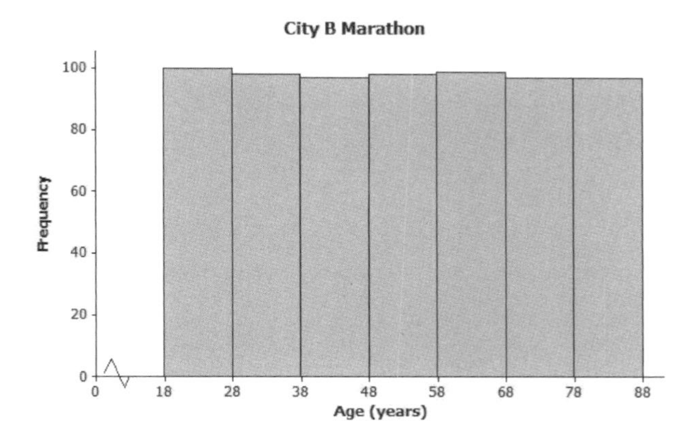

c. Approximately what was the mean age of the participants in the City B marathon? Approximately what was the standard deviation of the ages?

Mean is around 53 years; standard deviation is between 15 and 25 years.

d. Explain why the standard deviation of the ages in the City B marathon is greater than the standard deviation of the ages for the City A marathon.

In City A, there is greater clustering around the mean age than in City B. In City B, the deviations from the mean are generally greater than in City A, so the standard deviation for City B is greater than the standard deviation for City A.

Lesson 7: Measuring Variability for Skewed Distributions (Interquartile Range)

Student Outcomes

- Students explain why a median is a better description of a typical value for a skewed distribution.
- Students calculate the 5-number summary of a data set.
- Students construct a box plot based on the 5-number summary and calculate the interquartile range (IQR).
- Students interpret the IQR as a description of variability in the data.
- Students identify outliers in a data distribution.

Lesson Notes

Distributions that are not symmetrical pose some challenges in students' thinking about center and variability. The observation that the distribution is not symmetrical is straightforward. The difficult part is to select a measure of center and a measure of variability around that center. In Lesson 3, students learned that, because the mean can be affected by unusual values in the data set, the median is a better description of a typical data value for a skewed distribution. This lesson addresses what measure of variability is appropriate for a skewed data distribution. Students construct a box plot of the data using the 5-number summary and describe variability using the interquartile range.

Classwork

Exploratory Challenge 1/Exercises 1–3 (10 minutes): Skewed Data and Their Measure of Center

Verbally introduce the data set as described in the introductory paragraph and dot plot shown below.

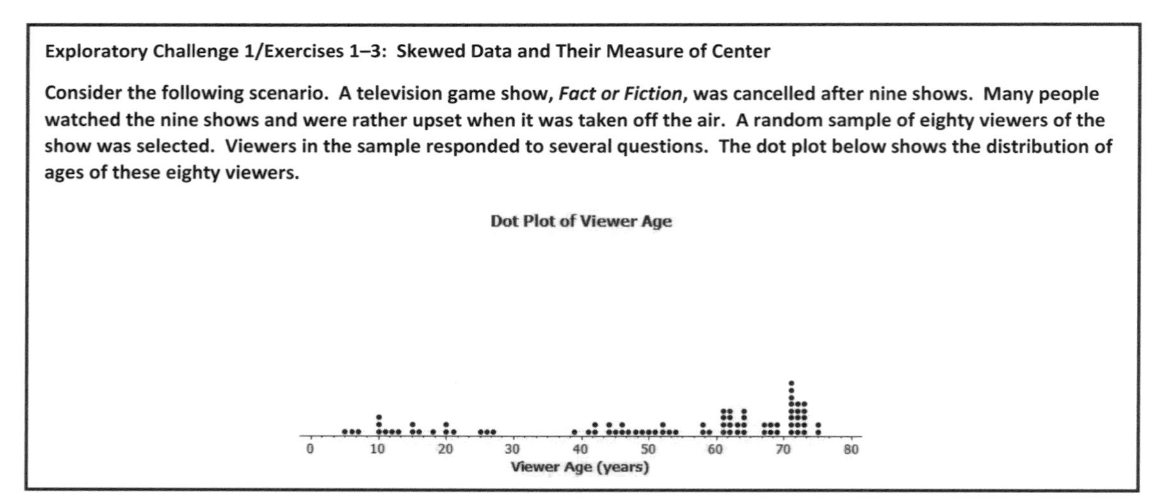

Exploratory Challenge 1/Exercises 1–3: Skewed Data and Their Measure of Center

Consider the following scenario. A television game show, *Fact or Fiction*, was cancelled after nine shows. Many people watched the nine shows and were rather upset when it was taken off the air. A random sample of eighty viewers of the show was selected. Viewers in the sample responded to several questions. The dot plot below shows the distribution of ages of these eighty viewers.

Then, discuss the following:

- What does the dot farthest to the left in this dot plot tell us?
  - *This dot tells us that one of the* 80 *viewers surveyed is only about* 5 *years old.*
- Is this distribution symmetrical?
  - *No. There are more viewers (a cluster of viewers) at the older ages.*
- What age would describe a typical age for this sample of viewers?
  - *The typical age is around* 70 *years old.*
- A reviewer of this show indicated that it was a *cross-generational show*. What do you think that term means?
  - *Viewers varied in age. People from more than one generation watched the show.*
- Do the data in the dot plot confirm or contradict the idea that it was a cross-generational show?
  - *The data confirm this idea. They show that viewers from as young as* 5 *years to as old as* 75 *years watch this show.*
- What could be the reason for the cancellation of the show? Allow students to brainstorm ideas. If no one suggests it, provide the following as a possible reason:
  - *Cross-generational shows are harder to get sponsors for. Sponsors like to purchase airtime for shows designed for their target audience.*

Give careful attention to the use of language in the following discussion; transition from less formal to more formal. Begin by emphasizing the language of "Which side is stretched?" and "Which side has the tail?" Then, make a connection to the phrasing *skewed to the left* or *left-skewed,* meaning the data are stretched on the left side and/or have their tail on the left side.

- A data distribution that is not symmetrical is described as *skewed*. In a skewed distribution, data "stretch" either to the left or to the right. The stretched side of the distribution is called a *tail*.
- Would you describe the age data distribution as a skewed distribution?
  - *Yes*
- Which side is stretched? Which side has the tail?
  - *The left side is stretched. The tail is on the left side.*

MP.3

- So, would you say it is skewed to the left or skewed to the right?
  - *The data are stretched to the left, with the tail on the left side, so these are skewed to the left, or left-skewed.*

Allow students to work independently or in pairs to answer Exploratory Challenge 1. Then, discuss and confirm answers as a class. The following are sample responses to Exercises 1–3:

1. Approximately where would you locate the mean (balance point) in the above distribution?

An estimate that indicates an understanding of how the balance would need to be closer to the cluster points on the high end is addressing balance. An estimate around 45 ***to*** 60 ***would indicate that students are taking the challenge of balance into account.***

2. How does the direction of the tail affect the location of the mean age compared to the median age?

The tail is on the left, which means that the data are skewed to the left. The mean is typically in the direction of the tail, so the mean age would be to the left of the median age.

> **3. The mean age of the above sample is approximately 50. Do you think this age describes the typical viewer of this show? Explain your answer.**
>
> ***Students should compare the given mean to their estimate. The mean as an estimate of a typical value does not adequately reflect the older ages of more than half the viewers.***

Exploratory Challenge 2/Exercises 4–8 (10 minutes): Constructing and Interpreting the Box Plot

- Recall from Grade 6 that the values of the 5-number summary are used when constructing a box plot of a data set.
- What does a box plot look like? Who can draw a quick sketch of a box plot?
  - *Allow a student to come to the board to draw a sketch of what a box plot looks like.*
- What are the values in the 5-number summary, and how are they related to the creation of the box plot?
  - *Take input from the class, and add the correct input to the sketch on the board.*

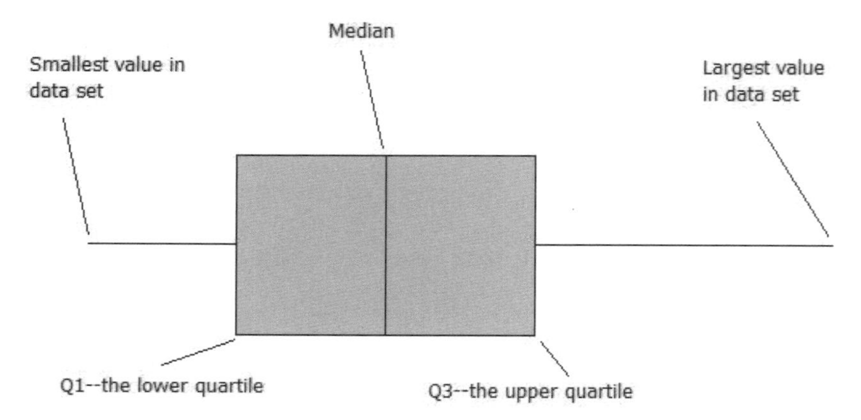

Students complete Exercise 4, constructing a box plot for the data set on top of the existing dot plot.

> **Exploratory Challenge 2/Exercises 4–8: Constructing and Interpreting the Box Plot**
>
> **4. Using the above dot plot, construct a box plot over the dot plot by completing the following steps:**
>
> **i. Locate the middle 40 observations, and draw a box around these values.**
>
> **ii. Calculate the median, and then draw a line in the box at the location of the median.**
>
> **iii. Draw a line that extends from the upper end of the box to the largest observation in the data set.**
>
> **iv. Draw a line that extends from the lower edge of the box to the minimum value in the data set.**

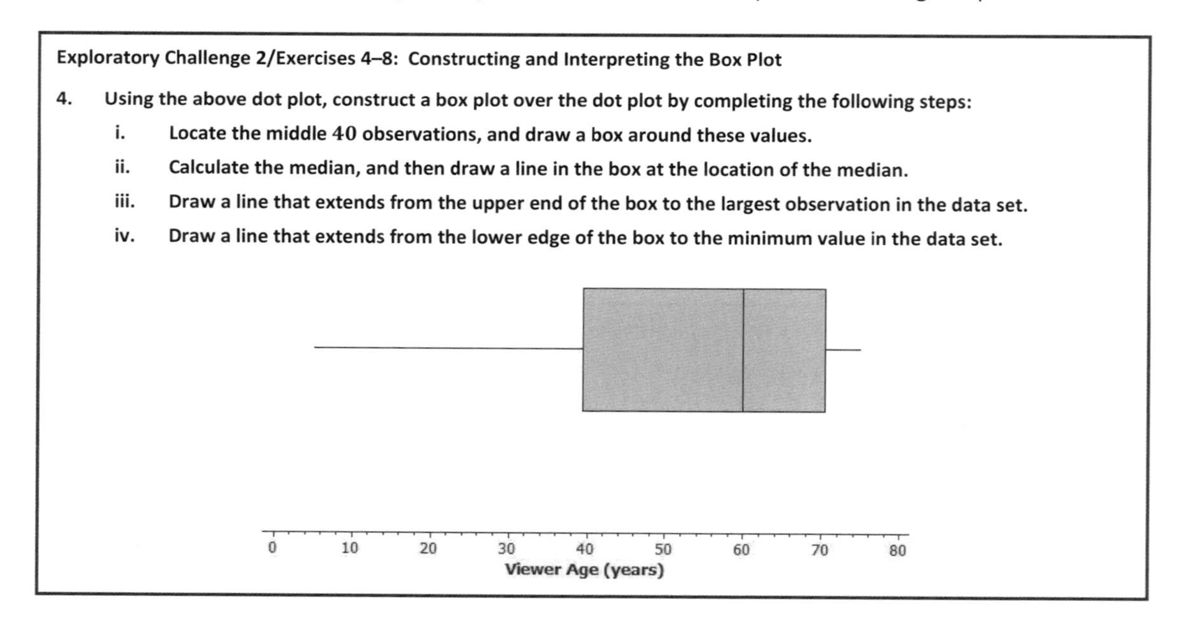

Students complete Exercises 5–8 and confirm answers with a peer or as a class.

5. **Recall that the 5 values used to construct the dot plot make up the 5-number summary. What is the 5-number summary for this data set of ages?**

Minimum age:	5
Lower quartile or Q1:	40
Median age:	60
Upper quartile or Q3:	70
Maximum age:	75

6. **What percent of the data does the box part of the box plot capture?**

   The box captures 50% *of the viewers.*

7. **What percent of the data fall between the minimum value and Q1?**

   25% *of the viewers fall between the minimum value and Q1.*

8. **What percent of the data fall between Q3 and the maximum value?**

   25% *of the viewers fall between Q3 and the maximum value.*

Exercises 9–14 (8 minutes)

These exercises (listed below) represent an application that should be discussed as students work through the exercise independently or in small groups. Discuss with students how advertising is linked to an audience. Consider the following questions to introduce this application:

- Have you ever bought something (e.g., clothes), attended a movie, or bought tickets to a concert based on an ad you saw on either the Internet or television? If yes, what did you buy, and what attracted you to the ad?
- A school is interested in drawing attention to an upcoming play. Where do you think they would place advertisements for the play? Why?

Exercises 9–14

An advertising agency researched the ages of viewers most interested in various types of television ads. Consider the following summaries:

Ages	Target Products or Services
30–45	Electronics, home goods, cars
46–55	Financial services, appliances, furniture
56–72	Retirement planning, cruises, health-care services

9. **The mean age of the people surveyed is approximately 50 years old. As a result, the producers of the show decided to obtain advertisers for a typical viewer of 50 years old. According to the table, what products or services do you think the producers will target? Based on the sample, what percent of the people surveyed about the *Fact or Fiction* show would have been interested in these commercials if the advertising table is accurate?**

   The target audience would be viewers 46 *to* 55 *years old, so the producers would focus on ads for financial services, appliances, and furniture.* 12 *out of* 80 *viewers, or* 15%, *are in that range.*

10. **The show failed to generate the interest the advertisers hoped. As a result, they stopped advertising on the show, and the show was cancelled. Kristin made the argument that a better age to describe the typical viewer is the median age. What is the median age of the sample? What products or services does the advertising table suggest for viewers if the median age is considered as a description of the typical viewer?**

    The median age is 60 years old. The target audience based on the median would include the ages 56 to 72 years old. Target products for this group are retirement planning, cruises, and health-care services.

11. **What percent of the people surveyed would be interested in the products or services suggested by the advertising table if the median age were used to describe a typical viewer?**

    31 of the 80 viewers are 56 to 72 years old, or approximately 39%.

12. **What percent of the viewers have ages between Q1 and Q3? The difference between Q3 and Q1, or Q3 – Q1, is called the interquartile range, or IQR. What is the IQR for this data distribution?**

    Approximately 50% of the viewers are located between Q1 and Q3. The IQR is $70 - 40$, or 30 years.

13. **The IQR provides a summary of the variability for a skewed data distribution. The IQR is a number that specifies the length of the interval that contains the middle half of the ages of viewers. Do you think producers of the show would prefer a show that has a small or large interquartile range? Explain your answer.**

    A smaller IQR indicates less variability, so it may be easier to target advertisements to a particular group.

    A larger IQR indicates more variability, which means the show is popular across generations but harder to target advertising.

14. **Do you agree with Kristin's argument that the median age provides a better description of a typical viewer? Explain your answer.**

    The median is a better description of a typical viewer for this audience because the distribution is skewed.

Exploratory Challenge 3/Exercises 15–20 (10 minutes): Outliers

In Grade 6, unusual data values were described as *extreme* data values. This example provides a more formal definition of an extreme value and shows how extreme values can be displayed in a box plot. Extreme values that fit this definition are called *outliers*. Identification of extreme values becomes important as students continue to work with box plots.

Discuss the data in the box plot, and have students work individually or in pairs to answer the questions.

Exploratory Challenge 3/Exercises 15–20: Outliers

Students at Waldo High School are involved in a special project that involves communicating with people in Kenya. Consider a box plot of the ages of 200 randomly selected people from Kenya.

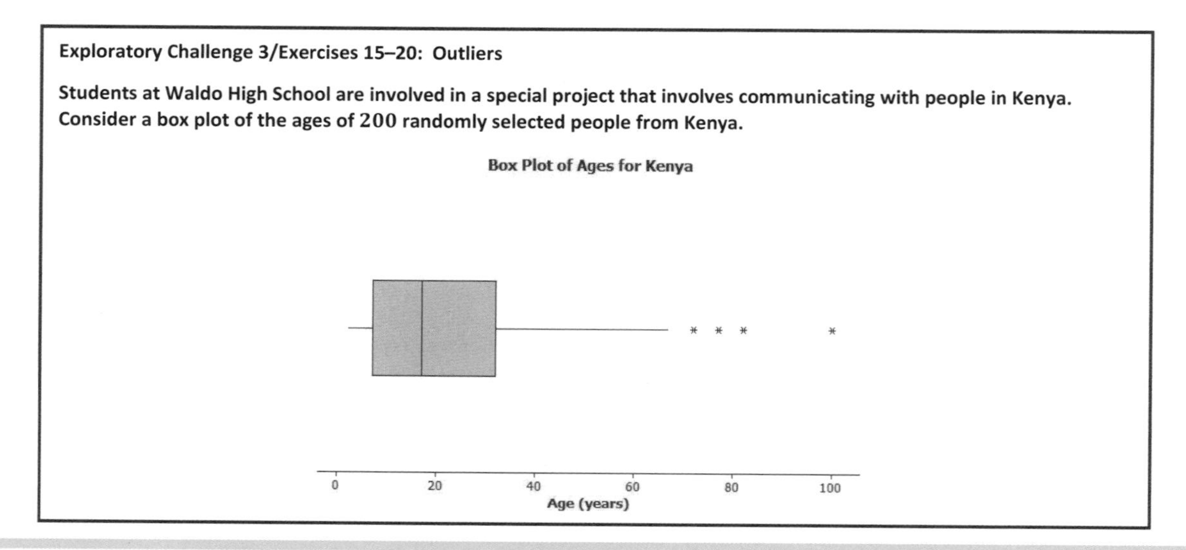

A data distribution may contain extreme data (specific data values that are unusually large or unusually small relative to the median and the interquartile range). A box plot can be used to display extreme data values that are identified as outliers.

Each "*" in the box plot represents the ages of four people from this sample. Based on the sample, these four ages were considered outliers.

15. Estimate the values of the four ages represented by an *.

    Allow for reasonable estimates. For example, 72, 77, 82, *and* 100 *years old would be reasonable estimates.*

An outlier is defined to be any data value that is more than $1.5 \times (IQR)$ away from the nearest quartile.

16. What is the median age of the sample of ages from Kenya? What are the approximate values of Q1 and Q3? What is the approximate IQR of this sample?

    The median age is approximately 18 *years old. Q1 is approximately* 7 *years old, and Q3 is approximately* 32 *years old. The approximate IQR is* 25 *years.*

17. Multiply the IQR by 1.5. What value do you get?

    1.5×25 *is* 37.5 *years.*

18. Add $1.5 \times (IQR)$ to the third quartile age (Q3). What do you notice about the four ages identified by an *?

    37.5 years $+ 32$ years *is* 69.5 *years, or approximately* 70 *years. The four ages identified by an * are all greater than this value.*

19. Are there any age values that are less than $Q1 - 1.5 \times (IQR)$? If so, these ages would also be considered outliers.

    7 years $- 37.5$ years is -30.5 *years. There are no ages less than this value.*

20. Explain why there is no * on the low side of the box plot for ages of the people in the sample from Kenya.

    An outlier on the lower end would have to be a negative age, which is not possible.

Closing (2 minutes)

Lesson Summary

- Nonsymmetrical data distributions are referred to as skewed.
- Left-skewed or skewed to the left means the data spread out longer (like a tail) on the left side.
- Right-skewed or skewed to the right means the data spread out longer (like a tail) on the right side.
- The center of a skewed data distribution is described by the median.
- Variability of a skewed data distribution is described by the interquartile range (IQR).
- The IQR describes variability by specifying the length of the interval that contains the middle 50% of the data values.
- Outliers in a data set are defined as those values more than $1.5 \times (IQR)$ from the nearest quartile. Outliers are usually identified by an "*" or a "•" in a box plot.

Exit Ticket (5 minutes)

Name ______________________________ Date ________________

Lesson 7: Measuring Variability for Skewed Distributions (Interquartile Range)

Exit Ticket

1. A data set consisting of the number of hours each of 40 students watched television over the weekend has a minimum value of 3 hours, a Q1 value of 5 hours, a median value of 6 hours, a Q3 value of 9 hours, and a maximum value of 12 hours. Draw a box plot representing this data distribution.

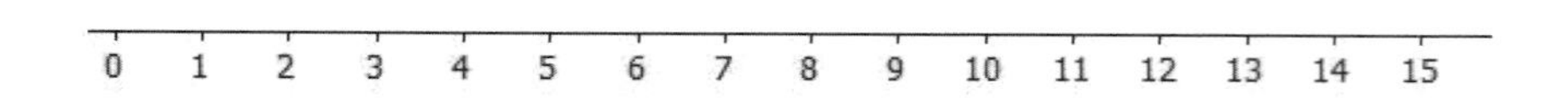

2. What is the interquartile range (IQR) for this distribution? What percent of the students fall within this interval?

3. Do you think the data distribution represented by the box plot is a skewed distribution? Why or why not?

4. Estimate the typical number of hours students watched television. Explain why you chose this value.

Exit Ticket Sample Solutions

1. **A data set consisting of the number of hours each of 40 students watched television over the weekend has a minimum value of 3 hours, a Q1 value of 5 hours, a median value of 6 hours, a Q3 value of 9 hours, and a maximum value of 12 hours. Draw a box plot representing this data distribution.**

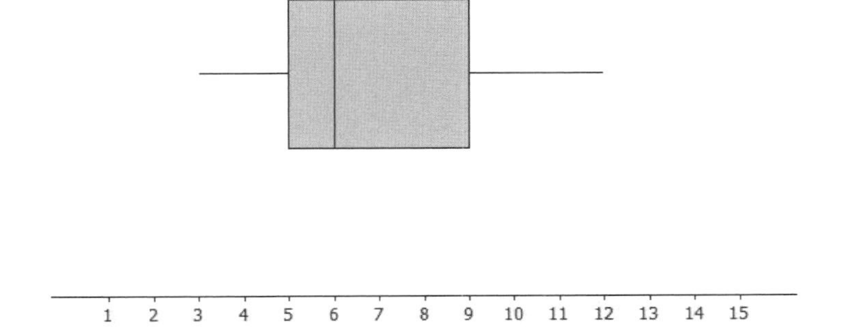

Students should sketch a box plot with the minimum value at 3 hours, a Q1 at 5 hours, a median at 6 hours, a Q3 at 9 hours, and a maximum value at 12 hours.

2. **What is the interquartile range (IQR) for this distribution? What percent of the students fall within this interval?**

The interquartile range is 4 hours. 50% of the students fall within this interval.

3. **Do you think the data distribution represented by the box plot is a skewed distribution? Why or why not?**

You would speculate that this distribution is skewed because 50% of the data would be between 3 and 6 hours, while 50% would be between 6 and 12 hours. There would be the same number of dots in the smaller interval from 3 to 6 as there would be in the wider interval of 6 to 12.

4. **Estimate the typical number of hours students watched television. Explain why you chose this value.**

Since this is a skewed data distribution, the most appropriate estimate of a typical number of hours would be the median, or 6 hours.

Problem Set Sample Solutions

Consider the following scenario. Transportation officials collect data on flight delays (the number of minutes a flight takes off after its scheduled time).

Consider the dot plot of the delay times in minutes for 60 BigAir flights during December 2012:

Dot Plot of December Delay Times

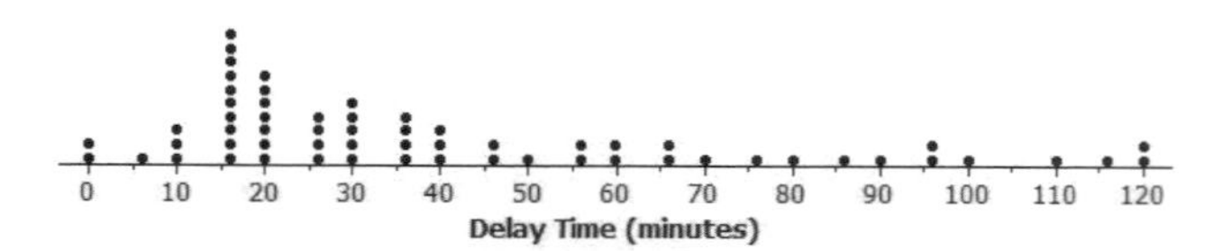

1. **How many flights left more than 60 minutes late?**

   14 flights left more than 60 minutes late.

2. **Why is this data distribution considered skewed?**

   This is a skewed distribution because there is a stretch of flights located to the right.

3. **Is the tail of this data distribution to the right or to the left? How would you describe several of the delay times in the tail?**

   The tail is to the right. The delay times in the tail represent flights with the longest delays.

4. **Draw a box plot over the dot plot of the flights for December.**

   A box plot of the December delay times is as follows:

Boxplot of Delay Time (December)

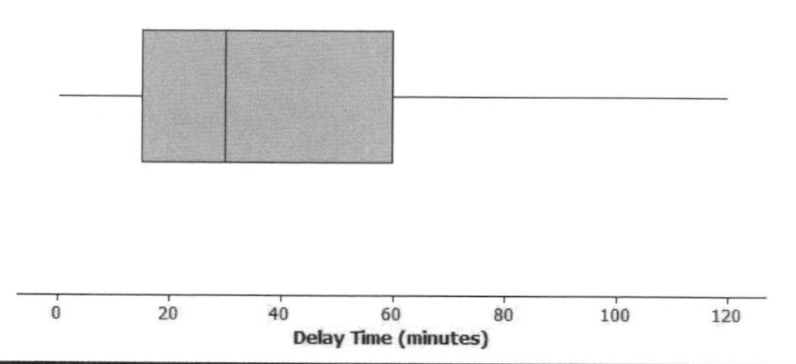

5. What is the interquartile range, or IQR, of this data set?

   The IQR is approximately $60 - 15$, or 45 minutes.

6. The mean of the 60 flight delays is approximately 42 minutes. Do you think that 42 minutes is typical of the number of minutes a BigAir flight was delayed? Why or why not?

   The mean value of 42 minutes is not a good description of a typical flight delay. It is pulled upward to a larger value because of flights with the very long delays.

7. Based on the December data, write a brief description of the BigAir flight distribution for December.

   Students should include a summary of the data in their reports. Included should be the median delay time of 30 minutes and that 50% of the flights are delayed between 15 minutes to 60 minutes, with a typical delay of approximately 30 minutes.

8. Calculate the percentage of flights with delays of more than 1 hour. Were there many flight delays of more than 1 hour?

   14 flights were delayed more than 60 minutes, or 1 hour. These 14 flights represent approximately 23% of the flights. This is not a large number, although the decision of whether or not 23% is large is subjective.

9. BigAir later indicated that there was a flight delay that was not included in the data. The flight not reported was delayed for 48 hours. If you had included that flight delay in the box plot, how would you have represented it? Explain your answer.

   A flight delay of 48 hours would be much larger than any delay in this data set and would be considered an extreme value, or outlier. To include this flight would require an extension of the scale to $2,880$ minutes. This flight might have been delayed due to an extreme mechanical problem with the plane or an extended problem with weather.

10. Consider a dot plot and the box plot of the delay times in minutes for 60 BigAir flights during January 2013.

    How is the January flight delay distribution different from the one summarizing the December flight delays? In terms of flight delays in January, did BigAir improve, stay the same, or do worse compared to December? Explain your answer.

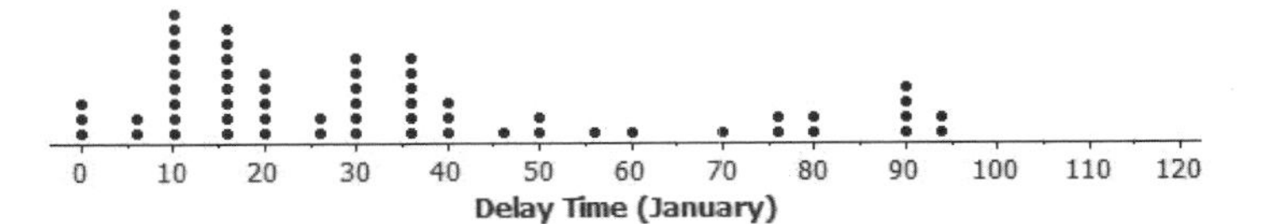

Box Plot of January Delay Times

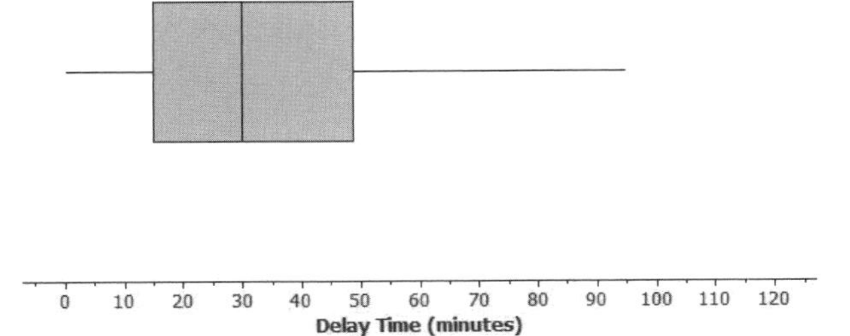

The median flight delay is the same as in December, which is 30 minutes. The IQR is less, or approximately 35 minutes. The maximum is also less. In general, this indicates a typical delay of 30 minutes with less variability.

Lesson 8: Comparing Distributions

Student Outcomes

- Students compare two or more distributions in terms of center, variability, and shape.
- Students interpret a measure of center as a typical value.
- Students interpret the IQR as a description of the variability of the data.
- Students answer questions that address differences and similarities for two or more distributions.

Classwork

Exploratory Challenge 1 (5 minutes): Country Data

Discuss the two histograms of ages for Kenya and the United States.

Exploratory Challenge 1: Country Data

A science museum has a Traveling Around the World exhibit. Using 3D technology, participants can make a virtual tour of cities and towns around the world. Students at Waldo High School registered with the museum to participate in a virtual tour of Kenya, visiting the capital city of Nairobi and several small towns. Before they take the tour, however, their mathematics class decided to study Kenya using demographic data from 2010 provided by the United States Census Bureau. They also obtained data for the United States from 2010 to compare to data for Kenya.

The following histograms represent the age distributions of the two countries.

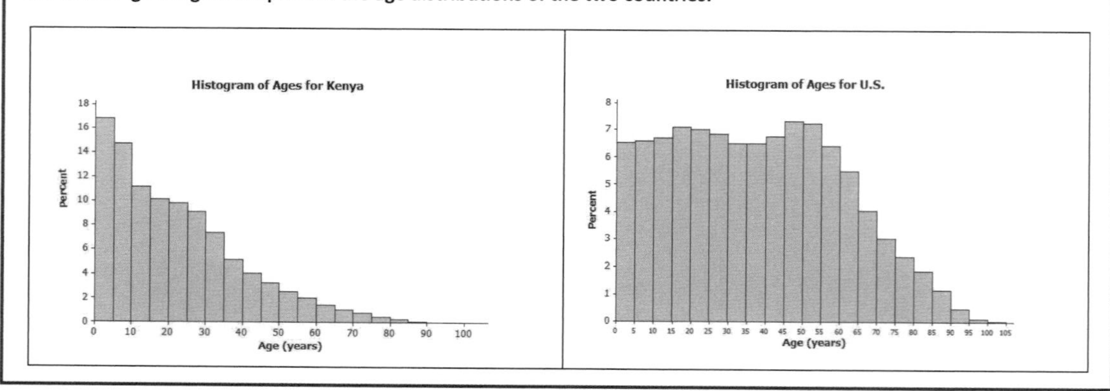

Review with students what each interval of ages represents. For example, the first interval represents people whose ages are $0 \leq x < 5$. Pose the following questions:

- What percent of people in Kenya are younger than 5?
  - *About* 17%
- What ages are represented by the intervals along the horizontal axis?
  - *If x represents age, then the first interval would be $0 \leq x < 5$, the second interval would be $5 \leq x < 10$, etc.*

- What does the first bar ($0 \le x < 5$) mean in the U.S. histogram?
    - *The percent of people in the U.S. who are younger than* 5

Exercises 1–8 (13 minutes)

Allow students to work independently or in small groups on Exercises 1–8. Then, discuss and confirm answers as a class.

Exercises 1–8

1. **How do the shapes of the two histograms differ?**

   The bars in the Kenya histogram slowly decline; the distribution is skewed with a tail to the right. The bars in the U.S. histogram are even for a while and then show a more rapid decline.

2. **Approximately what percent of people in Kenya are between the ages of 0 and 10 years?**

   Approximately 32% ***(***17% ***are ages*** 0 ***to*** 5 ***years, and*** 15% ***are ages*** 5 ***to*** 10 ***years.)***

3. **Approximately what percent of people in the United States are between the ages of 0 and 10 years?**

   Approximately 13%

4. **Approximately what percent of people in Kenya are 60 years or older?**

   Approximately 5%

5. **Approximately what percent of people in the United States are 60 years or older?**

   Approximately 20%

6. **The population of Kenya in 2010 was approximately 41 million people. What is the approximate number of people in Kenya between the ages of 0 and 10 years?**

   32% ***of*** 41 ***million people is approximately*** $13,120,000$ ***people.***

7. **The population of the United States in 2010 was approximately 309 million people. What is the approximate number of people in the United States between the ages of 0 and 10 years?**

   13% ***of*** 309 ***million people is approximately*** $40,170,000$ ***people.***

8. **The Waldo High School students started planning for their virtual visit of the neighborhoods in Nairobi and several towns in Kenya. Do you think they will see many teenagers? Will they see many senior citizens who are 70 or older? Explain your answer based on the histogram.**

   Adding a portion of the percent of people in the 10 ***to*** 14 ***years old group and the percent of people*** 15 ***to*** 19 ***years old approximates the estimate of the percent of teenagers. About*** 15% ***represents teenagers. Students are likely to see teenagers as this is a relatively large percent of the population. According to the histogram, approximately*** 3% ***of the population in Kenya is*** 70 ***or older. As a result, students are unlikely to see many senior citizens*** 70 ***or older.***

Exploratory Challenge 2 (5 minutes): Learning More About the Countries Using Box Plots and Histograms

Verbally introduce the box plots of Kenya ages and United States ages.

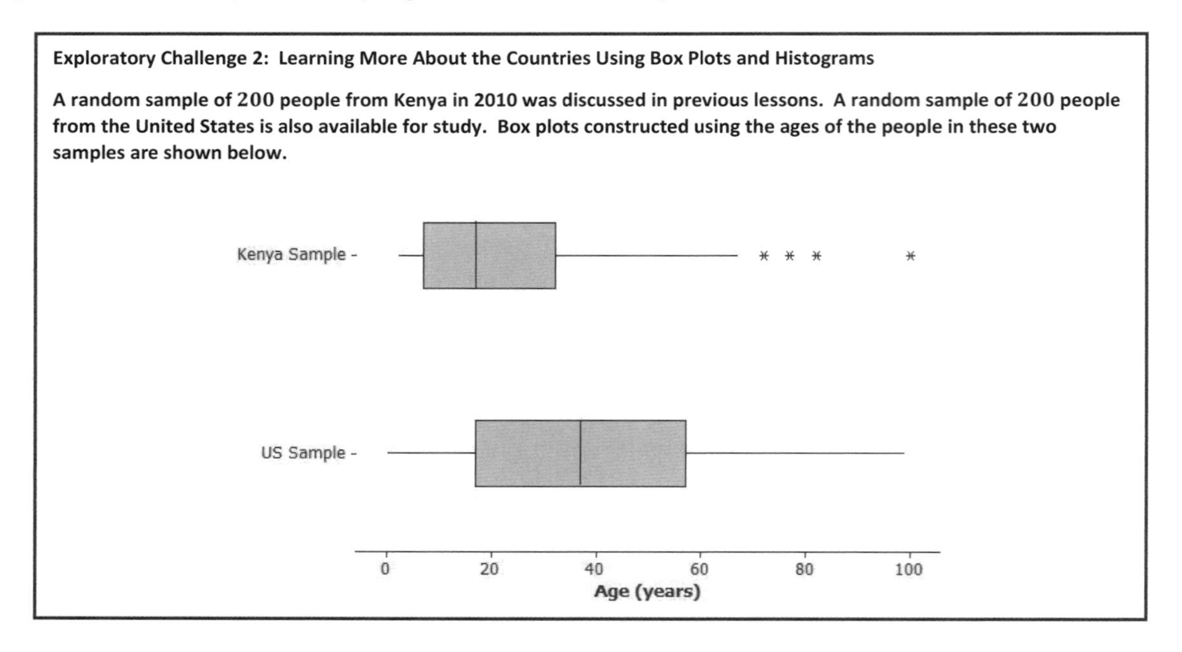
Exploratory Challenge 2: Learning More About the Countries Using Box Plots and Histograms

A random sample of 200 people from Kenya in 2010 was discussed in previous lessons. A random sample of 200 people from the United States is also available for study. Box plots constructed using the ages of the people in these two samples are shown below.

Then, discuss:

- What information is displayed in a box plot?
  - *Median, minimum, and maximum values, quartiles, and IQR are displayed.*
- What does the (*) represent on the box plot for Kenya?
  - *It represents extreme values or outliers.*
- Can we find this same information in the histograms from Example 1?
  - *No. Median, Q1, Q2, and minimum and maximum are not clear from a histogram. It could only be used to estimate these values.*
- Remind students that the histogram represents the entire population of Kenya, whereas the box plot only represents a sample of 200 people.

Exercises 9–16 (15 minutes)

Allow students to work independently or in small groups on Exercises 9–16. Then, discuss and confirm answers as a class.

Exercises 9–16

9. **Adrian, a senior at Waldo High School, stated that the box plots indicate that the United States has a lot of older people compared to Kenya. Would you agree? How would you describe the difference in the ages of people in these two countries based on the above box plots?**

   Yes. The population of the United States has a much greater percent of people in the older age intervals.

10. **Estimate the median age of a person in Kenya and the median age of a person in the United States using the box plots.**

    The median Kenyan age is slightly less than 20 years, while the median U.S. age is slightly less than 40 years.

11. **Using the box plot, 25% of the people in the United States are younger than what age? How did you determine that age?**

    25% are younger than approximately 18 years. I used the value of Q1, or the first quartile.

12. **Using the box plot, approximately what percent of people in Kenya are younger than 18 years old?**

    Approximately 50% of the people in Kenya are less than 18 years old.

13. **Could you have estimated the mean age of a person from Kenya using the box plot? Explain your answer.**

    No, the box plot does not provide an estimate of the mean age.

14. **The mean age of people in the United States is approximately 38 years. Using the histogram, estimate the percent of people in the United States who are younger than the mean age in the United States.**

    Approximately 50% of the U.S. population is less than 38 years old.

15. **If the median age is used to describe a typical person in Kenya, what percent of people in Kenya are younger than the median age? Is the mean or median age a better description of a typical person in Kenya? Explain your answer.**

    50% of the people in Kenya are less than the median age. The median is a better indicator of a typical age because the distribution is skewed.

16. **What is the IQR of the ages in the sample from the United States? What is the IQR of the ages in the sample from Kenya? If the IQRs are used to compare countries, what does a smaller IQR indicate about a country? Use Kenya and the United States to explain your answer.**

    The IQR for the United States is 58 years $-$ 18 years, or 40 years; the IQR for Kenya is 36 years $-$ 7 years, or 31 years. A smaller IQR indicates that more of the sample is around the median age, which you can see from looking at the histogram.

Closing (2 minutes)

Lesson Summary

- Histograms show the general shape of a distribution.
- Box plots are created from the 5-number summary of a data set.
- A box plot identifies the median, minimum, and maximum values and the upper and lower quartiles.
- The interquartile range (IQR) describes how the data are spread around the median; it is the length of the interval that contains 50% of the data values.
- The median is used as a measure of the center when a distribution is skewed or contains outliers.

Exit Ticket (5 minutes)

Name ______________________________ Date ______________

Lesson 8: Comparing Distributions

Exit Ticket

1. Using the histograms of the population distributions of the United States and Kenya in 2010, approximately what percent of the people in the United States were between 15 and 50 years old? Approximately what percent of the people in Kenya were between 15 and 50 years old?

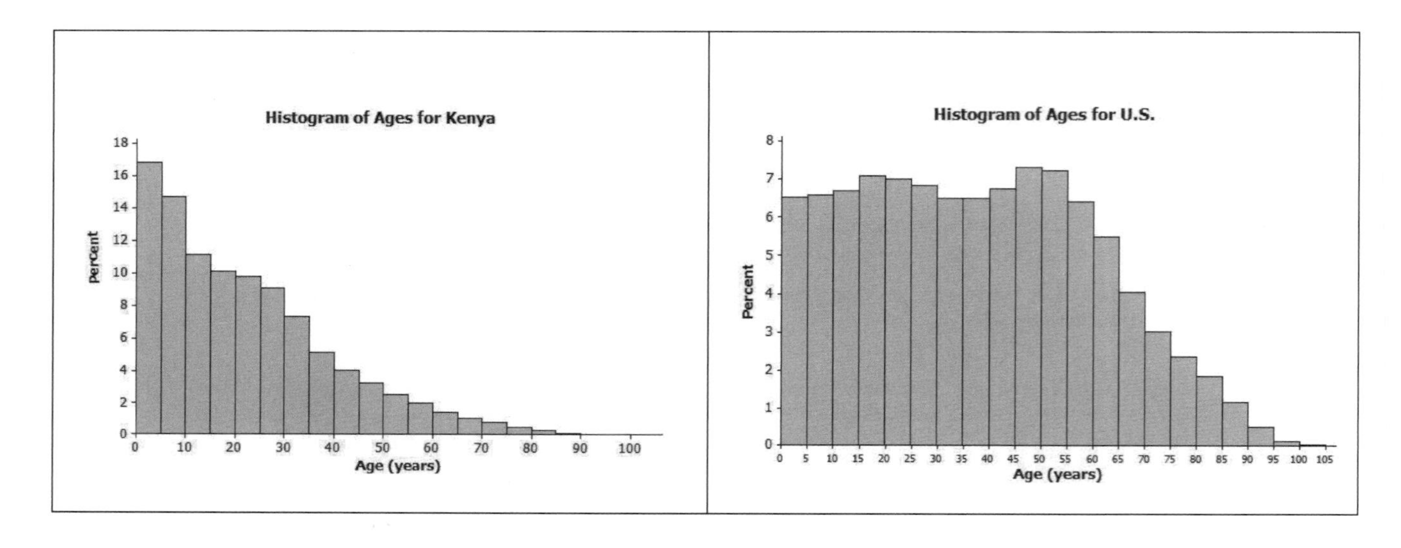

2. What 5-year interval of ages represented in the 2010 histogram of the United States age distribution has the most people?

3. Why is the mean age greater than the median age for people in Kenya?

Exit Ticket Sample Solutions

1. **Using the histograms of the population distributions of the United States and Kenya in 2010, approximately what percent of the people in the United States were between 15 and 50 years old? Approximately what percent of the people in Kenya were between 15 and 50 years old?**

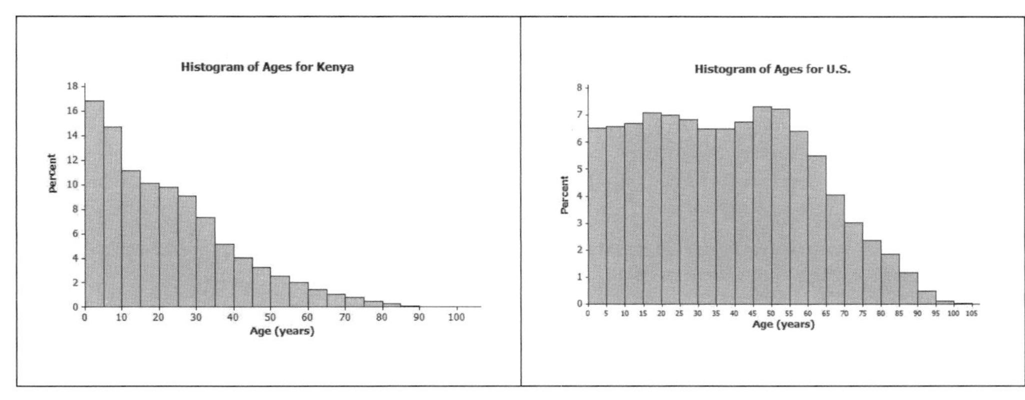

Approximately 47% of people in the United States were between 15 and 50 years old. Approximately 48% of people in Kenya were between 15 and 50 years old.

2. **What 5-year interval of ages represented in the 2010 histogram of the United States age distribution has the most people?**

The 5-year interval of ages with the most people is the people 45 to 50 years old.

3. **Why is the mean age greater than the median age for people in Kenya?**

The mean age is a balance point. The distribution is skewed to the right, and the value of the mean is affected by the older ages in the upper tail of the Kenya population histogram. The mean is greater than the median in this case.

Problem Set Sample Solutions

The following box plot summarizes ages for a random sample from a made-up country named Math Country.

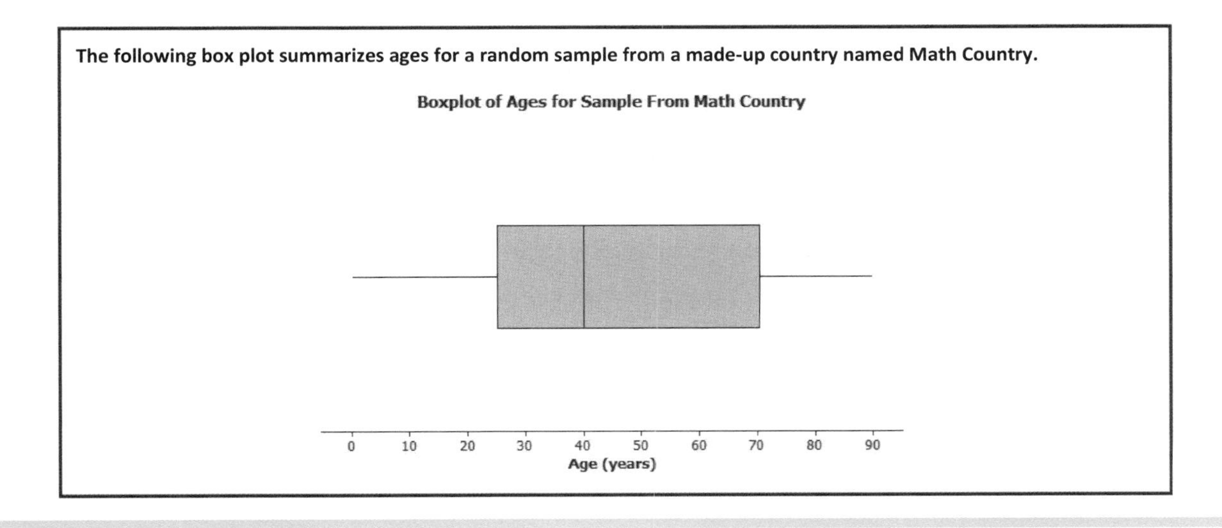

1. **Make up your own sample of forty ages that could be represented by the box plot for Math Country. Use a dot plot to represent the ages of the forty people in Math Country.**

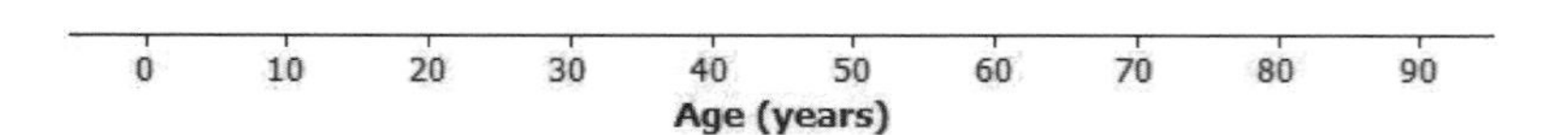

Many possible dot plots would be correct. Analyze individually. Ten of the ages need to be between 0 and 25 years old, ten of the ages need to be between 25 and 40 years old, ten of the ages need to be between 40 and 70 years old, and ten of the ages need to between 70 and 90 years old.

2. **Is the sample of forty ages represented in your dot plot of Math Country the only sample that could be represented by the box plot? Explain your answer.**

There are many possible dot plots that might be represented by this box plot. Any data set with the same 5-number summary would result in this same box plot.

3. **The following is a dot plot of sixty ages from a random sample of people from Japan in 2010.**
Draw a box plot over this dot plot.

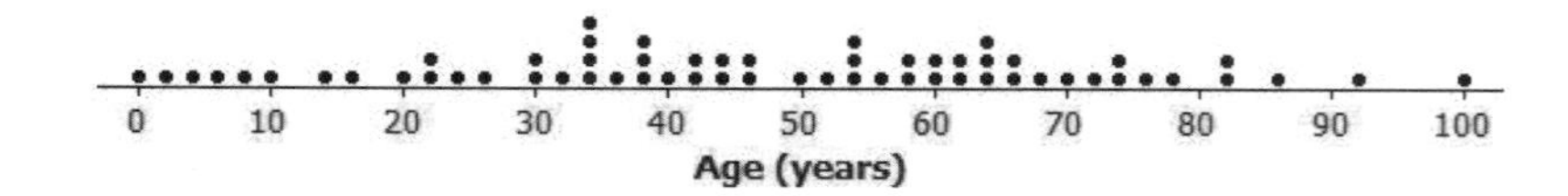

The following is the box plot of the ages of the sample of people from Japan:

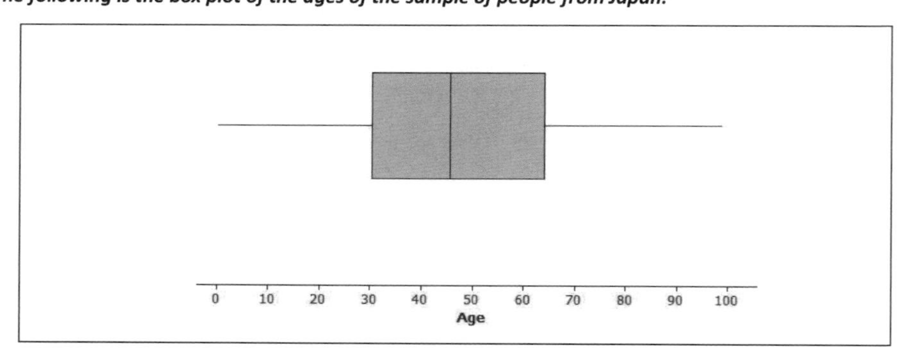

4. **Based on your box plot, would the median age of people in Japan be closer to the median age of people in Kenya or the United States? Justify your answer.**

The median age of Japan would be closer to the median age of the United States than to the median age of Kenya. The box plot indicates that the median age of Japan is approximately 45 years old. This median age is even greater than the median age of the United States.

5. **What does the box plot of this sample from Japan indicate about the possible differences in the age distributions of people from Japan and Kenya?**

A much greater percent of the people in Japan are in the older age groups than is the case for Kenya.

Name ______________________________ Date ____________

1. The scores of three quizzes are shown in the following data plot for a class of 10 students. Each quiz has a maximum possible score of 10. Possible dot plots of the data are shown below.

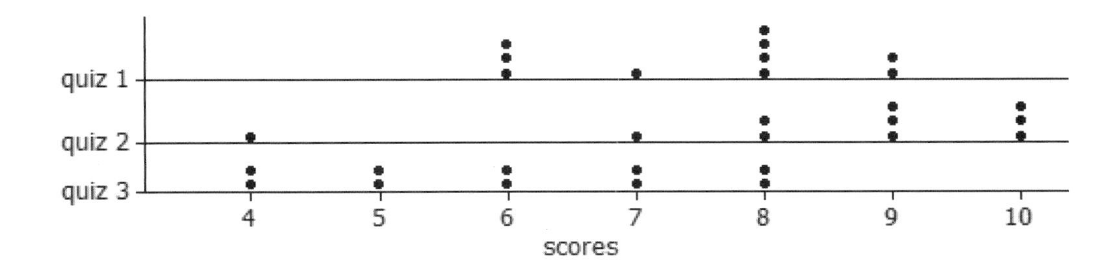

   a. On which quiz did students tend to score the lowest? Justify your choice.

   b. Without performing any calculations, which quiz tended to have the most variability in the students' scores? Justify your choice based on the graphs.

c. If you were to calculate a measure of variability for Quiz 2, would you recommend using the interquartile range or the standard deviation? Explain your choice.

d. For Quiz 3, move one dot to a new location so that the modified data set will have a larger standard deviation than before you moved the dot. Be clear which point you decide to move, where you decide to move it, and explain why.

e. On the axis below, arrange 10 dots, representing integer quiz scores between 0 and 10, so that the standard deviation is the largest possible value that it may have. You may use the same quiz score values more than once.

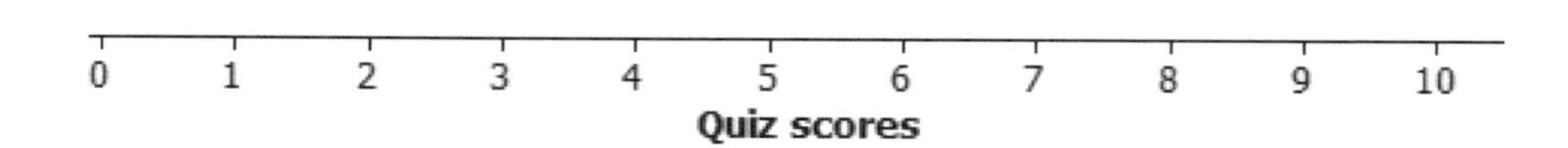

Use the following definitions to answer parts (f)–(h).

- The *midrange* of a data set is defined to be the average of the minimum and maximum values: $\frac{\text{min} + \text{max}}{2}$.
- The *midhinge* of a data set is defined to be the average of the first quartile (Q_1) and the third quartile (Q_3): $\frac{Q_1 + Q_3}{2}$.

f. Is the midrange a measure of center or a measure of spread? Explain.

g. Is the midhinge a measure of center or a measure of spread? Explain.

h. Suppose the lowest score for Quiz 2 was changed from 4 to 2, and the midrange and midhinge are recomputed. Which will change more?

A. Midrange
B. Midhinge
C. They will change the same amount.
D. Cannot be determined

2. The box plots below display the distributions of maximum speed for 145 roller coasters in the United States, separated by whether they are wooden coasters or steel coasters.

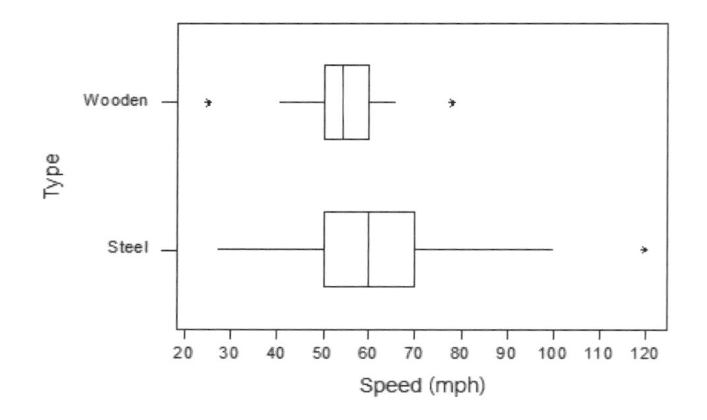

Based on the box plots, answer the following questions or indicate that you do not have enough information.

a. Which type of coaster has more observations?

A. Wooden
B. Steel
C. About the same
D. Cannot be determined

Explain your choice:

b. Which type of coaster has a higher percentage of coasters that go faster than 60 mph?

A. Wooden
B. Steel
C. About the same
D. Cannot be determined

Explain your choice:

c. Which type of coaster has a higher percentage of coasters that go faster than 50 mph?

A. Wooden
B. Steel
C. About the same
D. Cannot be determined

Explain your choice:

d. Which type of coaster has a higher percentage of coasters that go faster than 48 mph?

A. Wooden
B. Steel
C. About the same
D. Cannot be determined

Explain your choice:

e. Write 2–3 sentences comparing the two types of coasters with respect to which type of coaster normally goes faster.

A Progression Toward Mastery					
Assessment Task Item		**STEP 1** Missing or incorrect answer and little evidence of reasoning or application of mathematics to solve the problem	**STEP 2** Missing or incorrect answer but evidence of some reasoning or application of mathematics to solve the problem	**STEP 3** A correct answer with some evidence of reasoning or application of mathematics to solve the problem, OR an incorrect answer with substantial evidence of solid reasoning or application of mathematics to solve the problem	**STEP 4** A correct answer supported by substantial evidence of solid reasoning or application of mathematics to solve the problem
1	**a** **S-ID.A.2**	Student fails to address the tendency for lower scores.	Student picks Quiz 2 because of the low outlier at 4 points, rather than focusing on the overall distribution.	Student chooses Quiz 3 but does not give a full explanation for the choice.	Student uses an appropriate measure of center (e.g., mean or median) to explain the choice of Quiz 3.
	b **S-ID.A.3**	Student fails to address the idea of spread, variability, or clustering.	Student picks Quiz 1 because the heights of the stacks are most irregular.	Student picks Quiz 3 but does not give a full explanation for the choice. OR Student picks Quiz 2 based on one score (the low outlier), as opposed to the overall tendency.	Student chooses Quiz 3 and uses an appropriate justification such as stating that the data ranges from 4 to 8.
	c **S-ID.A.2**	Student does not make a clear choice between SD and IQR.	Student does not justify choice based on the shape of distribution or on the presence of an outlier.	Student considers the distribution symmetric and chooses the standard deviation.	Student chooses the IQR in an attempt to reduce the impact of the one extreme observation.
	d **S-ID.A.2**	Student does not clearly explain how the dot will be moved.	Student adds a dot near the center of the distribution (e.g., 5–7). OR Student moves a dot toward the center of the distribution.	Student's dot is moved to change the heights of the stacks of the dots.	Student's dot is moved to be further from the mean of the distribution (without much change in the mean of the distribution).

	e S-ID.A.2	Student's placement of dots does not appear to focus on spreading the values as far apart as possible.	Student focuses on having as many different values as possible. OR Student focuses on having as much change in the heights to the stacks as possible.	Student spreads the dots out as far as possible without using repeat values (with justification). OR Student does not split the dots into two equal pieces at the two extremes.	Student places half the dots at zero and half the dots at ten.
	f S-ID.A.2	Student selects measure of spread with a weaker explanation.	Student selects measure of spread because of the use of the max and min values.	Student selects measure of center but does not fully explain reasoning.	Student selects measure of center and discusses how the value will correspond to a "middle" number.
	g S-ID.A.2	Student selects measure of spread with a weaker explanation.	Student selects measure of spread because of the use of the quartile values.	Student selects measure of center but does not fully explain reasoning.	Student selects measure of center and discusses how the value will correspond to a "middle" number.
	h S-ID.A.2	Student fails to address the question.	Student selects midrange.	Student selects midrange but does not give a clear explanation.	Student selects midrange and discusses lack of impact on calculation of extreme values.
2	a S-ID.A.1	Student selects A or C.	N/A	Student selects B, thinking that the longer box plot indicates more observations.	Student selects D and states that the quartiles tell us about percentages, not about counts.
	b S-ID.A.1	Student selects A, C, or D.	N/A	Student selects B but justifies based on the steel coasters having a longer box to the right of 60.	Student selects B and compares the median of steel (50% above) to upper quartile of wooden (only 25% above).
	c S-ID.A.1	Student selects A or D.	N/A	Student selects B and justifies based on the steel coasters having a longer box to the right of 50.	Student selects C and cites the similarity of the two lower quartiles.
	d S-ID.A.1	Student selects A or C.	N/A	Student selects B, focusing on the length of the whisker.	Student selects D, which does not clearly correspond to one of the quartiles.

	e **S-ID.A.1**	Student does not address which type of coaster goes faster.	Student makes a weak comparison without clear justification or context. OR Student focuses on the one steel coaster at 120 mph.	Student describes shape, center, and spread but does not focus in on center or fails to give some numerical justification with the description of center.	Student describes the center of the distribution and gives some numerical evidence (e.g., median, Q3).

Name ______________________________ Date ______________

1. The scores of three quizzes are shown in the following data plot for a class of 10 students. Each quiz has a maximum possible score of 10. Possible dot plots of the data are shown below.

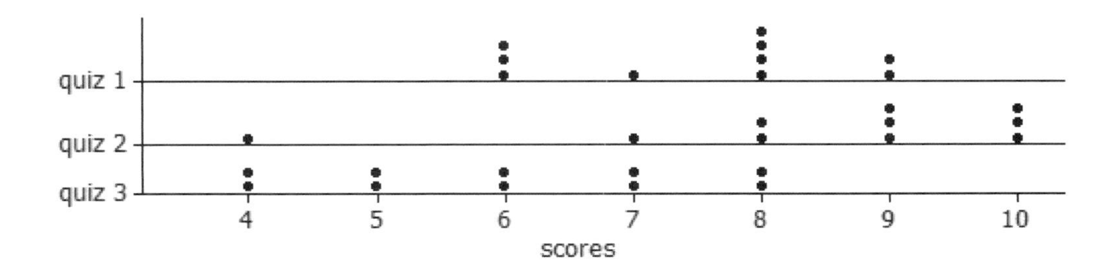

a. On which quiz did students tend to score the lowest? Justify your choice.

Even though Quiz 2 had one low value, the bulk of the Quiz 3 scores are lower than the other quizzes. Therefore, students tended to score lowest on Quiz 3.

b. Without performing any calculations, which quiz tended to have the most variability in the students' scores? Justify your choice based on the graphs.

Quiz 3 tended to have the most variability in the students' scores. The scores were over a wider range compared to the other two, which had a bit more clustering.

c. If you were to calculate a measure of variability for Quiz 2, would you recommend using the interquartile range or the standard deviation? Explain your choice.

I would recommend the interquartile range because the very low Quiz 2 score will inflate the standard deviation.

d. For Quiz 3, move one dot to a new location so that the modified data set will have a larger standard deviation than before you moved the dot. Be clear which point you decide to move, where you decide to move it, and explain why.

Move a dot from 8 to 9 to spread the scores out more.

e. On the axis below, arrange 10 dots, representing integer quiz scores between 0 and 10 so that the standard deviation is the largest possible value that it may have. You may use the same quiz score values more than once.

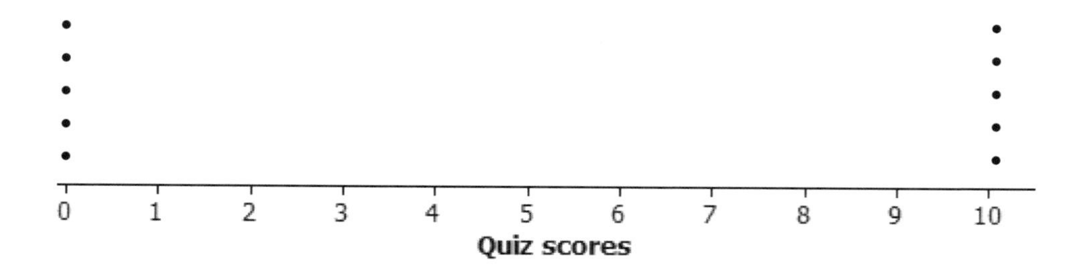

The dots are spread out from the center as much as possible, equally on both sides.

Use the following definitions to answer parts (f)–(h).

- The *midrange* of a data set is defined to be the average of the minimum and maximum values: $\frac{\text{min} + \text{max}}{2}$.
- The *midhinge* of a data set is defined to be the average of the first quartile (Q_1) and the third quartile (Q_3): $\frac{Q_1+Q_3}{2}$.

f. Is the midrange a measure of center or a measure of spread? Explain.

It is a measure of center because you are averaging two values and ending up in the middle.

g. Is the midhinge a measure of center or a measure of spread? Explain.

It is a measure of center for the same reason given for part (f).

h. Suppose the lowest score for Quiz 2 was changed from 4 to 2, and the midrange and midhinge are recomputed. Which will change more?

(A.) Midrange
B. Midhinge
C. They will change the same amount.
D. Cannot be determined

Midrange will change more because you have changed the value of min but not Q.

2. The box plots below display the distributions of maximum speed for 145 roller coasters in the United States, separated by whether they are wooden coasters or steel coasters.

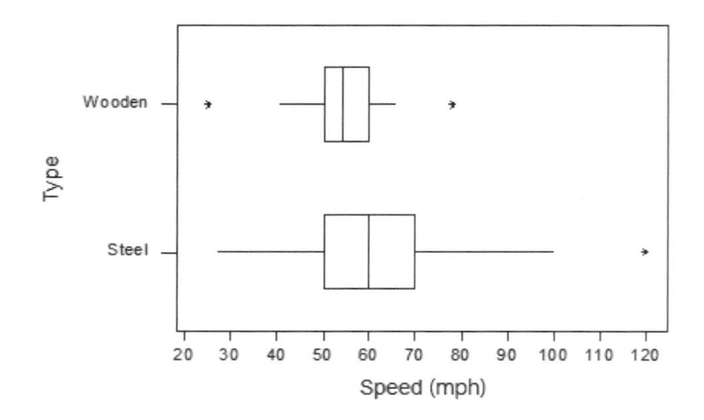

Based on the box plots, answer the following questions or indicate whether you do not have enough information.

a. Which type of coaster has more observations?

A. Wooden
B. Steel
C. About the same
(D.) Cannot be determined

Explain your choice: *We see how the values are split into pieces but not how many are in each piece.*

b. Which type of coaster has a higher percentage of coasters that go faster than 60 mph?

A. Wooden
(B.) Steel
C. About the same
D. Cannot be determined

Explain your choice: *60 = median for steel → 50% faster*

60 = Q_3 for wood → 25% faster

c. Which type of coaster has a higher percentage of coasters that go faster than 50 mph?

A. Wooden
B. Steel
(C.) About the same
D. Cannot be determined

Explain your choice: *50 is Q for both, so both have above 75% going faster.*

d. Which type of coaster has a higher percentage of coasters that go faster than 48 mph?

A. Wooden
B. Steel
C. About the same
(D.) Cannot be determined

Explain your choice: *The distributions do not land on one of the box edges, so I'm not sure what percent are faster than 48 mph.*

e. Write 2–3 sentences comparing the two types of coasters with respect to which type of coaster normally goes faster.

The median and Q_3 are larger for steel coasters, so they tend to go faster. However, both types have about 25% slower than 50 mph. One steel coaster could even reach 120 mph.

Topic C

Categorical Data on Two Variables

S-ID.B.5, S-ID.C.9

Focus Standards:	S-ID.B.5	Summarize categorical data for two categories in two-way frequency tables. Interpret relative frequencies in the context of the data (including joint, marginal, and conditional relative frequencies). Recognize possible associations and trends in the data.★
	S-ID.C.9	Distinguish between correlation and causation.★
Instructional Days:	3	
Lesson 9:	Summarizing Bivariate Categorical Data (E)[1]	
Lesson 10:	Summarizing Bivariate Categorical Data with Relative Frequencies (E)	
Lesson 11:	Conditional Relative Frequencies and Association (E)	

In Topic C, students reconnect with previous work in Grade 8 involving categorical data. Students use a two-way frequency table to organize data on two categorical variables. Students calculate the conditional relative frequencies from the frequency table. They explore a possible association between two categorical variables using differences in conditional relative frequencies. Students also come to understand the distinction between association of two categorical variables and a causal relationship between two variables. This provides a foundation for work on sampling and inference in later grades.

[1]Lesson Structure Key: **P**-Problem Set Lesson, **M**-Modeling Cycle Lesson, **E**-Exploration Lesson, **S**-Socratic Lesson

Lesson 9: Summarizing Bivariate Categorical Data

Student Outcomes

- Students distinguish between categorical data and numerical data.
- Students summarize data on two categorical variables collected from a sample using a two-way frequency table.

Lesson Notes

Categorical data are often summarized in the media, research studies, or general discussions. However, categorical data are summarized differently than numerical data. There is no mean or median that answers the question, "What is your favorite soft drink?" Methods for analyzing categorical data are developed in this lesson.

Categorical data were introduced to students in Grades 6 and 8. This lesson, along with Lessons 10 and 11, revisits and extends work students did in Grade 8 where data on two categorical variables were organized in a two-way table. Students also work with a random sample in this lesson and build on their understanding of a random sample developed in Grade 7. The data used in this lesson were obtained from the Census at School project. Census at School is further explained at the American Statistical Association website (www.amstat.org/censusatschool) and can be a source for data that might interest teenagers.

Classwork

Recall from your work in Grade 6 and Grade 8 that categorical data are data that are not numbers. Bivariate categorical data results from collecting data on two categorical variables. In this lesson, you will see examples involving categorical data collected from two survey questions.

Exploratory Challenge 1 (9 minutes): Superhero Powers

Exploratory Challenge 1: Superhero Powers

Superheroes have been popular characters in movies, television, books, and comics for many generations. Superman was one of the most popular series in the 1950s, while Batman was a top-rated series in the 1960s. Each of these characters was also popular in movies released from 1990 to 2013. Other notable characters portrayed in movies over the last several decades include Captain America, She-Ra, and the Fantastic Four. What is special about a superhero? Is there a special superhero power that makes these characters particularly popular?

High school students in the United States were invited to complete an online survey in 2010. Part of the survey included questions about superhero powers. More than $1,000$ students responded to this survey that included a question about a favorite superhero power. Researchers randomly selected 450 of the completed surveys. A rather confusing breakdown of the data by gender was compiled from the 450 surveys:

- **100 students indicated their favorite power was to fly. 49 of those students were females.**
- **131 students selected the power to freeze time as their favorite power. 71 of those students were males.**
- **75 students selected invisibility as their favorite power. 48 of those students were females.**

- **26 students indicated super strength as their favorite power. 25 of those students were males.**
- **And finally, 118 students indicated telepathy as their favorite power. 70 of those students were females.**

Direct students to read through the example and examine the data. Then, discuss the following questions to determine their understanding of the example:

- What is the most popular superpower?
  - *Freeze time*
- What is the least popular?
  - *Super strength*
- Why would the survey include gender?
  - *The survey includes gender in order to investigate whether or not there is a difference in the selection of a superpower for males or females.*
- Do you think gender plays a role in superhero power preference?
  - *Answers will vary, but in most cases, there are differences in the selection of a superpower by males or females.*

Exercises 1–4 (8 minutes)

Allow students to work independently or in small groups for two to three minutes on Exercises 1–4. Then, discuss and confirm answers as a class.

Exercises 1–4

Several superheroes portrayed in movies and television series had at least one extraordinary power. Some superheroes had more than one special power. Was Superman's power to fly the favorite power of his fans, or was it his super strength? Would females view the power to fly differently than males, or in the same way? Use the survey information given in Example 1 to answer the following questions.

1. **How many more females than males indicated their favorite power is telepathy?**

   22 more females indicated their favorite power was telepathy.

2. **How many more males than females indicated their favorite power was to fly?**

   Two more males indicated their favorite power was to fly.

3. **Write survey questions that you think might have been used to collect this data.**

   - ***What is your gender?*** ____ ***Male*** ____ ***Female***
   - ***If you could possess just one superpower, what would it be?***

     ____ ***To fly*** ____ ***Freeze time*** ____ ***Invisibility*** ____ ***Super strength*** ____ ***Telepathy***

4. **How do you think the 450 surveys used in Example 1 might have been selected? You can assume that there were $1,000$ surveys to select from.**

   A process involving random selection is needed.

Exploratory Challenge 2 (5 minutes): A Statistical Study Involving a Two-Way Frequency Table

Exploratory Challenge 2: A Statistical Study Involving a Two-Way Frequency Table

The data in Example 1 prompted students in a mathematics class to pose the statistical question, "Do high school males have different preferences for superhero powers than high school females?" Answering this statistical question involves collecting data as well as anticipating variability in the data collected.

The data consist of two responses from each student completing a survey. The first response indicates a student's gender, and the second response indicates the student's favorite superpower. For example, data collected from one student was *male* and *to fly*. The data are bivariate categorical data.

The first step in analyzing the statistical question posed by students in their mathematics class is to organize this data in a two-way frequency table.

A two-way frequency table that can be used to organize the categorical data is shown below. The letters below represent the frequency counts of the cells of the table.

	To Fly	Freeze Time	Invisibility	Super Strength	Telepathy	Total
Females	(a)	(b)	(c)	(d)	(e)	(f)
Males	(g)	(h)	(i)	(j)	(k)	(l)
Total	(m)	(n)	(o)	(p)	(q)	(r)

- **The shaded cells are called *marginal frequencies*. They are located around the margins of the table and represent the totals of the rows or columns of the table.**
- **The non-shaded cells *within* the table are called *joint frequencies*. Each joint cell is the frequency count of responses from the two categorical variables located by the intersection of a row and column.**

Ask students why the question posed is a statistical question. Remind students that a statistical question is a question that is answered by data and that it is anticipated that the data will vary. This question is a statistical question because the responses (data) are collected, and varied responses are expected (there are a variety of responses).

Explain the definition of categorical data and how it relates to Example 1.

Then, discuss the following:

- What is the difference between categorical and numerical data? (Remind students that answers to questions such as the superhero powers involve responses that are categories.)
- Provide examples of numerical data from past lessons to contrast with categorical data.

Have students examine the two-way frequency table.

Then, discuss the following:

- Is it possible to switch the row and column categories?
  - *Yes,* male *and* female *could be used as the column headings, and the superpowers could be represented in each row.*

Exercises 5–12 (15 minutes)

Allow students to work in small groups on Exercises 5–12. If students struggle with these questions, discuss them as a whole group.

Exercises 5–12

5. **Describe the data that would be counted in cell (a).**

   Cell (a) represents the number of females who chose to fly.

6. **Describe the data that would be counted in cell (j).**

   Cell (j) represents the number of males who chose super strength.

7. **Describe the data that would be counted in cell (l).**

   Cell (l) represents the total number of males who completed the survey in this sample.

8. **Describe the data that would be counted in cell (n).**

   Cell (n) represents the total number of students who chose freeze time as their favorite superpower.

9. **Describe the data that would be counted in cell (r).**

   Cell (r) represents the total number of students in the sample.

10. **Cell (i) is the number of male students who selected invisibility as their favorite superpower. Using the information given in Example 1, what is the value of this number?**

    Twenty-seven males selected invisibility.

11. **Cell (d) is the number of females whose favorite superpower is super strength. Using the information given in Example 1, what is the value of this number?**

    One female selected super strength.

12. **Complete the table below by determining a frequency count for each cell based on the summarized data.**

	To Fly	Freeze Time	Invisibility	Super Strength	Telepathy	Total
Females	49	60	48	1	70	228
Males	51	71	27	25	48	222
Total	100	131	75	26	118	450

Closing (3 minutes)

> **Lesson Summary**
>
> - ***Categorical data*** **are data that take on values that are categories rather than numbers. Examples include male or female for the categorical variable of gender or the five superpower categories for the categorical variable of superpower qualities.**
> - **A *two-way frequency table* is used to summarize bivariate categorical data.**
> - **The number in a two-way frequency table at the intersection of a row and column of the response to two categorical variables represents a *joint frequency*.**
> - **The total number of responses for each value of a categorical variable in the table represents the *marginal frequency* for that value.**

Exit Ticket (5 minutes)

Name ______________________________ Date______________

Lesson 9: Summarizing Bivariate Categorical Data

Exit Ticket

1. A survey asked the question, "How tall are you to the nearest inch?" A second question on this survey asked, "What sports do you play?" Indicate what type of data, numerical or categorical, would be collected from the first question? What type of data would be collected from the second question?

Another random sample of 100 surveys was selected. Jill had a copy of the frequency table that summarized these 100 surveys. Unfortunately, she spilled part of her lunch on the copy. The following summaries were still readable:

	To Fly	Freeze Time	Invisibility	Super Strength	Telepathy	Total
Females	12	15	(c)*	5	(e)*	55
Males	12	16	10	(j)*	3	45
Total	24	31	25	9	(q)*	100

2. Help Jill recreate the table by determining the frequencies for cells (c), (e), (j), and (q).

3. Of the cells (c), (e), (j), and (q), which cells represent joint frequencies?

4. Of the cells (c), (e), (j), and (q), which cells represent marginal frequencies?

Exit Ticket Sample Solutions

1. A survey asked the question, "How tall are you to the nearest inch?" A second question on this survey asked, "What sports do you play?" Indicate what type of data, numerical or categorical, would be collected from the first question? What type of data would be collected from the second question?

   The first question would result in numerical data; the second question would result in categorical data.

Another random sample of 100 surveys was selected. Jill had a copy of the frequency table that summarized these 100 surveys. Unfortunately, she spilled part of her lunch on the copy. The following summaries were still readable:

	To Fly	Freeze Time	Invisibility	Super Strength	Telepathy	Total
Females	12	15	*(c)**	5	*(e)**	55
Males	12	16	10	*(j)**	3	45
Total	24	31	25	9	*(q)**	100

2. Help Jill recreate the table by determining the frequencies for cells (c), (e), (j), and (q).

   Cell (c) has 15 students, (e) has 8 students, (j) has 4 students, and (q) has 11 students.

3. Of the cells (c), (e), (j), and (q), which cells represent joint frequencies?

   The cells (c), (e), and (j) are joint frequencies.

4. Of the cells (c), (e), (j), and (q), which cells represent marginal frequencies?

   Cell (q) is a marginal frequency.

Problem Set Sample Solutions

Several students at Rufus King High School were debating whether males or females were more involved in after-school activities. There are three organized activities in the after-school program—intramural basketball, chess club, and jazz band. Due to budget constraints, a student can only select one of these activities. The students were not able to ask every student in the school whether they participated in the after-school program or what activity they selected if they were involved.

1. Write questions that could be included in the survey to investigate the question the students are debating. Questions that could be used for this study include the following:

   What is your gender? (Circle one) Female Male

   Indicate if you participate in an after-school activity: (Circle one)

   Intramural basketball Chess club Jazz band I do not participate in after-school activities.

2. Rufus King High School has approximately $1,500$ students. Sam suggested that the first 100 students entering the cafeteria for lunch would provide a random sample to analyze. Janet suggested that they pick 100 students based on a school identification number. Who has a better strategy for selecting a random sample? How do you think 100 students could be randomly selected to complete the survey?

   Sam's suggestion is the least likely to generate a random sample because it will be primarily a convenience sample based on factors that influence who has lunch first (for example, certain grade levels, certain classes). Selections that involve ID numbers from the entire school are more likely to result in a more random selection. Contacting the 100 students selected by their IDs and asking them to complete the survey is not necessarily an easy or even workable process. I think I would ask students to take the survey just as they are leaving school. Nearly everyone in school gathers outside for a few minutes. I would try to get a completed survey from one out of every 50 students so that I would not get surveys just from one group.

3. Consider the following results from 100 randomly selected students:
   - Of the 60 female students selected, 20 of them played intramural basketball, 10 played chess, and 10 were in the jazz bland. The rest of them did not participate in the after-school program.
   - Of the male students, 10 did not participate in the after-school program, 20 played intramural basketball, 8 played in the jazz band, and the rest played chess.

   A two-way frequency table to summarize the survey data was started. Indicate what label is needed in the table cell identified with a ???.

	Intramural Basketball	Chess Club	Jazz Band	???	Total
Female	20	10	10	20	60
Male	20	2	8	10	40
Total	40	12	18	30	100

   The ??? could be labeled, "Do not participate in after-school program."

4. Complete the above table for the 100 students who were surveyed.

   Answers are provided in the table.

5. The table shows the responses to the after-school activity question for males and females. Do you think there is a difference in the responses of males and females? Explain your answer.

   Yes, I think that there are differences in the responses for males and females. Quite a few more females selected chess club. However, more females were surveyed than males. Also, half of the males selected basketball, while only a third of the females selected basketball. (Allow students to indicate that they are not sure how to compare the frequencies. For students forming an answer, the frequencies in the table are compared to the number of males or the number of females. Use this question to point out that more needs to be considered before we can really answer the question of whether or not there is a difference in the responses for males or females. Also, point out that a strategy for answering this type of question is developed in the next two lessons.)

Lesson 10: Summarizing Bivariate Categorical Data with Relative Frequencies

Student Outcomes

- Students summarize data on two categorical variables collected from a sample using a two-way frequency table.
- Given a two-way frequency table, students construct a relative frequency table and interpret relative frequencies.

Lesson Notes

Students continue the work with bivariate data from Lesson 9. Similar to Lesson 9, this lesson uses the superpower data to address the statistical question, "Do high school males have different preferences for superhero powers than high school females?" The two-way frequency table from Lesson 9 is used to develop a relative frequency table that allows students to compare the responses of males and females. However, the statistical question is still not clearly answered. As students complete the exercises in this lesson, they begin to see the need for conditional relative frequencies, which are introduced in Lesson 11. Students also begin to understand how conditional summaries are used to answer the statistical question.

This lesson revisits several topics that were developed in Grade 8. Students familiar with two-way tables move through these questions within the suggested time frame. Students not as familiar with this work may need more time to complete the exercises.

Classwork

This lesson expands on your work with two-way tables from Lesson 9.

Exploratory Challenge 1 (5 minutes): Extending the Frequency Table to a Relative Frequency Table

Exploratory Challenge 1: Extending the Frequency Table to a Relative Frequency Table

Determining the number of students in each cell presents the first step in organizing bivariate categorical data. Another way of analyzing the data in the table is to calculate the *relative frequency* for each cell. Relative frequencies relate each frequency count to the total number of observations. For each cell in this table, the relative frequency of a cell is found by dividing the frequency of that cell by the total number of responses.

Consider the two-way frequency table from the previous lesson.

Two-Way Frequency Table:

	To Fly	Freeze Time	Invisibility	Super Strength	Telepathy	Total
Females	49	60	48	1	70	228
Males	51	71	27	25	48	222
Total	100	131	75	26	118	450

The relative frequency table would be found by dividing each of the above cell values by 450. For example, the relative frequency of females selecting *to fly* is $\frac{49}{450}$, or approximately 0.109, to the nearest thousandth. A few of the other relative frequencies to the nearest thousandth are shown in the following relative frequency table:

	To Fly	Freeze Time	Invisibility	Super Strength	Telepathy	Total
Females	$\frac{49}{450} \approx 0.109$					$\frac{228}{450} \approx 0.507$
Males			$\frac{27}{450} \approx 0.060$			
Total		$\frac{131}{450} \approx 0.291$			$\frac{118}{450} \approx 0.262$	

Read through the Exploratory Challenge as a class.

Ask students to look at the relative frequency 49 out of 450 students, which is the first cell highlighted in the two-way frequency table. This cell represents females selecting the superpower to fly. Indicate to students that the relative frequency of this cell is a fraction, a decimal, or a percentage. The highlighted cell expresses the frequency as 0.109, to the nearest thousandth. The value could also be interpreted as approximately 10.9%, or about 11% of the students surveyed were females whose favorite superpower is the ability to fly. Work with students on the other examples of relative frequencies that appear in the two-way table. Point out that approximately 0.06, or 6% of the students surveyed were males whose favorite superpower is invisibility. Indicate that 131 of the 450 students, or 0.291, approximately 29%, selected freeze time as their favorite superpower. Then, discuss the following:

- A relative frequency is found by dividing the frequency count by the total number of observations.
- A relative frequency can be expressed as a decimal or a percentage or a fraction.
- Explore the following question: How would the relative frequencies look if males and females had the same opinions about their favorite superpowers? This question is a prelude to Lesson 11. Use the question to indicate that because the number of females and the number of males are not the same, relative frequencies are difficult to interpret to answer this question. Some students may begin to indicate that a comparison to the total number of males or to the total number of females is more appropriate. This observation is addressed in the next lesson.

Exercises 1–7 (10 minutes)

Allow students to work independently on Exercises 1–7. Then, discuss and confirm answers as a class. Sample responses are indicated.

Exercises 1–7

1. **Calculate the remaining relative frequencies in the table below. Write the value in the table as a decimal rounded to the nearest thousandth or as a percent.**

   Two-Way Frequency Table:

	To Fly	Freeze Time	Invisibility	Super Strength	Telepathy	Total
Females	0.109 10.9%	0.133 13.3%	0.107 10.7%	0.002 0.2%	0.156 15.6%	0.507 50.7%
Males	0.113 11.3%	0.158 15.8%	0.060 6.0%	0.056 5.6%	0.107 10.7%	0.493 49.3%
Total	0.222 22.2%	0.291 29.1%	0.167 16.7%	0.058 5.8%	0.262 26.2%	1.00 100%

2. **Based on previous work with frequency tables, which cells in this table would represent the joint relative frequencies?**

   The joint relative frequency cells are represented by the unshaded cells within the body of the table.

3. **Which cells in the relative frequency table would represent the marginal relative frequencies?**

   The marginal relative frequency cells are represented by the shaded cells in the total row and total column.

4. **What is the joint relative frequency for females who selected invisibility as their favorite superpower?**

   The joint relative frequency for females who selected invisibility as their favorite superpower is 0.107*, or approximately* 10.7%*. This indicates that approximately* 11% *of the students sampled were female who selected invisibility as their favorite superpower.*

5. **What is the marginal relative frequency for freeze time? Interpret the meaning of this value.**

   29.1%*, or approximately* 29% *of the total number of people surveyed, selected freeze time as their favorite superpower.*

6. **What is the difference in the joint relative frequencies for males and for females who selected to fly as their favorite superpower?**

   The difference in the relative frequencies is 0.004*, or* 0.4%*, or* $0.113 - 0.109$*.*

7. **Is there a noticeable difference between the genders and their favorite superpowers?**

   Yes. The most noticeable differences are in the following superpowers: invisibility, super strength, and telepathy.

Exploratory Challenge 2 (10 minutes): Interpreting Data

> **Exploratory Challenge 2: Interpreting Data**
>
> **Interest in superheroes continues at Rufus King High School. The students who analyzed the data in the previous lesson decided to create a comic strip for the school website that involves a superhero. They thought the summaries developed from the data would be helpful in designing the comic strip.**
>
> **Only one power will be given to the superhero. A debate arose as to what power the school's superhero would possess. Students used the two-way frequency table and the relative frequency table to continue the discussion. Take another look at those tables.**
>
> **Scott initially indicated that the character created should have super strength as the special power. This suggestion was not well received by the other students planning this project. In particular, Jill argued, "Well, if you don't want to ignore more than half of the readers, then I suggest telepathy is the better power for our character."**

Read through the Exploratory Challenge as a class.

Then, discuss the following:

- Why would several students argue against Scott's initial suggestion of choosing super strength?
  - 0.2% *of the responses were females who preferred this power.*
- Why might Scott have made this suggestion?
  - *Answers will vary. A reasonable answer could be personal preference.*
- Why would Jill say to use telepathy?
  - *It has the largest frequency count for females.*
- Do you think there is a difference in the superpowers selected by males and those selected by females?
  - *There are indications that males and females have differences in what superpowers they select. Less than* 1% *of the sample was females who selected* to fly, *while over* 5% *of the sample was males who selected* to fly. *The large difference suggests more males than females selected this superpower. However, point out to students that comparing the relative frequencies does not answer our question. Students may struggle to understand this question. (That is okay because the use of the relative frequency tables is limited.) Indicate that as we move into the next lesson, a direct comparison of these cells using conditional relative frequencies will provide a better indication of the gender differences in selection of superpowers.*

Exercises 8–10 (10 minutes)

Allow students to work in pairs. Then, discuss and confirm answers as a class.

> **Exercises 8–10**
>
> **Scott acknowledged that super strength was probably not the best choice based on the data. "The data indicate that freeze time is the most popular power for a superhero," continued Scott. Jill, however, still did not agree with Scott that this was a good choice. She argued that telepathy was a better choice.**
>
> 8. **How do the data support Scott's claim? Why do you think he selected freeze time as the special power for the comic strip superhero?**
>
>   ***Freeze time was the most popular choice among male students and among all students surveyed.***

9. **How do the data support Jill's claim? Why do you think she selected telepathy as the special power for the comic strip superhero?**

   Jill's claim was based on the observation that telepathy was the most popular choice of female students.

10. **Of the two special powers freeze time and telepathy, select one and justify why you think it is a better choice based on the data.**

    Answers will vary. The two categories each represent 26% to 29% of the sample. More females selected telepathy, while more males selected freeze time.

Closing (5 minutes)

Lesson Summary

- ***Categorical data*** **are data that take on values that are categories rather than numbers. Examples include male or female for the categorical variable of gender or the five superpower categories for the categorical variable of superpower qualities.**
- **A *two-way frequency table* is used to summarize bivariate categorical data.**
- **A *relative frequency* compares a frequency count to the total number of observations. It can be written as a decimal or percent. A two-way table summarizing the relative frequencies of each cell is called a *relative frequency table*.**
- **The marginal cells in a two-way relative frequency table are called the *marginal relative frequencies*, while the joint cells are called the *joint relative frequencies*.**

Exit Ticket (5 minutes)

Name ______________________________ Date______________

Lesson 10: Summarizing Bivariate Categorical Data with Relative Frequencies

Exit Ticket

Juniors and seniors were asked if they plan to attend college immediately after graduation, seek full-time employment, or choose some other option. A random sample of 100 students was selected from those who completed the survey. Scott started to calculate the relative frequencies to the nearest thousandth.

	Plan to Attend College	Plan to Seek Full-Time Employment	Other Options	Totals
Seniors	$\frac{25}{100} = 0.250$	$\frac{10}{100} = 0.100$		
Juniors				$\frac{45}{100} = 0.450$
Totals	$\frac{60}{100} = 0.600$	$\frac{15}{100} = 0.150$	$\frac{25}{100} = 0.250$	$\frac{100}{100} = 1.000$

1. Complete the calculations of the relative frequencies for each of the blank cells. Round your answers to the nearest thousandth.

2. A school website article indicated that "A Vast Majority of Students from our School Plan to Attend College." Do you agree or disagree with that article? Explain why you agree or disagree.

3. Do you think juniors and seniors differ regarding after-graduation options? Explain.

Exit Ticket Sample Solutions

Juniors and seniors were asked if they plan to attend college immediately after graduation, seek full-time employment, or choose some other option. A random sample of 100 students was selected from those who completed the survey. Scott started to calculate the relative frequencies to the nearest thousandth.

1. **Complete the calculations of the relative frequencies for each of the blank cells. Round your answers to the nearest thousandth.**

   The following is a completed chart:

	Plan to Attend College	Plan to Seek Full-Time Employment	Other Options	Totals
Seniors	$\frac{25}{100} = 0.250$	$\frac{10}{100} = 0.100$	$\frac{20}{100} = 0.200$	$\frac{55}{100} = 0.550$
Juniors	$\frac{35}{100} = 0.350$	$\frac{5}{100} = 0.050$	$\frac{5}{100} = 0.050$	$\frac{45}{100} = 0.450$
Totals	$\frac{60}{100} = 0.600$	$\frac{15}{100} = 0.150$	$\frac{25}{100} = 0.250$	$\frac{100}{100} = 1.000$

2. **A school website article indicated that "A Vast Majority of Students from our School Plan to Attend College." Do you agree or disagree with that article? Explain why you agree or disagree.**

   Most of the students in the school plan to attend college after graduation (60% of sample). That is a clear majority. It is interesting, however, that a larger number of junior students plan to attend college, yet there were fewer juniors in the sample.

3. **Do you think juniors and seniors differ regarding after-graduation options? Explain.**

   There are some interesting differences. One difference is noted above concerning college. Another is the selection of other options. A very small percentage of the students selecting that option were juniors.

Problem Set Sample Solutions

1. **Consider the Rufus King High School data from the previous lesson regarding after-school activities:**

	Intramural Basketball	Chess Club	Jazz Band	Not Involved	Total
Males	20	2	8	10	40
Females	20	10	10	20	60
Total	40	12	18	30	100

Calculate the relative frequencies for each of the cells to the nearest thousandth. Place the relative frequencies in the cells of the following table. (The first cell has been completed as an example.)

	Intramural Basketball	Chess Club	Jazz Band	Not Involved	Total
Males	$\frac{20}{100} = 0.200$	$\frac{2}{100} = 0.020$	$\frac{8}{100} = 0.080$	$\frac{10}{100} = 0.100$	$\frac{40}{100} = 0.400$
Females	$\frac{20}{100} = 0.200$	$\frac{10}{100} = 0.100$	$\frac{10}{100} = 0.100$	$\frac{20}{100} = 0.200$	$\frac{60}{100} = 0.600$
Total	$\frac{40}{100} = 0.400$	$\frac{12}{100} = 0.120$	$\frac{18}{100} = 0.180$	$\frac{30}{100} = 0.300$	$\frac{100}{100} = 1.000$

2. **Based on your relative frequency table, what is the relative frequency of students who indicated they play basketball?**

   0.40, *or* 40%

3. **Based on your table, what is the relative frequency of males who play basketball?**

   0.20, *or* 20%

4. **If a student were randomly selected from the students at the school, do you think the student selected would be a male or a female?**

   The selection could be a female because 0.60, ***or*** 60%, ***of the students in the sample were females.***

5. **If a student were selected at random from school, do you think this student would be involved in an after-school program? Explain your answer.**

   Yes, 70% ***of the students participate in an after-school program.***

6. **Why might someone question whether or not the students who completed the survey were randomly selected? If the students completing the survey were randomly selected, what do the marginal relative frequencies possibly tell you about the school? Explain your answer.**

   A person may question the sample based on the assumption that you would anticipate 50% ***of the students would be female and*** 50% ***would be male. The marginal relative frequencies indicate that the sample was*** 60% ***female and*** 40% ***male. Possibly, the school has more females than males.***

7. **Why might females think they are more involved in after-school activities than males? Explain your answer.**

   More females were involved in the after-school activities. 40 ***females were involved in the after-school activities, while*** 30 ***males were involved. (Note: Indicate to students that this will be explored in the next lesson.)***

Lesson 11: Conditional Relative Frequencies and Association

Student Outcomes

- Students calculate and interpret conditional relative frequencies from two-way frequency tables.
- Students evaluate conditional relative frequencies as an indication of possible association between two variables.
- Students explain why association does not imply causation.

Lesson Notes

Students continue the analysis of the bivariate categorical data that they began in Lessons 9 and 10. Lesson 9 summarized the data in a two-way frequency table. Relative frequencies were then introduced in Lesson 10. In each case, however, the question posed about whether there is a difference in the favorite superpower responses of males and females remains unclear. This lesson develops and interprets conditional relative frequencies to answer the statistical question posed in the previous lessons. Students familiar with two-way tables from Grade 8 move through these questions within the suggested time frame. Students not as familiar with this work may need more time to complete these exercises.

The focus of this lesson is conditional relative frequencies and how they indicate a possible association. Definitions of conditional relative frequencies and association are provided in this lesson. Differences in conditional relative frequencies are used as evidence of possible association. Instructors should challenge students to think critically about the meaning of an association between two categorical variables and to be careful not to draw unwarranted conclusions about possible cause-and-effect relationships between two categorical variables. The last example and exercise discuss the issue of cause-and-effect.

Classwork

After further discussion, the students involved in designing the superhero comic strip decided that before any decision is made, a more careful look at the data on the special powers a superhero character could possess was needed. There is an association between gender and superpower response if the superpower responses of males are not the same as the superpower responses of females. Examining each row of the table can help determine whether or not there is an association.

Exploratory Challenge 1 (5 minutes): Conditional Relative Frequencies

Exploratory Challenge 1: Conditional Relative Frequencies

Recall the two-way table from the previous lesson.

	To Fly	Freeze Time	Invisibility	Super Strength	Telepathy	Total
Females	49	60	48	1	70	228
Males	51	71	27	25	48	222
Total	100	131	75	26	118	450

A *conditional relative frequency* compares a frequency count to the marginal total that represents the condition of interest. For example, the condition of interest in the first row is females. The row conditional relative frequency of females responding invisibility as the favorite superpower is $\frac{48}{228}$, or approximately 0.211. This conditional relative frequency indicates that approximately 21.1% of females prefer invisibility as their favorite superpower. Similarly, $\frac{27}{222}$, or approximately 0.122 or 12.2%, of males prefer invisibility as their favorite superpower.

Let students read through the introductory paragraph and Example 1.

Then, discuss the following:

- How is relative frequency calculated?
  - *It is calculated by dividing the frequency by the total observations.*
- How could we determine a relative frequency for only the female students?
  - *We could determine this by dividing the frequency by the total number of females.*
- Conditional relative frequencies are found by dividing the frequency by the marginal total.

Work with students to calculate the conditional relative frequency of females who chose to fly as a superpower:

$$\frac{49}{228} \approx 0.215, \text{ or } 21.5\%.$$

Then, discuss the following:

- How would we interpret the conditional relative frequency?
  - 21.5% *of the females surveyed chose to fly as their favorite superpower.*
- How does this compare with the same cell in the relative frequency table from Example 1?
  - 10.9% *of the students surveyed were females who chose to fly as their favorite superpower.*

Exercises 1–5 (10 minutes)

Let students continue to work in pairs on Exercises 1–5. Work with students more directly on the first set of questions.

Exercises 1–5

1. **Use the frequency counts from the table in Exploratory Challenge 1 to calculate the missing row of conditional relative frequencies. Round the answers to the nearest thousandth.**

	To Fly	Freeze Time	Invisibility	Super Strength	Telepathy	Total
Females	$\frac{49}{228} \approx 0.215$	$\frac{60}{228} \approx 0.263$	$\frac{48}{228} \approx 0.211$	$\frac{1}{228} \approx 0.004$	$\frac{70}{228} \approx 0.307$	$\frac{228}{228} = 1.000$
Males	$\frac{51}{222} \approx 0.230$	$\frac{71}{222} \approx 0.320$	$\frac{27}{222} \approx 0.122$	$\frac{25}{222} \approx 0.113$	$\frac{48}{222} \approx 0.216$	$\frac{222}{222} = 1.000$
Total	$\frac{100}{450} \approx 0.222$	$\frac{131}{450} \approx 0.291$	$\frac{75}{450} \approx 0.167$	$\frac{26}{450} \approx 0.058$	$\frac{118}{450} \approx 0.262$	$\frac{450}{450} = 1.000$

2. **Suppose that a student is selected at random from those who completed the survey. What do you think is the gender of the student selected? What would you predict for this student's response to the superpower question?**

   Since there were almost the same number of males and females, the selected student could be male or female. If the responses of both males and females were combined, students would probably select freeze time because the relative frequency of freeze time is $\frac{131}{450}$ *(or approximately* 29%*) of all students. This superpower was selected by more of the males and females than any other superpower.*

3. **Suppose that a student is selected at random from those who completed the survey. If the selected student is male, what do you think was his response to the selection of a favorite superpower? Explain your answer.**

   Freeze time was also the most popular selection for male students.

4. **Suppose that a student is selected at random from those who completed the survey. If the selected student is female, what do you think was her response to the selection of a favorite superpower? Explain your answer.**

   Telepathy was the most popular selection for female students.

5. **What superpower was selected by approximately one-third of the females? What superpower was selected by approximately one-third of the males? How did you determine each answer from the conditional relative frequency table?**

   Telepathy was selected by approximately one-third of the females. Freeze time was selected by approximately one-third of the males. These selections were based on row conditional relative frequencies approximately equal to 0.333 *for females and for males.*

Exploratory Challenge 2 (5 minutes): Possible Association Based on Conditional Relative Frequencies

> **Exploratory Challenge 2: Possible Association Based on Conditional Relative Frequencies**
>
> **Two categorical variables are associated if the row conditional relative frequencies (or column relative frequencies) are different for the rows (or columns) of the table. For example, if the selection of superpowers selected for females is different than the selection of superpowers for males, then gender and superpower favorites are associated. This difference indicates that knowing the gender of a person in the sample indicates something about their superpower preference.**
>
> **The evidence of an association is strongest when the conditional relative frequencies are quite different. If the conditional relative frequencies are nearly equal for all categories, then there is probably not an association between variables.**

Verbally summarize the paragraphs and how they relate to the theme of the lesson.

Association can be a challenging concept for students. Discuss additional examples of association involving the *condition* of gender:

- If you know that a person is female, could you predict that she spends more than thirty minutes getting ready for school?
  - *Maybe. Girls may tend to spend more time getting ready than boys, and, if so, there is an association between gender and whether a student spends more than thirty minutes getting ready for school.*
- If you know that a person is male, could you predict that country music is his favorite type of music?
  - *Probably not. There is no association between gender and music preference.*

Discuss other examples of questions that investigate association:

- If dogs are classified as large, medium, or small based on weight, are small dogs more likely to pass an obedience course?
- If users of a social network are classed as active, average, or inactive, is a person classified as an *active* user more likely to be a good writer than those classified in the other categories?

Then, discuss the evidence that supports association:

- There is strong evidence of association when there is a *noticeable* difference in conditional relative frequencies.
- What is a *noticeable* difference in conditional relative frequencies? This is subjective; students should use their best judgment at this time. Students evaluate the differences more formally in Algebra II as well as Precalculus and Advanced Topics.

Exercises 6–10 (7 minutes)

Allow students to work independently on Exercises 6–10. Then, discuss and confirm answers as a class.

> **Exercises 6–10**
>
> **Examine the conditional relative frequencies in the two-way table of conditional relative frequencies you created in Exercise 1. Note that for each superpower, the conditional relative frequencies are different for females and males.**

6. **For what superpowers would you say that the conditional relative frequencies for females and males are very different?**

   The most noticeable differences in conditional relative frequencies would be for invisibility, super strength, and telepathy. Students may also indicate a noticeable difference for freeze time.

7. **For what superpowers are the conditional relative frequencies nearly equal for males and females?**

   The superpower to fly has nearly the same conditional relative frequencies for males and females.

8. **Suppose a student is selected at random from the students who completed the survey. Would knowing the student's gender be helpful in predicting which superpower this student selected? Explain your answer.**

   Due to the noticeable differences in the conditional relative frequencies of selecting a particular superpower based on gender, it would be helpful to know a student's gender when predicting the selection of a superpower.

9. **Is there evidence of an association between gender and a favorite superpower? Explain why or why not.**

   Based on the definition of association presented in this lesson, there appears to be an association between superpower selected and gender. Knowing the gender of a student helps predict the superpower response.

10. **What superpower would you recommend the students at Rufus King High School select for their superhero character? Justify your choice.**

    Consider several answers. Students are expected to justify their answers based on the conditional relative frequencies or the relative frequencies for all students.

Exploratory Challenge 3 (5 minutes): Association and Cause-and-Effect

Exploratory Challenge 3: Association and Cause-and-Effect

Students were given the opportunity to prepare for a college placement test in mathematics by taking a review course. Not all students took advantage of this opportunity. The following results were obtained from a random sample of students who took the placement test.

	Placed in Math 200	Placed in Math 100	Placed in Math 50	Total
Took Review Course	40	13	7	60
Did Not Take Review Course	10	15	15	40
Total	50	28	22	100

This example introduces the important idea that you should not infer a cause-and-effect relationship from an association between two categorical variables.

Read through the example with students.

Pose the following questions to the class. Let students discuss their ideas.

- Is there an association between taking the review course and a student's placement in a math class?

- Would knowing that a student took a review course make a difference in predicting which math course they were placed in?
- Does taking a review course *cause* a student to place higher in a math placement?

Exercises 11–16 (6 minutes)

Let students work in pairs. Then, discuss and confirm answers to Exercises 11–13 and 14–16.

Exercises 11–16

11. Construct a row conditional relative frequency table of the above data.

	Placed in Math 200	Placed in Math 100	Placed in Math 50	Total
Took Review Course	$\frac{40}{60} \approx 0.667$	$\frac{13}{60} \approx 0.217$	$\frac{7}{60} \approx 0.117$	$\frac{60}{60} = 1.000$
Did Not Take Review Course	$\frac{10}{40} = 0.250$	$\frac{15}{40} = 0.375$	$\frac{15}{40} = 0.375$	$\frac{40}{40} = 1.000$
Total	$\frac{50}{100} = 0.500$	$\frac{28}{100} = 0.280$	$\frac{22}{100} = 0.220$	$\frac{100}{100} = 1.000$

12. Based on the conditional relative frequencies, is there evidence of an association between whether a student takes the review course and the math course in which the student was placed? Explain your answer.

There is evidence of association because the conditional relative frequencies are noticeably different for those students who took the course and for those students who did not take the course.

13. Looking at the conditional relative frequencies, the proportion of students who placed into Math 200 is much higher for those who took the review course than for those who did not. One possible explanation is that taking the review course caused improvement in placement test scores. What is another possible explanation?

Another possible explanation is that students who took the review course are more interested in mathematics or were already better prepared in mathematics and, therefore, performed better on the mathematics placement test.

- Do you think that this is an example of a cause-and-effect relationship? Be sure that students understand that even though there is an association, this does not mean that there is a cause-and-effect relationship.

Now consider the following statistical study:

Fifty students were selected at random from students at a large middle school. Each of these students was classified according to sugar consumption (high or low) and exercise level (high or low). The resulting data are summarized in the following frequency table.

		Exercise Level		
		High	Low	Total
Sugar Consumption	High	14	18	32
	Low	14	4	18
	Total	28	22	50

14. **Calculate the row conditional relative frequencies, and display them in a row conditional relative frequency table.**

		Exercise Level		
		High	Low	Total
Sugar Consumption	High	$\frac{14}{32} \approx 0.438$	$\frac{18}{32} \approx 0.563$	$\frac{32}{32} = 1.000$
	Low	$\frac{14}{18} \approx 0.778$	$\frac{4}{18} \approx 0.222$	$\frac{18}{18} = 1.000$
	Total	$\frac{28}{50} = 0.560$	$\frac{22}{50} = 0.440$	$\frac{50}{50} = 1.000$

15. **Is there evidence of an association between sugar consumption category and exercise level? Support your answer using conditional relative frequencies.**

    There is a noticeable difference in the conditional relative frequencies based on whether a person selected had high or low sugar consumption. The differences suggest an association between sugar consumption and exercise level.

16. **Is it reasonable to conclude that high sugar consumption is the cause of the observed differences in the conditional relative frequencies? What other explanations could explain a difference in the conditional relative frequencies? Explain your answer.**

    Students are encouraged to think about their responses to this exercise based on their understanding that the results should not be interpreted as a cause-and-effect relationship. Other factors such as eating habits and lifestyle could be mentioned by students.

If time permits, discuss the following with your students:

- Is it possible that students in the above study who are more health conscious tend to be in the low sugar consumption category and also tend to be in the high exercise level category?
- It is not possible to determine if the difference in the conditional relative frequencies is due to a cause-and-effect relationship.
- The data summarized in this study were collected in an observational study. In an observational study, any observed differences in conditional relative frequencies might be explained by some factor other than the variables examined in the study. With an observational study, evidence of an association may exist, but it is not possible to imply that there is a cause-and-effect relationship.

Closing (2 minutes)

Discuss with students the Lesson Summary.

> **Lesson Summary**
>
> - **A conditional relative frequency compares a frequency count to the marginal total that represents the *condition* of interest.**
> - **The differences in conditional relative frequencies are used to assess whether or not there is an association between two categorical variables.**
> - **The greater the differences in the conditional relative frequencies, the stronger the evidence that an association exits.**
> - **An observed association between two variables does not necessarily mean that there is a cause-and-effect relationship between the two variables.**

Exit Ticket (5 minutes)

Name ______________________________ Date ______________

Lesson 11: Conditional Relative Frequencies and Association

Exit Ticket

Juniors and seniors were asked if they plan to attend college immediately after graduation, seek full-time employment, or choose some other option. A random sample of 100 students was selected from those who completed the survey. Scott started to calculate the row conditional relative frequencies to the nearest thousandth.

	Plan to Attend College	Plan to Seek Full-Time Employment	Other Options	Totals
Seniors	$\frac{25}{55} \approx 0.455$	$\frac{10}{55} \approx 0.182$	$\frac{20}{\quad} \approx ???$	$\frac{55}{55} = 1.000$
Juniors	$\frac{35}{\quad} \approx ???$	$\frac{5}{\quad} \approx ???$	$\frac{5}{45} \approx 0.111$	$\frac{45}{45} = 1.000$
Totals	$\frac{60}{100} = 0.600$	$\frac{15}{100} = 0.150$	$\frac{25}{100} = 0.250$	$\frac{100}{100} = 1.000$

1. Complete the calculations of the row conditional relative frequencies. Round your answers to the nearest thousandth.

2. Are the row conditional relative frequencies for juniors and seniors similar, or are they very different?

3. Do you think there is a possible association between grade level (junior or senior) and after high school plans? Explain your answer.

Exit Ticket Sample Solutions

Juniors and seniors were asked if they plan to attend college immediately after graduation, seek full-time employment, or choose some other option. A random sample of 100 students was selected from those who completed the survey. Scott started to calculate the row conditional relative frequencies to the nearest thousandth.

1. Complete the calculations of the row conditional relative frequencies. Round your answers to the nearest thousandth.

	Plan to Attend College	Plan to Seek Full-Time Employment	Other Options	Totals
Seniors	$\frac{25}{55} \approx 0.455$	$\frac{10}{55} \approx 0.182$	$\frac{20}{55} \approx 0.364$	$\frac{55}{55} = 1.000$
Juniors	$\frac{35}{45} \approx 0.778$	$\frac{5}{45} \approx 0.111$	$\frac{5}{45} \approx 0.111$	$\frac{45}{45} = 1.000$
Totals	$\frac{60}{100} = 0.600$	$\frac{15}{100} = 0.150$	$\frac{25}{100} = 0.250$	$\frac{100}{100} = 1.000$

2. Are the row conditional relative frequencies for juniors and seniors similar, or are they very different?

   The conditional relative frequencies are noticeably different for juniors and seniors.

3. Do you think there is a possible association between grade level (junior or senior) and after high school plans? Explain your answer.

   The differences in the conditional relative frequencies suggest that there is an association.

Problem Set Sample Solutions

Consider again the summary of data from the 100 randomly selected students in the Rufus King High School investigation of after-school activities and gender.

	Intramural Basketball	Chess Club	Jazz Band	Not Involved	Total
Females	20	10	10	20	60
Males	20	2	8	10	40
Total	40	12	18	30	100

1. Construct a row conditional relative frequency table for this data. Decimal values are given to the nearest thousandth.

	Intramural Basketball	Chess Club	Jazz Band	Not Involved	Total
Females	$\frac{20}{60} \approx 0.333$	$\frac{10}{60} \approx 0.167$	$\frac{10}{60} \approx 0.167$	$\frac{20}{60} \approx 0.333$	$\frac{60}{60} = 1.000$
Males	$\frac{20}{40} = 0.500$	$\frac{2}{40} = 0.050$	$\frac{8}{40} = 0.200$	$\frac{10}{40} = 0.250$	$\frac{40}{40} = 1.000$
Total	$\frac{40}{100} = 0.400$	$\frac{12}{100} = 0.120$	$\frac{18}{100} = 0.180$	$\frac{30}{100} = 0.300$	$\frac{100}{100} = 1.000$

2. **For what after-school activities do you think the row conditional relative frequencies for females and males are very different? What might explain why males or females select different activities?**

   There are noticeable differences in several of the after-school activity conditional relative frequencies for the two genders, suggesting that there is an association. (The most noticeable differences are in intramural basketball and chess club.) They could be different based on a student's interest in being with friends, having a specific coach, following a popular leader, or participating in a more popular tradition established at the school.

3. **If John, a male student at Rufus King High School, completed the after-school survey, what would you predict was his response? Explain your answer.**

   50%*, or half, of the males indicated they participated in intramural basketball. Since this was the greatest conditional relative frequency for males, you would anticipate that John, a male student, would select this response.*

4. **If Beth, a female student at Rufus King High School, completed the after-school survey, what would you predict was her response? Explain your answer.**

   Females selected intramural basketball *or* not involved *equally often. You would anticipate that Beth, a female student, would select one of these two responses.*

5. **Notice that 20 female students participate in intramural basketball and that 20 male students participate in intramural basketball. Is it accurate to say that females and males are equally involved in intramural basketball? Explain your answer.**

   It is not accurate to say they are equally involved because there are more females in the sample. Thus, the 20 *female students who participate in intramural basketball represent one-third of the females, while the* 20 *male students represent one-half of the males.*

6. **Do you think there is an association between gender and choice of after-school program? Explain.**

   There is a difference in the conditional relative frequencies, but the differences are not as obvious as in the other examples. (This is a problem in which students would be expected to justify how they would indicate association between gender and the after-school selections.)

Column conditional relative frequencies **can also be computed by dividing each frequency in a frequency table by the corresponding column total to create a column conditional relative frequency table. Column conditional relative frequencies indicate the proportions, or relative frequencies, based on the column totals.**

7. **If you wanted to know the relative frequency of females surveyed who participated in chess club, would you use a row conditional relative frequency or a column conditional relative frequency?**

   You would use a row conditional relative frequency. Of the 60 *females surveyed,* 10 *participated in the chess club. (The given condition is that the student is female.) The relative frequency of* $\frac{10}{60}$ *would be the conditional relative frequency of females who participated in chess club.*

8. **If you wanted to know the relative frequency of band members surveyed who were female, would you use a row conditional relative frequency or a column conditional relative frequency?**

   You would use a column conditional relative frequency. Of the 18 *band members,* 10 *were females. (The given condition is that the student is in band.) The conditional relative frequency of* $\frac{10}{18}$ *would be the conditional relative frequency of band members who were females.*

9. **For the superpower survey data, write a question that would be answered using a row conditional relative frequency.**

   An example of a row conditional relative frequency question would be "What proportion of females selected telepathy as their favorite superpower?"

10. **For the superpower survey data, write a question that would be answered using a column conditional relative frequency.**

    An example of a column conditional relative frequency would be "What proportion of those who selected telepathy are female?"

Mathematics Curriculum

Topic D

Numerical Data on Two Variables

S-ID.B.6, S-ID.C.7, S-ID.C.8, S-ID.C.9

Focus Standards:	S-ID.B.6	Represent data on two quantitative variables on a scatter plot, and describe how the variables are related.★ a. Fit the function to the data; use functions fitted to data to solve problems in the context of the data. *Use given functions or choose a function suggested by the context. Emphasize linear, quadratic, and exponential models.* b. Informally assess the fit of a function by plotting and analyzing residuals. c. Fit a linear function for a scatter plot that suggests a linear association.
	S-ID.C.7	Interpret the slope (rate of change) and the intercept (constant term) of a linear model in the context of the data.★
	S-ID.C.8	Compute (using technology) and interpret the correlation coefficient of a linear fit.★
	S-ID.C.9	Distinguish between correlation and causation.★
Instructional Days:	9	
Lessons 12–13:	Relationships Between Two Numerical Variables (P, P)[1]	
Lesson 14:	Modeling Relationships with a Line (P)	
Lesson 15:	Interpreting Residuals from a Line (P)	
Lesson 16:	More on Modeling Relationships with a Line (P)	
Lessons 17–18:	Analyzing Residuals (P, P)	
Lesson 19:	Interpreting Correlation (P)	
Lesson 20:	Analyzing Data Collected on Two Variables (E)	

In Topic D, students analyze relationships between two quantitative variables by using scatter plots and by summarizing linear relationships using the least squares regression line. Models are proposed based on an understanding of the equations representing the models and the observed pattern in the scatter plot. Students calculate and analyze residuals based on an interpretation of residuals as prediction errors.

[1]Lesson Structure Key: **P**-Problem Set Lesson, **M**-Modeling Cycle Lesson, **E**-Exploration Lesson, **S**-Socratic Lesson

Lesson 12: Relationships Between Two Numerical Variables

Student Outcomes

- Students distinguish between scatter plots that display a relationship that can be reasonably modeled by a linear equation and those that should be modeled by a nonlinear equation.

Lesson Notes

This lesson builds on students' work from Grade 8 and their work with bivariate data and its relationships. Previous studies of relationships have primarily focused on linear models. For this lesson, students begin their work with nonlinear relationships, specifically exponential and quadratic models.

Lesson 20 encourages students to select an example from this lesson or the next one to summarize as examples in a poster or a similar presentation. As students work through these examples, encourage them to consider each as a possible problem for a poster or presentation.

Classwork

A scatter plot is an informative way to display numerical data with two variables. In your previous work in Grade 8, you saw how to construct and interpret scatter plots. Recall that if the two numerical variables are denoted by x and y, the scatter plot of the data is a plot of the (x, y) data pairs.

Example 1 (5 minutes): Looking for Patterns in a Scatter Plot

Briefly introduce the data in the table. Explain how plotting the ordered pairs of data creates a scatter plot.

Example 1: Looking for Patterns in a Scatter Plot

The National Climate Data Center collects data on weather conditions at various locations. They classify each day as clear, partly cloudy, or cloudy. Using data taken over a number of years, they provide data on the following variables.

x represents elevation above sea level (in feet).

y represents mean number of clear days per year.

w represents mean number of partly cloudy days per year.

z represents mean number of cloudy days per year.

The table below shows data for 14 U.S. cities.

City	x (Elevation Above Sea Level in Feet)	y (Mean Number of Clear Days per Year)	w (Mean Number of Partly Cloudy Days per Year)	z (Mean Number of Cloudy Days per Year)
Albany, NY	275	69	111	185
Albuquerque, NM	$5,311$	167	111	87
Anchorage, AK	114	40	60	265
Boise, ID	$2,838$	120	90	155
Boston, MA	15	98	103	164
Helena, MT	$3,828$	82	104	179
Lander, WY	$5,557$	114	122	129
Milwaukee, WI	672	90	100	175
New Orleans, LA	4	101	118	146
Raleigh, NC	434	111	106	149
Rapid City, SD	$3,162$	111	115	139
Salt Lake City, UT	$4,221$	125	101	139
Spokane, WA	$2,356$	86	88	191
Tampa, FL	19	101	143	121

Here is a scatter plot of the data on elevation and mean number of clear days.

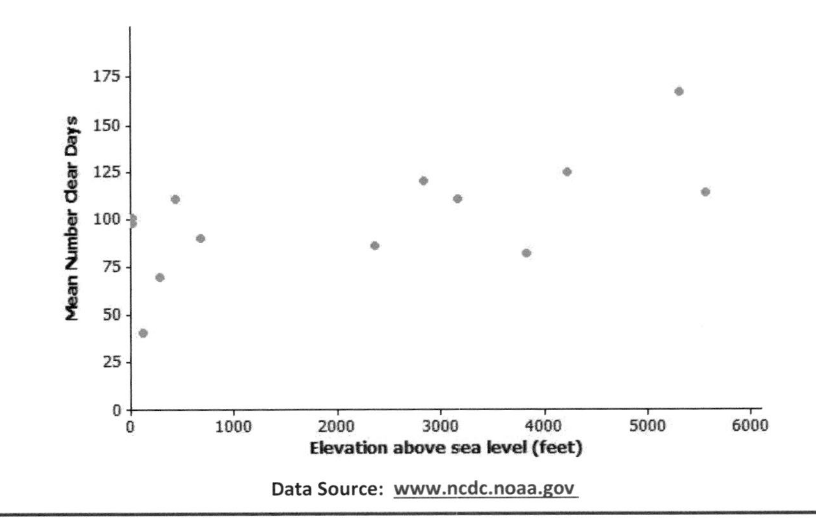

Data Source: www.ncdc.noaa.gov

Exercises 1–3 (7 minutes)

Let students work independently on Exercises 1–3. Then discuss and confirm as a class.

Exercises 1–3

1. **Do you see a pattern in the scatter plot, or does it look like the data points are scattered?**

   The scatter plot does not have a strong pattern. Students may respond that it looks like the data points are randomly scattered. If students look carefully, however, there is a pattern that suggests as elevation increases, the number of clear days also appears to increase. Motivate the discussion by looking at various data points, with several at lower elevations, and several others at higher elevations to indicate the possible relationship.

2. **How would you describe the relationship between elevation and mean number of clear days for these 14 cities? That is, does the mean number of clear days tend to increase as elevation increases, or does the mean number of clear days tend to decrease as elevation increases?**

   As the elevation increases, the number of clear days generally increases.

MP.4

3. **Do you think that a straight line would be a good way to describe the relationship between the mean number of clear days and elevation? Why do you think this?**

   Although the pattern is not strong, a straight line would describe the general pattern that was observed in the discussion of the first two exercises.

Exercises 4–7 (7 minutes): Thinking about Linear Relationships

Let students work in pairs on Exercises 4–7. Then, discuss as a class. Allow for more than one student to offer an answer for each question.

Remind students to state what each axis represents in each question.

Exercises 4–7: Thinking about Linear Relationships

Below are three scatter plots. Each one represents a data set with eight observations.

The scales on the x- and y-axes have been left off these plots on purpose, so you have to think carefully about the relationships.

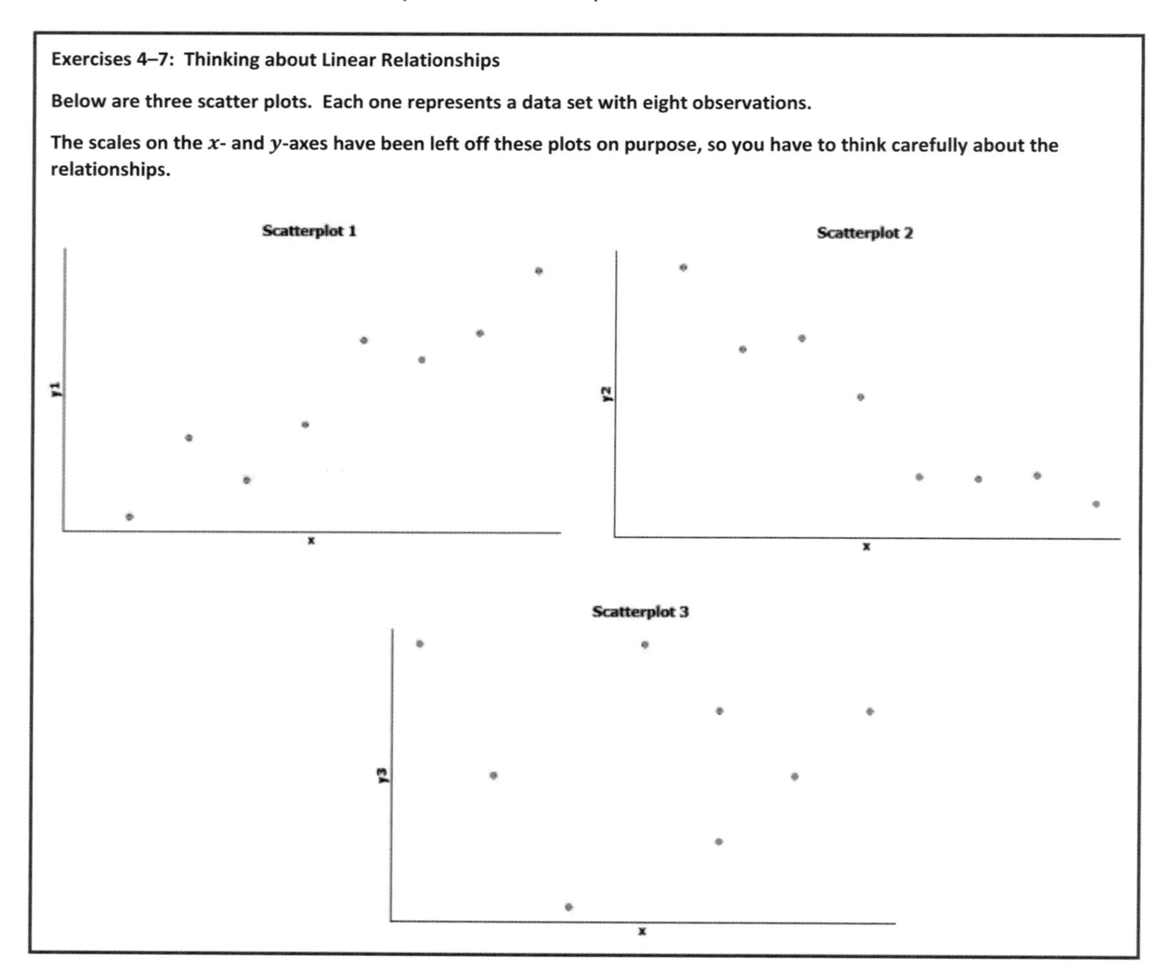

4. If one of these scatter plots represents the relationship between height and weight for eight adults, which scatter plot do you think it is and why?

   Scatter Plot 1—weight or height could be assigned to either axis, as height increases so does weight.

   Scatter Plot 3—weight or height could be assigned to either axis. There is no relationship.

   We expect the relationship to follow Scatter Plot 1. While a large population would likely show a relationship between height and weight, it is possible that in a small sample size, no clear pattern would emerge.

5. If one of these scatter plots represents the relationship between height and SAT math score for eight high school seniors, which scatter plot do you think it is and why?

   Scatter Plot 3—weight or score could be assigned to either axis, there is no relationship.

6. If one of these scatter plots represents the relationship between the weight of a car and fuel efficiency for eight cars, which scatter plot do you think it is and why?

   Scatter Plot 2—weight or fuel efficiency could be assigned to either axis, as weight increases, fuel efficiency decreases.

7. Which of these three scatter plots does not appear to represent a linear relationship? Explain the reasoning behind your choice.

   Scatter Plot 3 indicates that there is no relationship between the variables that could reasonably be described by a line.

Exercises 8–13 (18 minutes): Not Every Relationship Is Linear

Let students work independently. Then discuss and confirm as a class.

Exercises 8–13: Not Every Relationship Is Linear

When a straight line provides a reasonable summary of the relationship between two numerical variables, we say that the two variables are *linearly related* or that there is a *linear relationship* between the two variables.

Take a look at the scatter plots below, and answer the questions that follow.

Scatter Plot 1

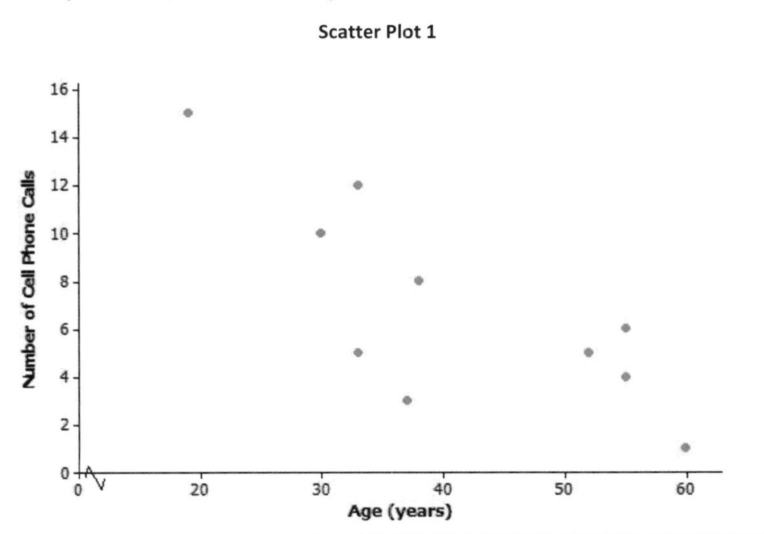

8. **Is there a relationship between the number of cell phone calls and age, or does it look like the data points are scattered?**

   There is a relationship.

9. **If there is a relationship between the number of cell phone calls and age, does the relationship appear to be linear?**

   The pattern is linear—as age increases, the number of cell phone calls decrease.

Scatter Plot 2

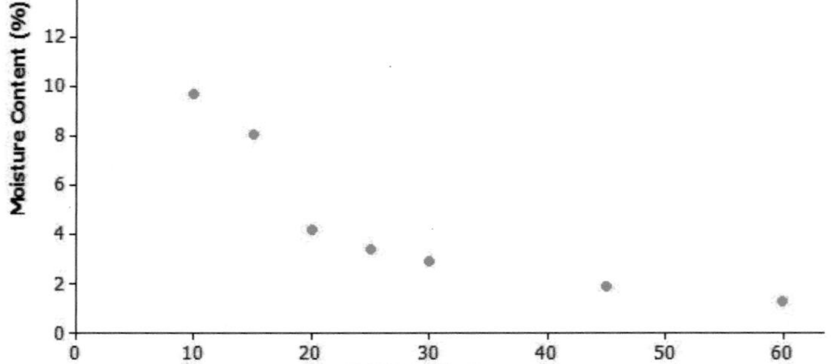

Data Source: R.G. Moreira, J. Palau, V.E. Sweat, and X. Sun, "Thermal and Physical Properties of Tortilla Chips as a Function of Frying Time," *Journal of Food Processing and Preservation,* 19 (1995): 175.

10. **Is there a relationship between moisture content and frying time, or do the data points look scattered?**

    There is a relationship.

Help students understand the concept of moisture content. For example, if a cake mixture is left in the oven too long, the cake becomes very dry. Here, the moisture evaporates during the frying time.

11. **If there is a relationship between moisture content and frying time, does the relationship look linear?**

    As the frying time increases, the moisture content decreases. It is not linear.

- Have you seen this shape before?
  - *Exponential curve*

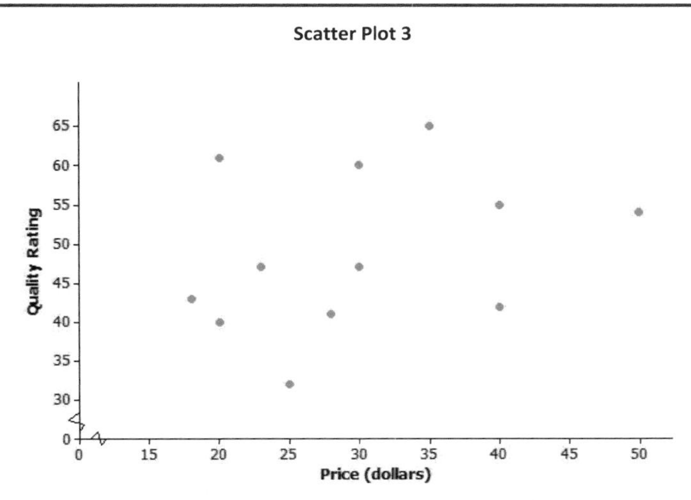

Data Source: www.consumerreports.org/health

12. Scatter Plot 3 shows data for the prices of bike helmets and the quality ratings of the helmets (based on a scale that estimates helmet quality). Is there a relationship between quality rating and price, or are the data points scattered?

    There is no relationship; the points are scattered.

13. If there is a relationship between quality rating and price for bike helmets, does the relationship appear to be linear?

    Because there does not appear to be a relationship between quality rating and price, it does not make sense to say the relationship is either linear or not linear.

- What does this tell us about rating and price?
  - *There is no relationship between rating and price that we can summarize.*
- Is an expensive helmet going to provide the best protection?
  - *Based on data, an expensive helmet may not necessarily provide the best protection.*

Closing (3 minutes)

Review the Lesson Summary. Highlight how to use scatter plot to investigate the relationship between two numerical variables (using any of the examples or exercises). Also, use one of the problems to summarize how a linear relationship can be described.

Lesson Summary

- **A scatter plot can be used to investigate whether or not there is a relationship between two numerical variables.**
- **A relationship between two numerical variables can be described as a linear or nonlinear relationship.**

Exit Ticket (5 minutes)

Name ______________________________ Date ______________

Lesson 12: Relationships Between Two Numerical Variables

Exit Ticket

1. You are traveling around the United States with friends. After spending a day in a town that is 2,000 ft. above sea level, you plan to spend the next several days in a town that is 5,000 ft. above sea level. Is this town likely to have more or fewer clear days per year than the town that is 2,000 ft. above sea level? Explain your answer.

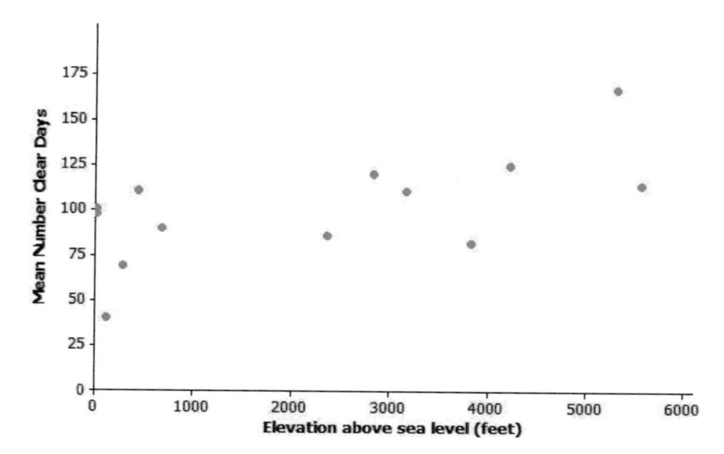

2. You plan to buy a bike helmet. Based on data presented in this lesson, will buying the most expensive bike helmet give you a helmet with the highest quality rating? Explain your answer.

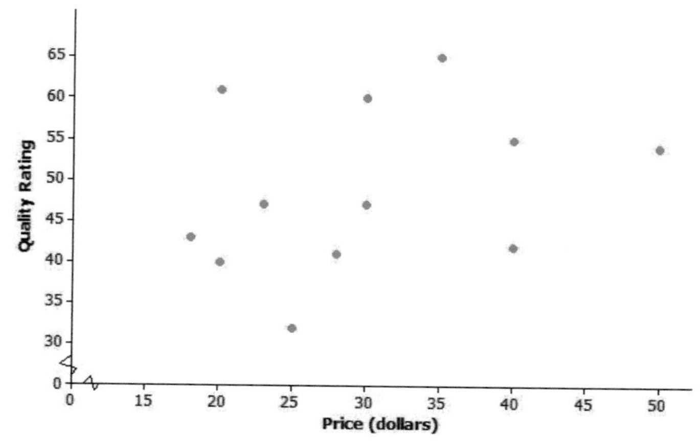

Data Source: www.consumerreports.org/health

Exit Ticket Sample Solutions

Consider providing the data set from the student lesson.

1. **You are traveling around the United States with friends. After spending a day in a town that is $2,000$ ft. above sea level, you plan to spend the next several days in a town that is $5,000$ ft. above sea level. Is this town likely to have more or fewer clear days per year than the town that is $2,000$ ft. above sea level? Explain your answer.**

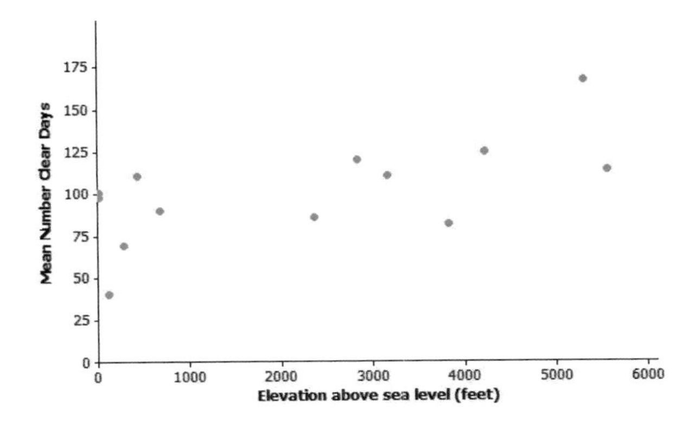

I would expect the number of clear days per year to increase. The relationship between elevation above sea level and the mean number of clear days per year appears to be linear. The scatter plot indicates that as the elevation increases, the number of clear days per year also generally increases.

2. **You plan to buy a bike helmet. Based on data presented in this lesson, will buying the most expensive bike helmet give you a helmet with the highest quality rating? Explain your answer.**

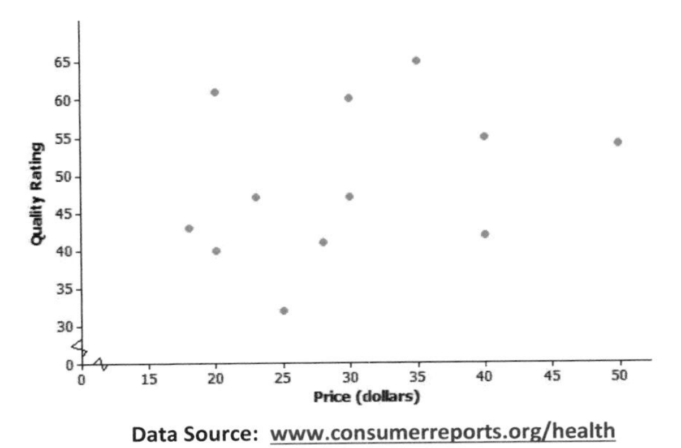

Data Source: www.consumerreports.org/health

I think there is a good chance I would not be buying the bike helmet with the highest price. The scatter plot indicates that there is no relationship between price and quality rating.

Problem Set Sample Solutions

1. Construct a scatter plot that displays the data for x (elevation above sea level in feet) and w (mean number of partly cloudy days per year).

City	x (Elevation Above Sea Level in Feet)	y (Mean Number of Clear Days per Year)	w (Mean Number of Partly Cloudy Days per Year)	z (Mean Number of Cloudy Days per Year)
Albany, NY	275	69	111	185
Albuquerque, NM	$5,311$	167	111	87
Anchorage, AK	114	40	60	265
Boise, ID	$2,838$	120	90	155
Boston, MA	15	98	103	164
Helena, MT	$3,828$	82	104	179
Lander, WY	$5,557$	114	122	129
Milwaukee, WI	672	90	100	175
New Orleans, LA	4	101	118	146
Raleigh, NC	434	111	106	149
Rapid City, SD	$3,162$	111	115	139
Salt Lake City, UT	$4,221$	125	101	139
Spokane, WA	$2,356$	86	88	191
Tampa, FL	19	101	143	121

Provide students with graph paper or have students construct the scatter plot using a graphing calculator or graphing software. The following represents the scatter plot.

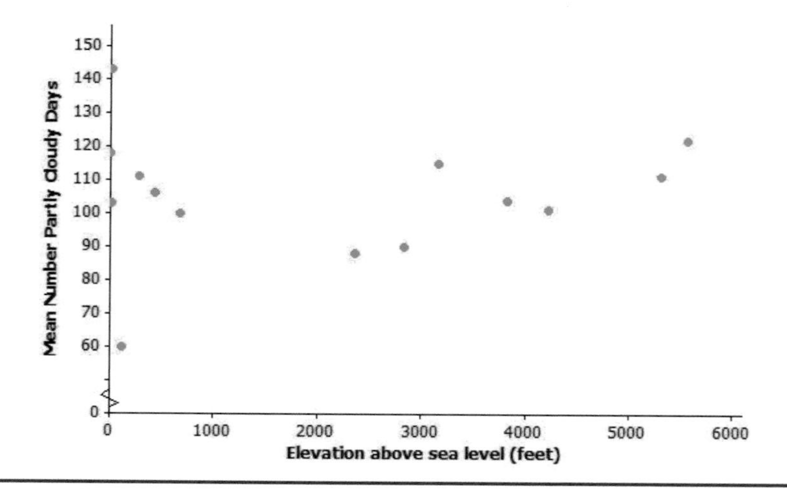

2. **Based on the scatter plot you constructed in Problem 1, is there a relationship between elevation and the mean number of partly cloudy days per year? If so, how would you describe the relationship? Explain your reasoning.**

   There appears to be a relationship. As the elevation increases, the number of partly cloudy days tends to decrease from approximately 0 to $3,000$ ft. above sea level. Then at approximately $3,000$ ft. above sea level, as the elevation increases, the number of partly cloudy days also appears to increase. This pattern suggests a quadratic model. Some cities, however, do not follow this pattern. (Students should discuss the overall pattern.)

Consider the following scatter plot for Problems 3 and 4.

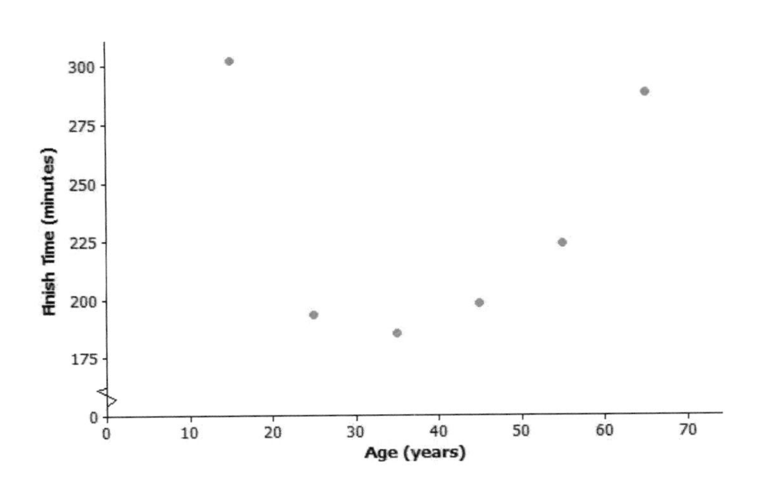

Data Source: Sample of six women who ran the 2003 NYC marathon

3. **Is there a relationship between finish time and age, or are the data points scattered?**

   At 35 years old, the finish time begins to increase.

4. **Do you think there is a relationship between finish time and age? If so, does it look linear?**

   The pattern does not look linear.

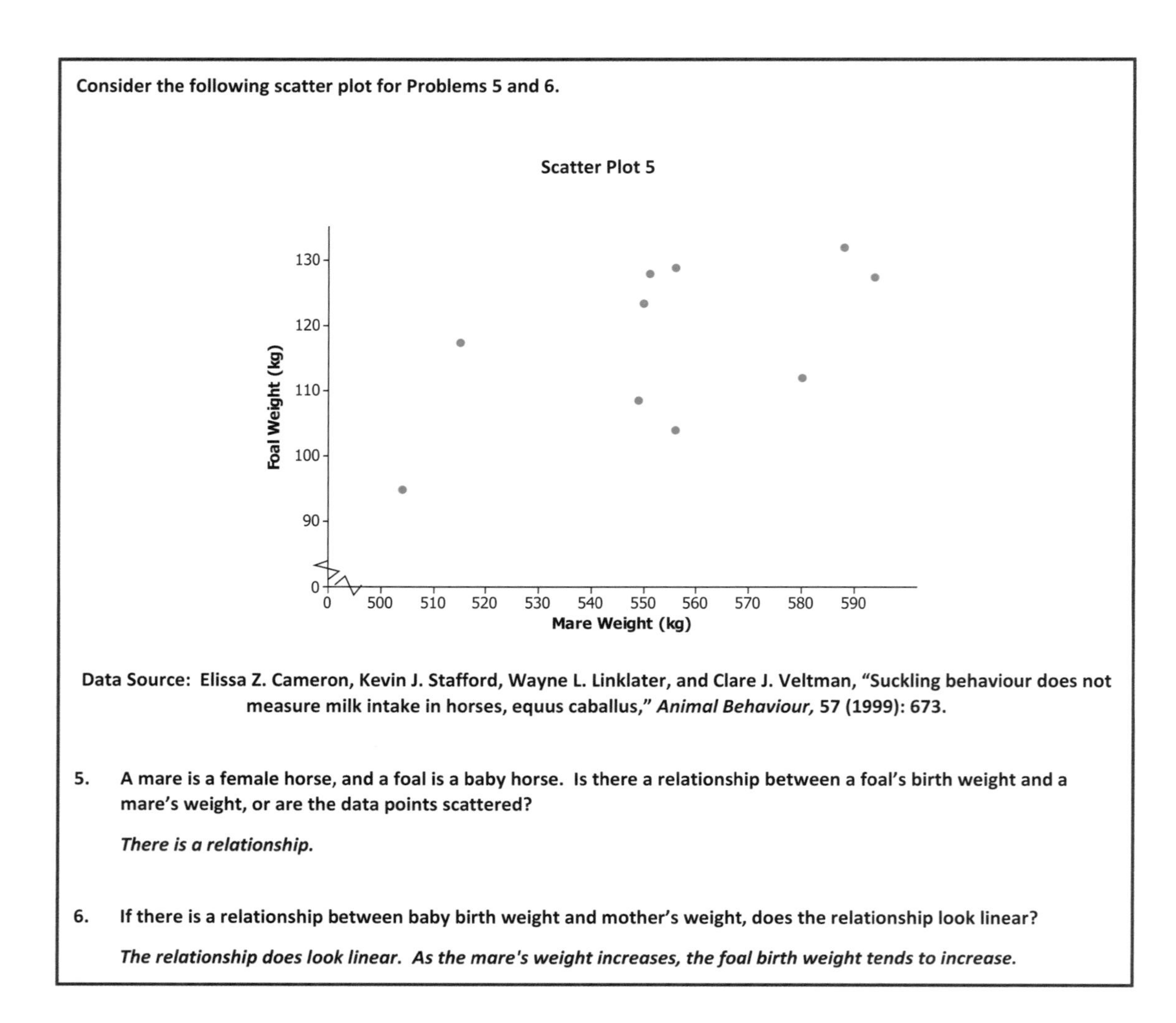

Consider the following scatter plot for Problems 5 and 6.

Data Source: Elissa Z. Cameron, Kevin J. Stafford, Wayne L. Linklater, and Clare J. Veltman, "Suckling behaviour does not measure milk intake in horses, equus caballus," ***Animal Behaviour,*** **57 (1999): 673.**

5. **A mare is a female horse, and a foal is a baby horse. Is there a relationship between a foal's birth weight and a mare's weight, or are the data points scattered?**

   There is a relationship.

6. **If there is a relationship between baby birth weight and mother's weight, does the relationship look linear?**

   The relationship does look linear. As the mare's weight increases, the foal birth weight tends to increase.

Note to teacher: The next lesson is a continuation of the objectives of this lesson. Lesson 13 connects specific modeling equations to several of the scatter plots used in this lesson.

Lesson 13: Relationships Between Two Numerical Variables

Student Outcomes

- Students distinguish between scatter plots that display a relationship that can be reasonably modeled by a linear equation and those that should be modeled by a nonlinear equation.
- Students use an equation given as a model for a nonlinear relationship to answer questions based on an understanding of the specific equation and the context of the data.

Lesson Notes

The work in this lesson builds on students' work with bivariate data and its relationships. The models addressed in this lesson also build on the scatter plots presented in Lesson 12. Lesson 12 asked students to think about whether or not there was a relationship between variables. If there was, students identified that relationship as linear or nonlinear. Previous relationship studies focused primarily on linear models. In this lesson, students begin to analyze nonlinear relationships, specifically exponential and quadratic models.

Lesson 18 encourages students to select an example from this lesson or the next one to summarize on a poster. As students work with these examples, encourage them to consider each example as a possible problem for a poster or presentation. The poster provides an opportunity to explain a problem, the data presented with the problem, the relationship between the variables and what the relationship indicates. The focus for this project is numerical, bivariate data.

Classwork

Not all relationships between two numerical variables are *linear*. There are many situations where the pattern in the scatter plot would best be described by a curve. Two types of functions often used in modeling nonlinear relationships are *quadratic* and *exponential* functions.

Example 1 (7 minutes): Modeling Relationships

As a group, discuss the functions presented in this example and their graphs. Students' previous work in algebra and functions used these functions. Ask students to describe the functions based on their graphs. For students unfamiliar with these functions, discuss the graphs of the quadratic and exponential functions, and explain how they are different from a linear function.

Example 1: Modeling Relationships

Sometimes the pattern in a scatter plot looks like the graph of a quadratic function (with the points falling roughly in the shape of a *U* that opens up or down), as in the graph below.

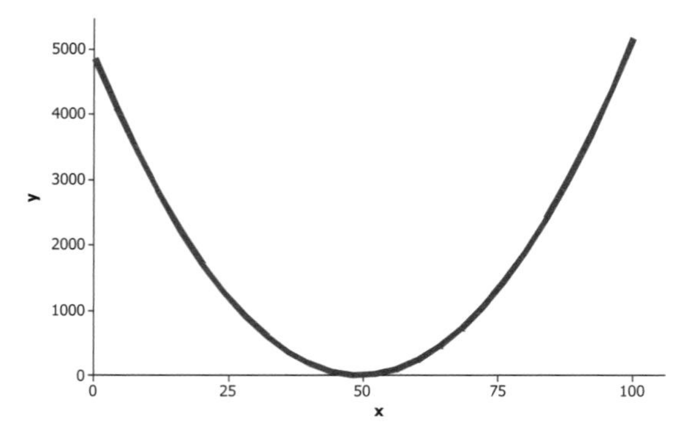

In other situations, the pattern in the scatter plot might look like the graphs of exponential functions that either are upward sloping (Graph 1) or downward sloping (Graph 2).

Graph 1: Exponential—upward sloping

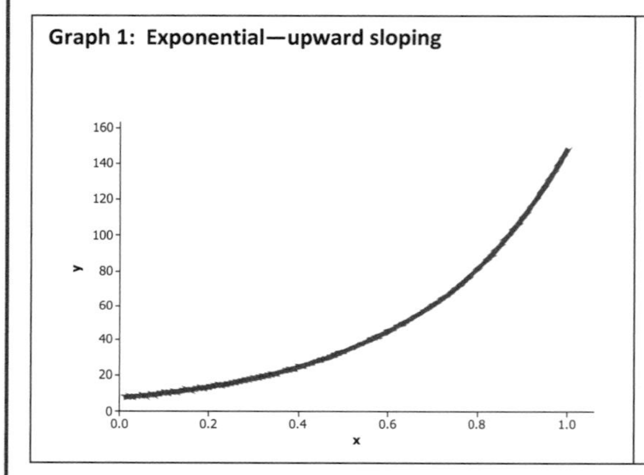

Graph 2: Exponential—downward sloping

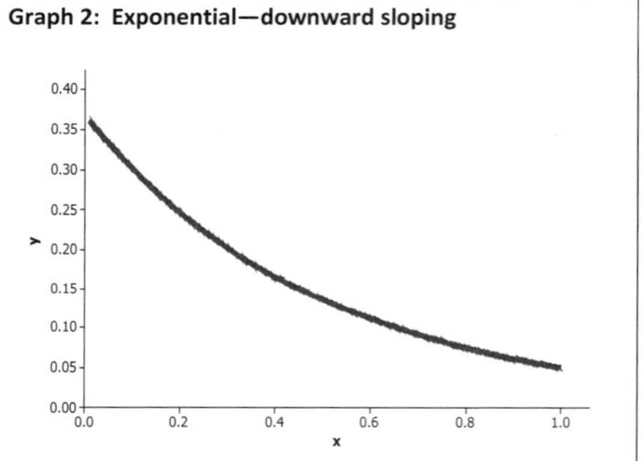

Exercises 1–6 (12 minutes)

Provide students time to work individually or in small groups on the questions of this exercise. Discuss the questions as a group after students have developed their responses.

Exercises 1–6

Consider again the five scatter plots discussed in the previous lesson.

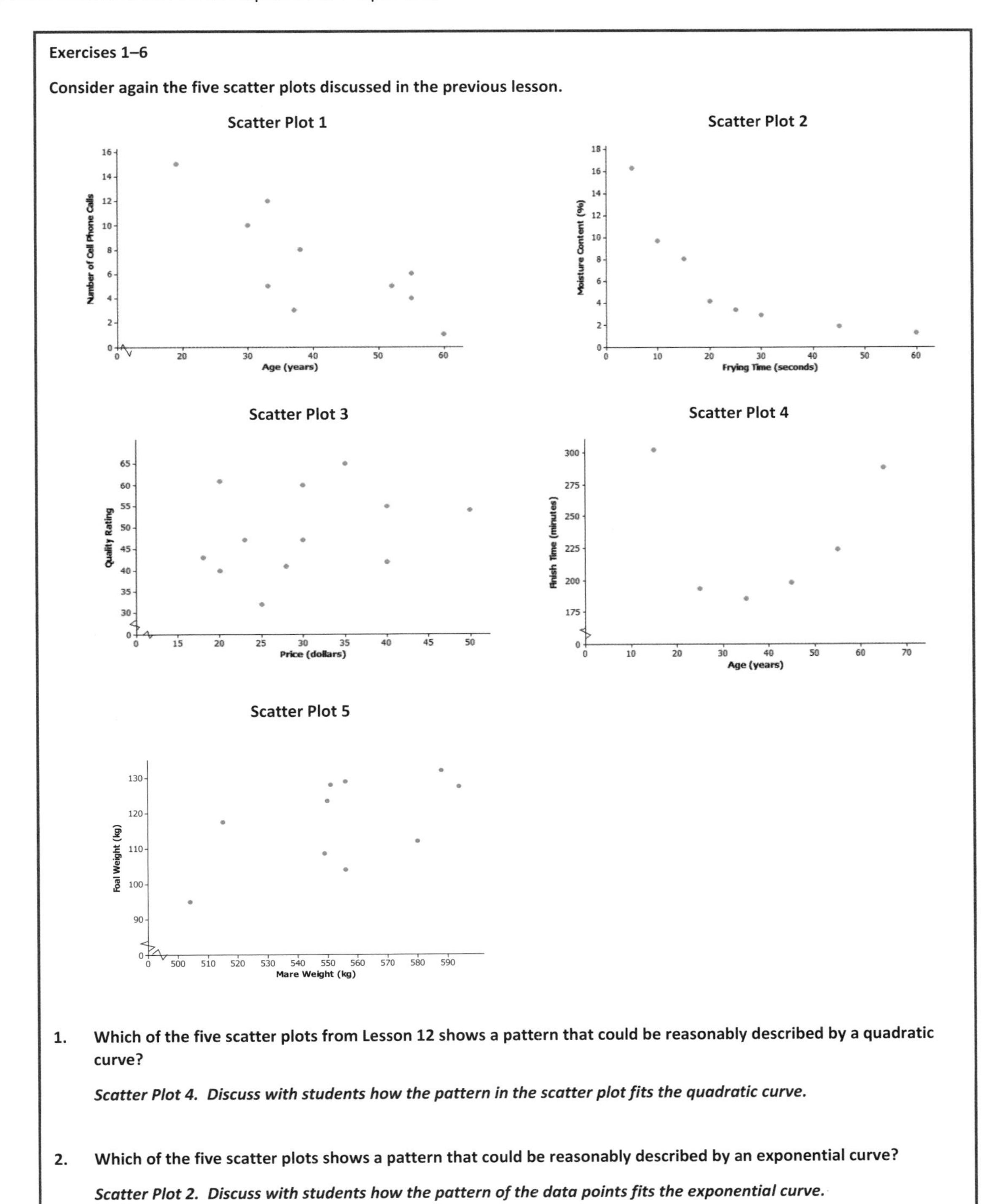

1. **Which of the five scatter plots from Lesson 12 shows a pattern that could be reasonably described by a quadratic curve?**

   Scatter Plot 4. Discuss with students how the pattern in the scatter plot fits the quadratic curve.

2. **Which of the five scatter plots shows a pattern that could be reasonably described by an exponential curve?**

   Scatter Plot 2. Discuss with students how the pattern of the data points fits the exponential curve.

Discuss how predictions can be found using a model. Ask students:

- How can a graph be used to make a prediction?
  - *Estimate the value from the line or curve.*
- How can a model be used to make a prediction?
  - *A value can be substituted for a variable in the model to solve for the other variable.*

Let's revisit the data on elevation (in feet above sea level) and mean number of clear days per year. The scatter plot of this data is shown below. The plot also shows a straight line that can be used to model the relationship between elevation and mean number of clear days. (In Grade 8, you informally fit a straight line to model the relationship between two variables. The next lesson shows a more formal way to fit a straight line.) The equation of this line is $y = 83.6 + 0.008x$.

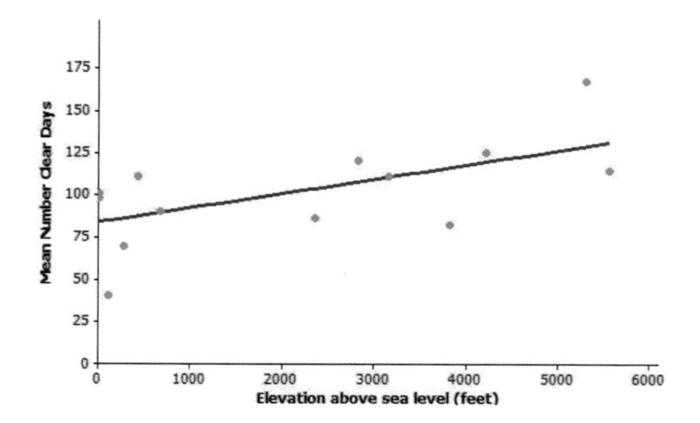

3. **Assuming that the 14 cities used in this scatter plot are representative of cities across the United States, should you see more clear days per year in Los Angeles, which is near sea level, or in Denver, which is known as the mile-high city? Justify your choice with a line showing the relationship between elevation and mean number of clear days.**

   Denver, since the number of clear days increases as elevation increases.

   Provide the data set from the previous lesson. Using the data, students can see which city is plotted on the graph.

   From the graph and data set, Los Angeles had about 84 clear days; Denver had about 125 clear days.

   From the linear model, Los Angeles ($x = 0$) had 83.6 clear days, and Denver ($x = 5,280$) had 125.84 clear days.

4. **One of the cities in the data set was Albany, New York, which has an elevation of 275 ft. If you did not know the mean number of clear days for Albany, what would you predict this number to be based on the line that describes the relationship between elevation and mean number of clear days?**

   Let $x = 275$ and substitute the value into the model. The predicted number of clear days is 85.8 days or about 86 days.

5. **Another city in the data set was Albuquerque, New Mexico. Albuquerque has an elevation of $5,311$ ft. If you did not know the mean number of clear days for Albuquerque, what would you predict this number to be based on the line that describes the relationship between elevation and mean number of clear days?**

   Let $x = 5,311$ and substitute the value into the model. The predicted number of clear days is 126.088 or about 126 days.

6. **Was the prediction of the mean number of clear days based on the line closer to the actual value for Albany with 69 clear days or for Albuquerque with 167 clear days? How could you tell this from looking at the scatter plot with the line shown above?**

The prediction (86 clear days) was closer for Albany, which had 69 actual clear days. The distance from the predicted point on the line to the point representing Albany showed a smaller distance than the point corresponding to Albuquerque.

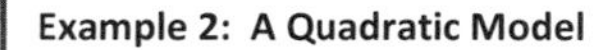

Example 2 (3 minutes): A Quadratic Model

Discuss the data presented in this exercise.

- Is fertilizer good for plants?
- Can a plant be *over-fertilized*?
- How can we find the amount of fertilizer that produces the most corn?

Example 2: A Quadratic Model

Farmers sometimes use fertilizers to increase crop yield but often wonder just how much fertilizer they should use. The data shown in the scatter plot below are from a study of the effect of fertilizer on the yield of corn.

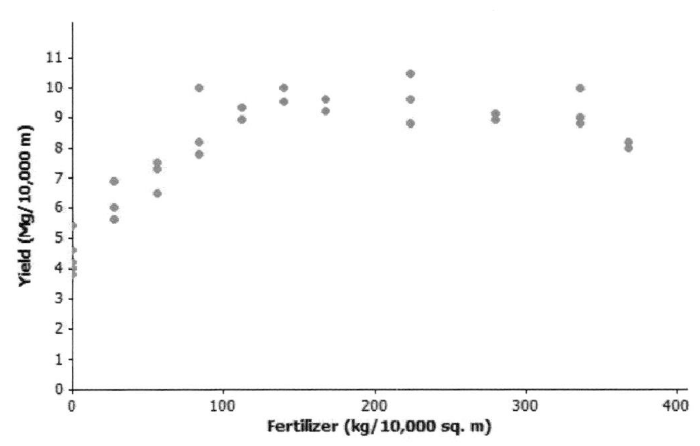

Data Source: M.E. Cerrato and A.M. Blackmer, "Comparison of Models for Describing Corn Yield Response to Nitrogen Fertilizer" ***Agronomy Journal,*** **82 (1990): 138.**

Exercises 7–9 (7 minutes)

Let students work in pairs on Exercises 7–9. Then discuss and confirm Exercises 8 and 9 as a class.

Exercises 7–9

7. **The researchers who conducted this study decided to use a quadratic curve to describe the relationship between yield and amount of fertilizer. Explain why they made this choice.**

In the beginning, as the amount of fertilizer (x) increases, so does the yield (y). But then around 250 kg, the yield begins to decrease as the amount of fertilizer increases.

8. The model that the researchers used to describe the relationship was $y = 4.7 + 0.05x - 0.0001x^2$, where x represents the amount of fertilizer (kg per $10,000$ sq. m) and y represents corn yield (Mg per $10,000$ sq. m). Use this quadratic model to complete the following table. Then sketch the graph of this quadratic equation on the scatter plot.

Encourage students to also use a graphing calculator or statistical software to construct the table and the curve. Students can also construct the curve by plotting the points in the table.

x	y
0	4.7
100	8.7
200	10.7
300	10.7
400	8.7

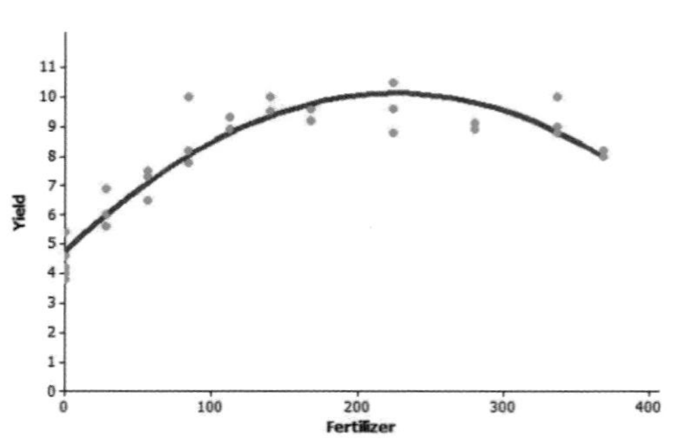

9. Based on this quadratic model, how much fertilizer per $10,000$ sq. m would you recommend that a farmer use on his cornfields in order to maximize crop yield? Justify your choice.

About 225–250 kg *per* $10,000$ sq. m

Example 3 (3 minutes): An Exponential Model

Discuss the data presented in the exercise. Ask students:

- What is meant by *regulating lobster trapping*?
  - *Preventing commercial fisherman from harvesting too many lobsters*
- Why would biologists care about the age of a lobster?
  - *This information can be used to decide whether a lobster can be harvested or thrown back into the ocean.*

Example 3: An Exponential Model

How do you tell how old a lobster is? This question is important to biologists and to those who regulate lobster trapping. To answer this question, researchers recorded data on the shell length of 27 lobsters that were raised in a laboratory and whose ages were known.

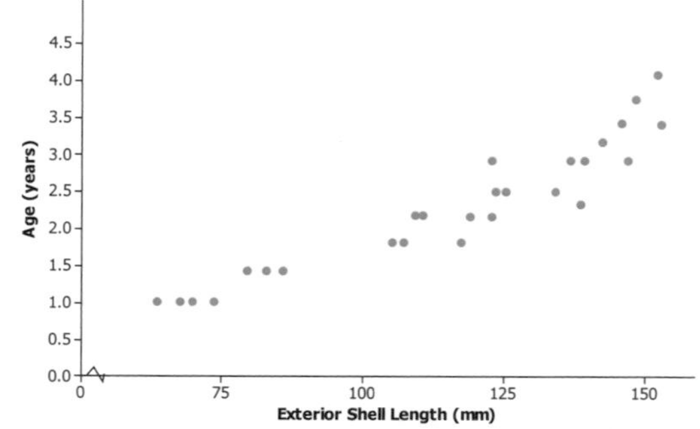

Data Source: Kerry E. Maxwell, Thomas R. Matthews, Matt R.J. Sheehy, Rodney D. Bertelsen, and Charles D. Derby, "Neurolipofuscin is a Measure of Age in *Panulirus argus*, the Caribbean Spiny Lobster, in Florida" *Biological Bulletin,* 213 (2007): 55.

Exercises 10–13 (8 minutes)

Let students work independently on Exercises 10–13. Then discuss and confirm as a class.

Exercises 10–13

10. **The researchers who conducted this study decided to use an exponential curve to describe the relationship between age and exterior shell length. Explain why they made this choice.**

    As the length of the exterior shell increases, the age of the lobster tends to increase. The change in age is greater as the shell length increases, suggesting the exponential model.

11. **The model that the researchers used to describe the relationship is $y = 10^{-0.403 + 0.0063x}$, where x represents the exterior shell length (mm), and y represents the age of the lobster (in years). The exponential curve is shown on the scatter plot below. Does this model provide a good description of the relationship between age and exterior shell length? Explain why or why not.**

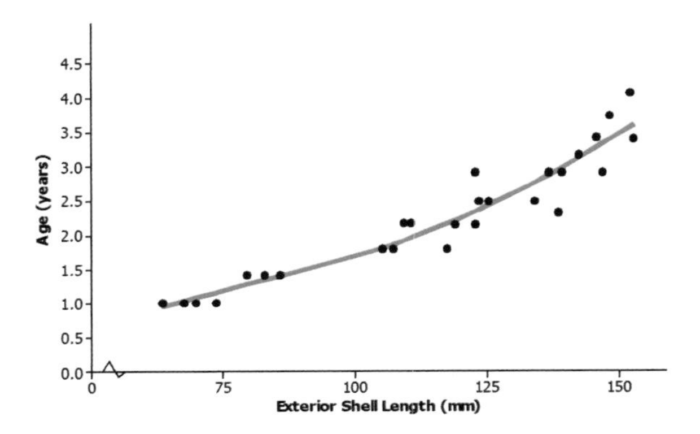

    The model does a good job of describing the relationship; the data points lie reasonably close to the model.

12. **Based on this exponential model, what age is a lobster with an exterior shell length of 100 mm?**

    From the graph: About 1.75 years old

    From the model: $y = 10^{-0.403 + 0.0063x}$

    Therefore, $y = 10^{-0.403 + 0.0063(100)}$*, or approximately 1.69 years old.*

13. **Suppose that trapping regulations require that any lobster with an exterior shell length less than 75 mm or more than 150 mm must be released. Based on the exponential model, what are the ages of lobsters with exterior shell lengths less than 75 mm? What are the ages of lobsters with exterior shell lengths greater than 150 mm? Explain how you arrived at your answer.**

    Lobsters less than 75 mm would be about 1 year or less in age. Lobsters that are more than 150 mm would be approximately 3.5 years or older.

Students can use the model or estimate from the graph. Share with students that not only are lobsters released if they are too small (or young) but also if they are too large.

Closing (2 minutes)

> **Lesson Summary**
>
> - **A scatter plot can be used to investigate whether or not there is a relationship between two numerical variables.**
> - **Linear, quadratic, and exponential functions are common models that can be used to describe the relationship between variables.**
> - **Models can be used to answer questions about how two variables are related.**

Exit Ticket (3 minutes)

Name ______________________________ Date ______________

Lesson 13: Relationships Between Two Numerical Variables

Exit Ticket

1. Here is the scatter plot of age (in years) and finish time (in minutes) of the NY City Marathon that you first saw in an example. What type of model (linear, quadratic, or exponential) would best describe the relationship between age and finish time? Explain your reasoning.

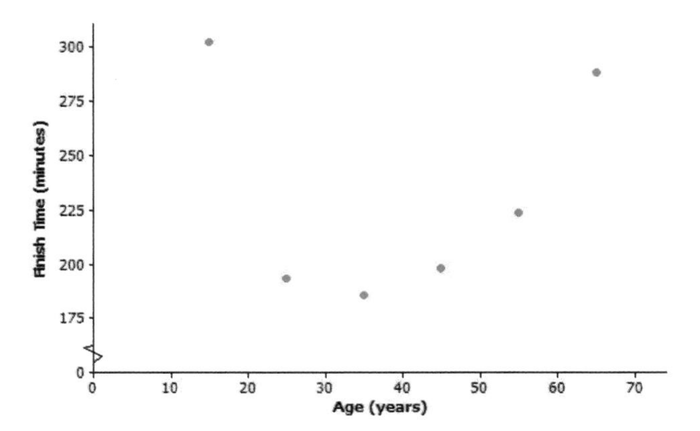

2. Here is the scatter plot of frying time (in seconds) and moisture content (as a percentage) you first saw in Lesson 12. What type of model (linear, quadratic, or exponential) would best describe the relationship between frying time and moisture content? Explain your reasoning.

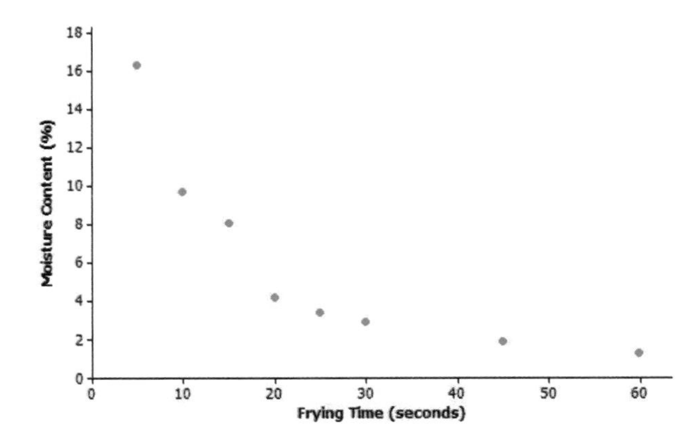

Exit Ticket Sample Solutions

1. **Here is the scatter plot of age (in years) and finish time (in minutes) of the NY City Marathon that you first saw in an example. What type of model (linear, quadratic, or exponential) would best describe the relationship between age and finish time? Explain your reasoning.**

   The relationship between age and finish time is best described by a quadratic model. As age increases, finish times decrease until they reach a minimum value and then begin to increase.

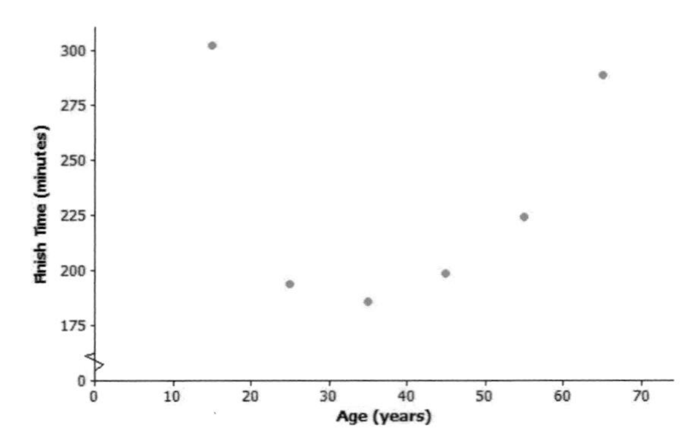

2. **Here is the scatter plot of frying time (in seconds) and moisture content (as a percentage) you first saw in Lesson 12. What type of model (linear, quadratic, or exponential) would best describe the relationship between frying time and moisture content? Explain your reasoning.**

   The relationship between frying time and moisture content is exponential. As the frying time increases, the moisture content decreases. The amount of decrease is slowing as the frying time increases; therefore, it is an exponential decrease.

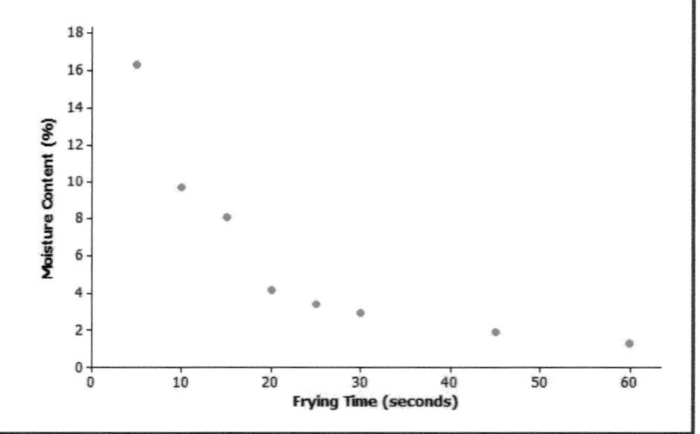

Problem Set Sample Solutions

Biologists conducted a study of the nesting behavior of a type of bird called a flycatcher. They examined a large number of nests and recorded the latitude for the location of the nest and the number of chicks in the nest.

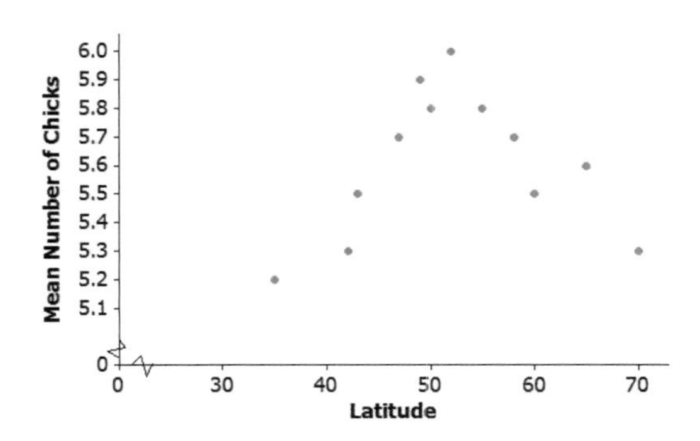

Data Source: Juan José Sanz, "Geographic variation in breeding parameters of the pied flycatcher *Ficedula hypoleuca*" *Ibis,* 139 (1997): 107.

1. **What type of model (linear, quadratic, or exponential) would best describe the relationship between latitude and mean number of chicks?**

   The relationship between latitude in degrees and mean number of chicks is best described by a quadratic model.

2. **One model that could be used to describe the relationship between mean number of chicks and latitude is $y = 0.175 + 0.21x - 0.002x^2$, where x represents the latitude of the location of the nest and y represents the number of chicks in the nest. Use the quadratic model to complete the following table. Then sketch a graph of the quadratic curve on the scatter plot at the beginning of the Problem Set.**

x (degrees)	y
30	4.675
40	5.375
50	5.675
60	5.575
70	5.075

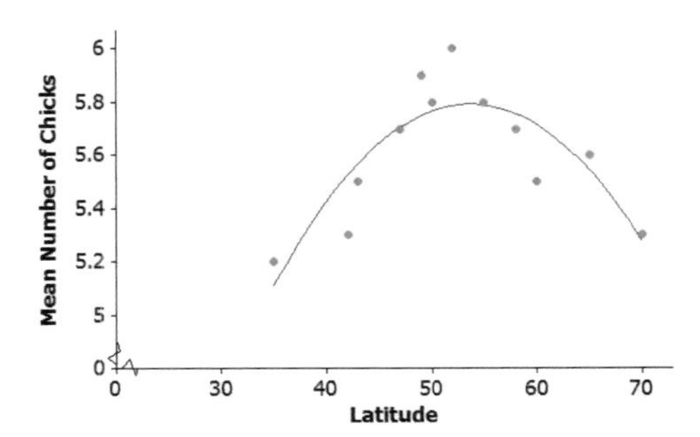

3. **Based on this quadratic model, what is the best latitude for hatching the most flycatcher chicks? Justify your choice.**

   The best latitude is the highest point, which is 55 degrees latitude.

Suppose that social scientists conducted a study of senior citizens to see how the time (in minutes) required to solve a word puzzle changes with age. The scatter plot below displays data from this study.

Let x equal the age of the citizen and y equal the time (in minutes) required to solve a word puzzle for the seven study participants.

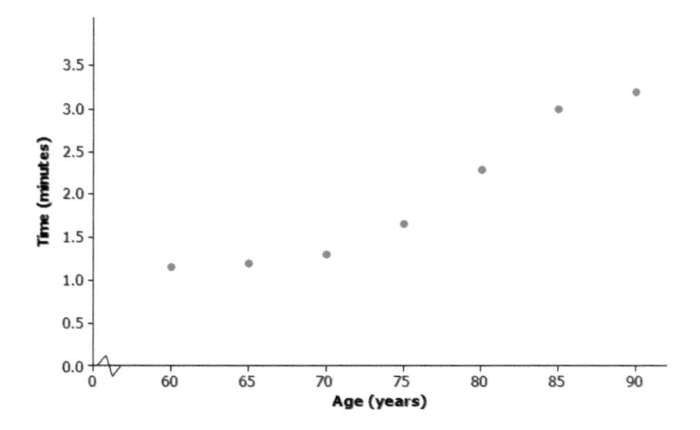

4. What type of model (linear, quadratic, or exponential) would you use to describe the relationship between age and time required to complete the word puzzle?

   Exponential

5. One model that could describe the relationship between age and time to complete the word puzzle is $y = 10^{-1.01 + 0.017x}$. This exponential curve is shown on the scatter plot below. Does this model do a good job of describing the relationship between age and time to complete the word puzzle? Explain why or why not.

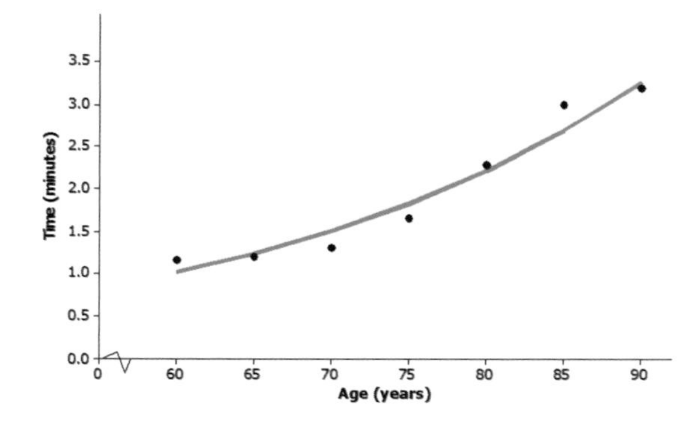

   Evaluation is subjective; the data points are close to the model; therefore, it does a good job of describing the relationship between age and time to complete the word puzzle.

6. Based on this exponential model, what time would you predict for a person who is 78 years old?

   Based on the graph, an estimate of about 2 min. *would be reasonable. Using the model equation,* $y = 10^{-1.01 + 0.017(78)}$, *or approximately* 2 min.

Lesson 14: Modeling Relationships with a Line

Student Outcomes

- Students use technology to determine the least squares regression line from a given set of data.
- Students use the least squares regression line to make predictions.

Lesson Notes

Lesson 12 introduced the concept of using linear functions to model the relationship between two numerical variables. In this lesson, students use technology to determine a least squares regression line to make predictions. Residuals are introduced in this lesson as the rationale for choosing the best-fit line. Students further evaluate models based on residuals in Lessons 15–16. Depending on students' proficiency with technology, consider breaking this lesson into two days.

As students work with problems in this lesson, encourage them to consider these examples as a potential context for their poster or presentation of Lesson 20.

Classwork

Example 1 (2 minutes): Using a Line to Describe a Relationship

Briefly summarize the data and the graph.

Example 1: Using a Line to Describe a Relationship

Kendra likes to watch crime scene investigation shows on television. She watched a show where investigators used a shoe print to help identify a suspect in a case. She questioned how possible it is to predict someone's height from his shoe print.

To investigate, she collected data on shoe length (in inches) and height (in inches) from 10 adult men. Her data appear in the table and scatter plot below.

x (Shoe Length)	y (Height)
12.6	74
11.8	65
12.2	71
11.6	67
12.2	69
11.4	68
12.8	70
12.2	69
12.6	72
11.8	71

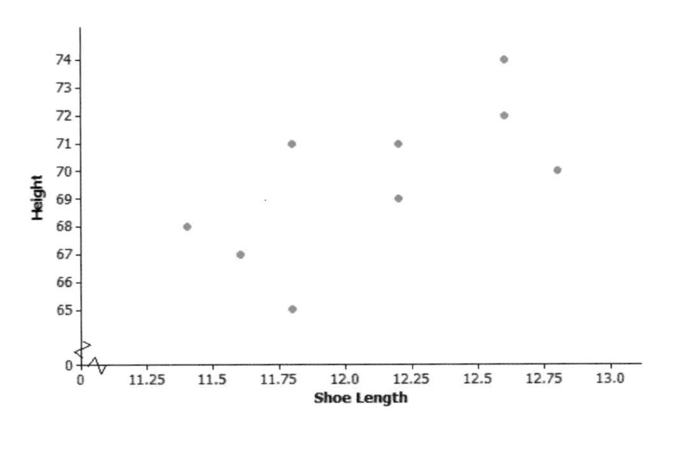

Exercises 1–2 (2 minutes)

Discuss the questions as a class.

Exercises 1–2

1. **Is there a relationship between shoe length and height?**

   Yes, it looks like there is a relationship between shoe length and height.

2. **How would you describe the relationship? Do the men with longer shoe lengths tend be taller?**

   As shoe length increases, height tends to increase. Men with longer shoe lengths tend to be taller.

Example 2 (3 minutes): Using Models to Make Predictions

Example 2: Using Models to Make Predictions

When two variables x and y are linearly related, you can use a line to describe their relationship. You can also use the equation of the line to predict the value of the y-variable based on the value of the x-variable.

For example, the line $y = 25.3 + 3.66x$ might be used to describe the relationship between shoe length and height, where x represents shoe length and y represents height. To predict the height of a man with a shoe length of 12 in., you would substitute 12 for x in the equation of the line and then calculate the value of y.

$$y = 25.3 + 3.66x = 25.3 + 3.66(12) = 69.22$$

You would predict a height of 69.22 in. for a man with a shoe length of 12 in.

Remind students that a model (equation) can be used to describe the relationship between variables.

- Explain that the model can be used to make predictions by substituting a value for one variable to solve for the other.
- Discuss how to use the model given in the student lesson to predict a man's height using a shoe length of 12 in.

Exercises 3–7 (7 minutes)

Introduce the scatter plot and models in Exercise 3. Discuss why neither line is a perfect model. Let students work in pairs to answer Exercises 3–7. After they complete their work, confirm as a class.

Exercises 3–7

3. **Below is a scatter plot of the data with two linear models, $y = 130 - 5x$ and $y = 25.3 + 3.66x$. Which of these two models does a better job of describing how shoe length (x) and height (y) are related? Explain your choice.**

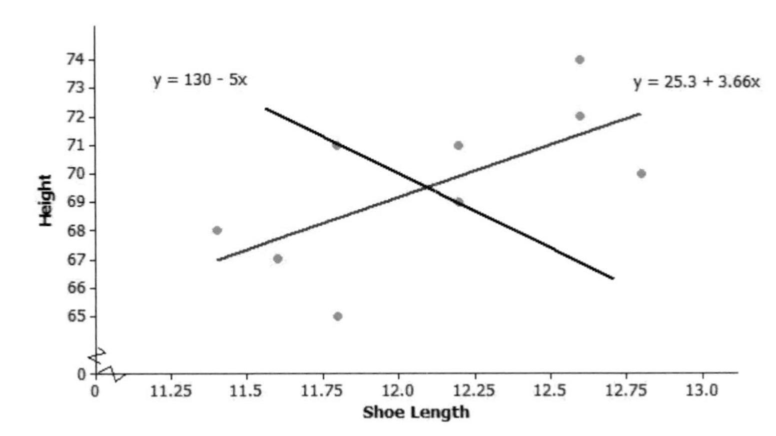

The line of $y = 25.3 + 3.66x$ is a better choice because as shoe length increases, height tends to increase.

4. **One of the men in the sample has a shoe length of 11.8 in. and a height of 71 in. Circle the point in the scatter plot in Exercise 3 that represents this man.**

The point $(11.8, 71)$ should be circled on the scatter plot.

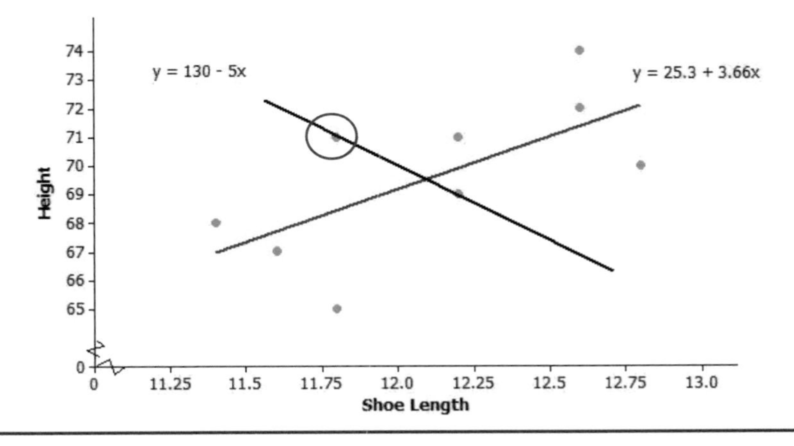

5. Suppose that you do not know this man's height but do know that his shoe length is 11.8 in. If you use the model $y = 25.3 + 3.66x$, what would you predict his height to be? If you use the model $y = 130 - 5x$, what would you predict his height to be?

   For the first model: $y = 25.3 + 3.66(11.8) = 68.488$

   For the second model: $y = 130 - 5(11.8) = 71$

   Using the first model, the man's predicted height is 68.488 in. *Using the second model, his predicted height is* 71 in.

6. Which model was closer to the actual height of 71 in.? Is that model a better fit to the data? Explain your answer.

   The model $y = 130 - 5x$ *was closer to the actual value, but that is not the better model because* $y = 25.3 + 3.66x$ *is closer to more points.*

7. Is there a better way to decide which of two lines provides a better description of a relationship (rather than just comparing the predicted value to the actual value for one data point in the sample)?

   The better line (or the line with the best fit) is the one in which the distances from the points to the line are as short as possible. Highlight a few of the points and the distances from the points to the line. Highlight the vertical distances from various points to the line to show students how the values of residuals help us evaluate a line's fit.

Example 3 (3 minutes): Residuals

Explain the definition of residual. Work through the example in the text with students. Note that the first row of the table in Exercise 8 represents the example. If students struggle, work through another row of the table.

Example 3: Residuals

One way to think about how useful a line is for describing a relationship between two variables is to use the line to predict the y-values for the points in the scatter plot. These predicted values could then be compared to the actual y-values.

For example, the first data point in the table represents a man with a shoe length of 12.6 in. and height of 74 in. If you use the line $y = 25.3 + 3.66x$ to predict this man's height, you would get:

$$\begin{aligned} y &= 25.3 + 3.66x \\ &= 25.3 + 3.66(12.6) \\ &= 71.42 \end{aligned}$$

His predicted height is 71.42 in. Because his actual height was 74 in., you can calculate the prediction error by subtracting the predicted value from the actual value. This prediction error is called a *residual*. For the first data point, the residual is calculated as follows:

$$\begin{aligned} \text{Residual} &= \text{actual } y\text{-value} - \text{predicted } y\text{-value} \\ &= 74 - 71.42 \\ &= 2.58 \end{aligned}$$

Exercises 8–10 (7 minutes)

Let students work in pairs to complete Exercises 8–10. Then discuss and confirm Exercises 9–10 as a class.

Exercises 8–10

8. **For the line $y = 25.3 + 3.66x$, calculate the missing values, and add them to complete the table.**

x (Shoe Length)	y (Height)	Predicted y-value	Residual
12.6	74	71.42	2.58
11.8	65	68.49	-3.49
12.2	71	69.95	1.05
11.6	67	67.76	-0.76
12.2	69	69.95	-0.95
11.4	68	67.02	0.98
12.8	70	72.15	-2.15
12.2	69	69.95	-0.95
12.6	72	71.42	0.58
11.8	71	68.49	2.51

9. **Why is the residual in the table's first row positive and the residual in the second row negative?**

   The actual value is larger than the predicted value in the first row, so the difference is positive. In the second row, the actual value is less than the predicted value, so the difference is negative.

10. **What is the sum of the residuals? Why did you get a number close to zero for this sum? Does this mean that all of the residuals were close to 0?**

    The sum of the residuals is -0.6. This number is close to 0 because the positive and negative values of the residuals balance each other out. Not all residuals are close to zero. (Refer to the table.)

Exercises 11–13 (5 minutes)

Work on the exercises as a class. Allow for multiple student responses.

Explain that the line of best fit will be the model where the absolute values of the residuals (vertical distances to the line) are small. Refer back to the two linear models in Exercise 3. The residuals for the line of best fit ($y = 25.3 + 3.66x$) are much smaller than those for the other line ($y = 130 - 5x$) because, in general, the points lie closer to the better model. Pose the question in Exercise 11 to the class.

Exercises 11–13

When you use a line to describe the relationship between two numerical variables, the *best* line is the line that makes the residuals as small as possible overall.

11. **If the residuals tend to be small, what does that say about the fit of the line to the data?**

    If the residuals are small, the points tend to be close to the line.

Explain that it is the sum of the *squared* residuals that leads to choosing the line of best fit. Tell students to square the residuals in the table (Exercise 8) and place their answers in a column they construct to the right of the table. Pose the following questions one at time to the class.

The most common choice for the *best* line is the line that makes the sum of the *squared* residuals as small as possible. Add a column on the right of the table in Exercise 8. Calculate the square of each residual and place the answer in the column.

Residual	*Square of Residual*
2.58	6.6564
-3.49	12.1801
1.05	1.1025
-0.76	0.5776
-0.95	0.9025
0.98	0.9604
-2.15	4.6225
-0.95	0.9025
0.58	0.3364
2.51	6.3001

12. **Why do we use the sum of the squared residuals instead of just the sum of the residuals (without squaring)? Hint: Think about whether the sum of the residuals for a line can be small even if the prediction errors are large. Can this happen for squared residuals?**

    If you just add all of the residuals, positive and negative residuals can offset one another, and you can get a small sum even if some of the residuals are big. Squaring the residuals gives positive values that still reflect how far the data points are from the line.

13. **What is the sum of the squared residuals for the line $y = 25.3 + 3.66x$ and the data of Exercise 11?**

    The sum of the squared residuals (rounded to the nearest hundredth) is 34.54.

Example 4 (5 minutes): The Least Squares Line (Best-Fit Line)

The line that has a smaller sum of squared residuals than any other line is called the *least squares line*. Tell students that there are formulas for determining the least squares line, but the formulas are tedious and time-consuming, so they will instead use a graphing calculator or statistical software to generate the best-fit line.

Example 4

The line that has a smaller sum of squared residuals for this data set than any other line is called the *least squares line*. This line can also be called the *best-fit line* or the *line of best fit* (or regression line).

For the shoe-length and height data for the sample of 10 men, the line $y = 25.3 + 3.66x$ is the least squares line. No other line would have a smaller sum of squared residuals for this data set than this line.

There are equations that can be used to calculate the value for the slope and the intercept of the least squares line, but these formulas require a lot of tedious calculations. Fortunately, a graphing calculator can be used to find the equation of the least squares line.

Your teacher will show you how to enter data and obtain the equation of the least squares line using your graphing calculator or other statistics program.

The following outlines how to determine the least squares regression using a TI-84 Plus. Most graphing calculators use a similar process. Having students use software that emulates a graphing calculator is also an option. Use this outline as a guide for working with students. Modify these steps for the available technology.

Finding the Regression Line (TI-84 Plus)

1. From your home screen, press STAT.
2. From the STAT menu, select the EDIT option. (EDIT, ENTER)
3. Enter the x-values of the data set in L1.
4. Enter the y-values of the data set in L2.
5. Select STAT. Move cursor to the menu item CALC, and then move the cursor to option 4: LinReg($ax + b$) or option 8: LinReg($a + bx$). Press ENTER. (Discuss with students that both options 4 and 8 are representations of a linear equation. Anticipate that most students will be familiar with option 4, or the slope y-intercept form. Option 8 is essentially the same representation using different letters to represent slope and y-intercept. Option 8 is the preferred option in statistical studies.)
6. With option 4 or option 8 on the screen, enter L1, L2, and Y1 as described in the following notes.

LinReg($a + bx$) L1, L2, Y1

Select ENTER to see results. The least squares regression will be stored in Y1. Work with students in graphing the scatter plot and Y1.

Note: L1 represents the x-values of the regression function, L2 the y-values, and Y1 represents the least squares regression function.

To obtain Y1, go to VARS, move cursor to Y-VARS, and then Functions (ENTER). You are now at the screen highlighting the y-variables. Move cursor to Y1 and hit ENTER.

Y1 is the linear regression line and will be stored in Y1.

Exercises 14–17 (5 minutes)

Let students work independently on Exercises 14–17. Assist students who need help using their calculators.

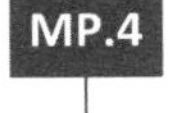

14. Enter the shoe-length and height data, and then use your calculator to find the equation of the least squares line. Did you get $y = 25.3 + 3.66x$? (The slope and y-intercept here have been rounded to the nearest hundredth.)

The exact equation of the least squares line is $Y1 = 25.276\,859\,504\,133 + 3.657\,024\,793\,388\,4x$. When rounded to the nearest tenth for the y-intercept and hundredth for the slope, the equation is $y = 25.3 + 3.66x$.

15. Assuming that the 10 men in the sample are representative of adult men in general, what height would you predict for a man whose shoe length is 12.5 in.? What height would you predict for a man whose shoe length is 11.9 in.?

The predicted height of a man whose shoe length is 12.5 in. is 71.05 in. The predicted height of a man whose shoe length is 11.9 in. is 68.86 in.

MP.4

Once you have found the equation of the least squares line, the values of the slope and y-intercept of the line often reveal something interesting about the relationship you are modeling.

The slope of the least squares line is the change in the predicted value of the y-variable associated with an increase of one in the value of the x-variable.

16. **Give an interpretation of the slope of the least squares line $y = 25.3 + 3.66x$ for predicting height from shoe size for adult men.**

    The slope is 3.66; for every 1 in. increase in a man's shoe length, you would estimate an increase of 3.66 in. in height.

The y-intercept of a line is the predicted value of y when x equals zero. When using a line as a model for the relationship between two numerical variables, it often does not make sense to interpret the y-intercept because a x-value of zero may not make any sense.

17. **Explain why it does not make sense to interpret the y-intercept of 25.3 as the predicted height for an adult male whose shoe length is zero.**

    The y-intercept is $(0, 25.3)$. Since x represents shoe length, it is impossible for the shoe length to be 0 in. when a man is 25.3 in. tall.

Closing (2 minutes)

Lesson Summary

When the relationship between two numerical variables x and y is linear, a straight line can be used to describe the relationship. Such a line can then be used to predict the value of y based on the value of x. When a prediction is made, the prediction error is the difference between the actual y-value and the predicted y-value. The prediction error is called a *residual*, and the residual is calculated as *residual* $=$ *actual y-value* $-$ *predicted y-value*. The *least squares line* is the line that is used to model a linear relationship. The least squares line is the *best* line in that it has a smaller sum of squared residuals than any other line.

Exit Ticket (4 minutes)

Name ____ Date____________________

Lesson 14: Modeling Relationships with a Line

Exit Ticket

1. The scatter plot below displays the elevation and mean number of clear days per year of 14 U.S. cities. Two lines are shown on the scatter plot. Which represents the least squares line? Explain your choice.

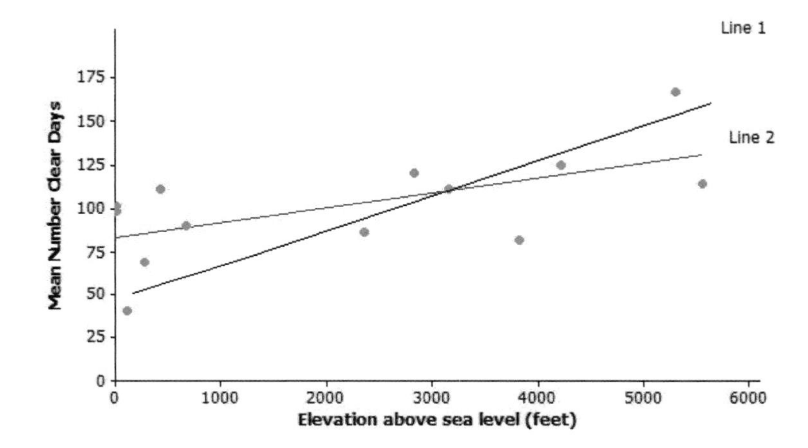

2. Below is a scatter plot of foal birth weight and mare's weight.

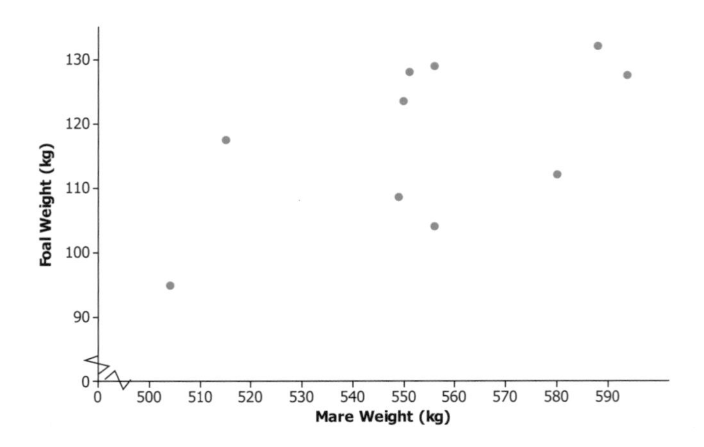

The equation of the least squares line for the data is $y = -19.6 + 0.248x$, where x represents the mare's weight (in kg) and y represents the foal's birth weight (in kg).

a. What foal birth weight would you predict for a mare that weighs 520 kg?

b. How would you interpret the value of the slope in the least squares line?

c. Does it make sense to interpret the value of the y-intercept in this context? Explain why or why not.

Exit Ticket Sample Solutions

1. **The scatter plot below displays the elevation and mean number of clear days per year of 14 U.S. cities. Two lines are shown on the scatter plot. Which represents the least squares line? Explain your choice.**

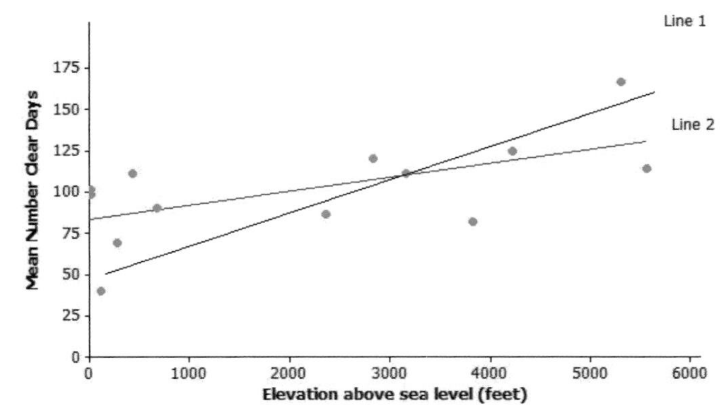

Line 2 represents the least squares line because it appears to have smaller residuals overall.

2. **Below is a scatter plot of foal birth weight and mare's weight.**

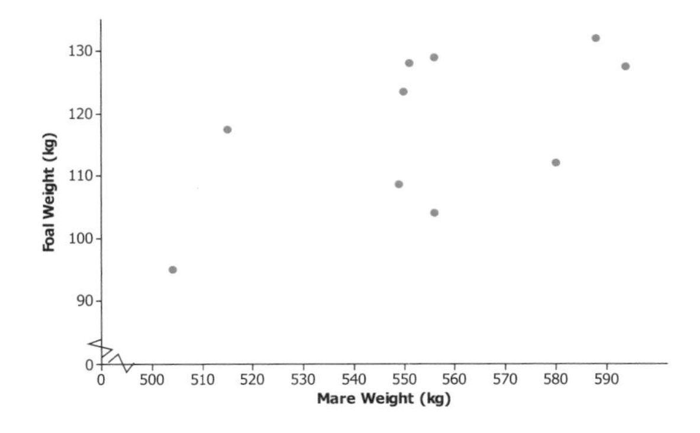

The equation of the least squares line for these data is $y = -19.6 + 0.248x$, where x represents the mare's weight (in kg) and y represents the foal's birth weight (in kg).

a. **What foal birth weight would you predict for a mare that weighs 520 kg?**

$y = -19.6 + 0.248(520) = 109.36$

For a mare that weighs 520 kg, the predicted foal birth weight would be 109.36 kg.

b. **How would you interpret the value of the slope in the least squares line?**

The value of the slope is 0.248, indicating that predicted foal weight increases by 0.248 kg for each 1 kg increase in the mare's weight.

c. **Does it make sense to interpret the value of the y-intercept in this context? Explain why or why not.**

It does not make sense to interpret the value of the y-intercept because it is equivalent to predicting the foal's weight for a mare's weight of zero, which does not make sense.

Problem Set Sample Solutions

If time permits, the following data set and questions provide an opportunity to give hands-on examples. Consider providing actual shoe prints from students or individuals (children and adults). Create a scenario in which the shoe print is *evidence*, and have the class figure out *who done it?*

Kendra wondered if the relationship between shoe length and height might be different for men and women. To investigate, she also collected data on shoe length (in inches) and height (in inches) for 12 women.

x (Shoe Length of Women)	y (Height of Women)
8.9	61
9.6	61
9.8	66
10.0	64
10.2	64
10.4	65
10.6	65
10.6	67
10.5	66
10.8	67
11.0	67
11.8	70

1. **Construct a scatter plot of these data.**

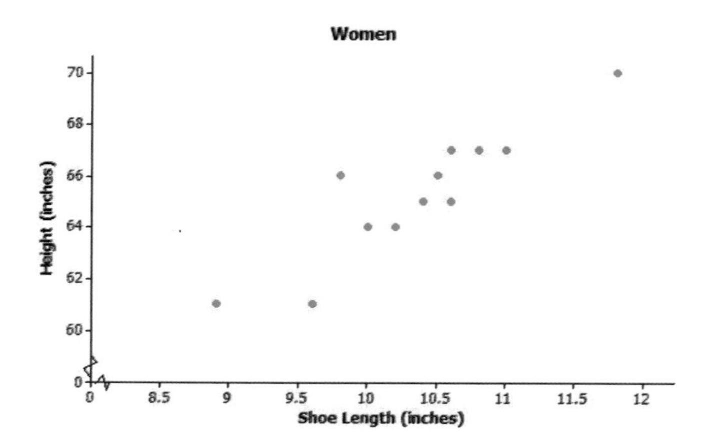

2. **Is there a relationship between shoe length and height for these 12 women?**

   Yes, as shoe length increases, height also tends to increase.

3. **Find the equation of the least squares line. (Round values to the nearest hundredth.)**

   The least squares line is $y = 32.68 + 3.15x$.

4. Suppose that these 12 women are representative of adult women in general. Based on the least squares line, what would you predict for the height of a woman whose shoe length is 10.5 in.? What would you predict for the height of a woman whose shoe length is 11.5 in.?

The predicted height for a woman whose shoe length is 10.5 in. would be 65.76 in., or 66 in. to the nearest inch. The predicted height for a woman whose shoe length is 11.5 in. would be 68.91 in., or 69 in. to the nearest inch.

5. One of the women in the sample had a shoe length of 9.8 in. Based on the regression line, what would you predict for her height?

$y = 32.68 + 3.15(9.8) = 63.55$

Her predicted height is 63.55 in.

6. What is the value of the residual associated with the observation for the woman with the shoe length of 9.8 in.?

The residual would be the actual value minus the predicted value, or 66 in. $-$ 63.55 in. $=$ 2.45 in.

7. Add the predicted value and the residual you just calculated to the table below. Then, calculate the sum of the squared residuals.

The sum of the squared residuals is 12.94. (Note: The predicted heights and residuals come from the rounded values in the model not the exact values generated from the regression line using the calculator.)

x (Shoe Length of Women)	y (Height of Women)	Predicted Height (in.)	Residual (in.)	Squared Residual
8.9	61	60.72	0.28	0.0784
9.6	61	62.92	-1.92	3.6864
9.8	66	63.55	2.45	6.0025
10.0	64	64.18	-0.18	0.0324
10.2	64	64.81	-0.81	0.6561
10.4	65	65.44	-0.44	0.1936
10.6	65	66.07	-1.07	1.1449
10.6	67	66.07	0.93	0.8649
10.5	66	65.76	0.24	0.0576
10.8	67	66.7	0.3	0.09
11.0	67	67.33	-0.33	0.1089
11.8	70	69.85	0.15	0.0225

8. Provide an interpretation of the slope of the least squares line.

We would predict an increase of 3.15 in. in height for an increase of 1 in. in shoe length.

9. Does it make sense to interpret the y-intercept of the least squares line in this context? Explain why or why not.

The intercept would be based on a shoe length of zero inches. This would not make sense.

10. Would the sum of the squared residuals for the line $y = 25 + 2.8x$ be greater than, about the same as, or less than the sum you computed in Problem 7? Explain how you know this. You should be able to answer this question without calculating the sum of squared residuals for this new line.

The sum of squared residuals will be greater for the line $y = 25 + 2.8x$. The equation $y = 32.68 + 3.15x$ is the approximate equation of the least squares line, so it has a smaller sum of squared residuals than any other line.

11. **For the men, the least squares line that describes the relationship between x, which represents shoe length (in inches), and y, which represents height (in inches), was $y = 25.3 + 3.66x$. How does this compare to the equation of the least squares line for women? Would you use $y = 25.3 + 3.66x$ to predict the height of a woman based on her shoe length? Explain why or why not.**

    The slope is greater for men; a one-inch increase in shoe length translates to a greater increase in height for men compared to women. The y-intercept is greater for women. To predict the height of a woman, the least squares line for women must be used because it is the best fit.

12. **Below are dot plots of the shoe lengths for women and the shoe lengths for men. Suppose that you found a shoe print and that when you measured the shoe length, you got 10.8 in. Do you think that a man or a woman left this shoe print? Explain your choice.**

    It is more likely that a woman left the shoe print with length 10.8 in. based on the clustering around the value.

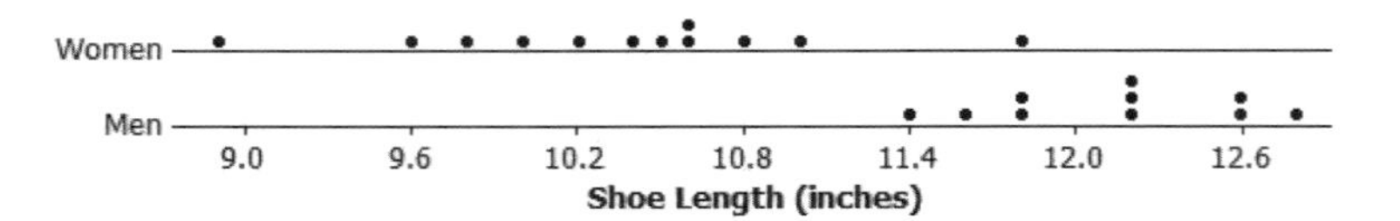

13. **Suppose that you find a shoe print and the shoe length for this print is 12 in. What would you predict for the height of the person who left this print? Explain how you arrived at this answer.**

    The print most likely belongs to a man. Use the least squares line for men to predict a height, or $y = 25.3 + 3.66(12)$, which is 69.22 in., to the nearest hundredth of an inch.

Lesson 15: Interpreting Residuals from a Line

Student Outcomes

- Students use the least squares line to predict values for a given data set.
- Students use residuals to evaluate the accuracy of predictions based on the least squares line.

Lesson Notes

Students continue their exploration of residuals. Lesson 14 introduced residuals as the rationale for choosing the best-fit line. In this lesson, students calculate prediction errors for a data set and generalize residuals to predict the error of a value not included in the original data set.

Classwork

Example 1 (3 minutes): Calculating Prediction Errors

Introduce the data and plot from the opening paragraph.

Example 1: Calculating Prediction Errors

The gestation time for an animal is the typical duration between conception and birth. The longevity of an animal is the typical lifespan for that animal. The gestation times (in days) and longevities (in years) for 13 types of animals are shown in the table below.

Animal	Gestation Time (days)	Longevity (years)
Baboon	187	20
Black Bear	219	18
Beaver	105	5
Bison	285	15
Cat	63	12
Chimpanzee	230	20
Cow	284	15
Dog	61	12
Fox (Red)	52	7
Goat	151	8
Lion	100	15
Sheep	154	12
Wolf	63	5

Data Source: *Core Math Tools*, http://nctm.org

Here is the scatter plot for this data set:

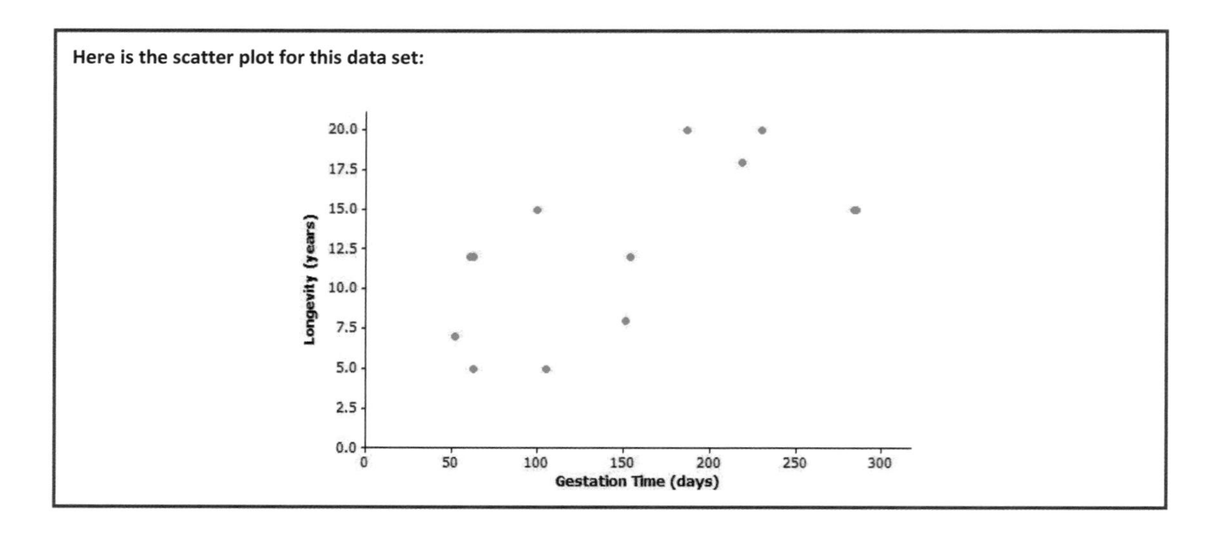

Exercises 1–4 (10 minutes)

Let students work independently on finding the regression line in Exercise 1.

Ask students to examine the scatter plot with the regression line. Then discuss:

- How accurate will this line be at predicting the longevities of types of animals?
- Look at the vertical distances of the points in the plot from the line—smaller distances lead to more accurate predictions.

Exercises 1–4

Finding the equation of the least squares line relating longevity to gestation time for these types of animals provides the equation to predict longevity. How good is the line? In other words, if you were given the gestation time for another type of animal not included in the original list, how accurate would the least squares line be at predicting the longevity of that type of animal?

1. **Using a graphing calculator, verify that the equation of the least squares line is $y = 6.642 + 0.03974x$, where x represents the gestation time (in days), and y represents longevity (in years).**

   The least squares line has been added to the scatter plot below.

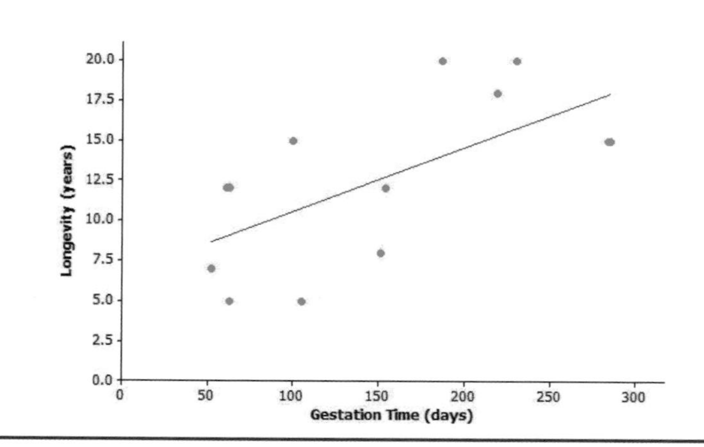

Let students work independently on Exercises 2–4. Then discuss and confirm as a class.

MP.4

2. Suppose a particular type of animal has a gestation time of 200 days. Approximately what value does the line predict for the longevity of that type of animal?

$y = 6.642 + 0.03974(200) = 14.59 \approx 14.6$

3. Would the value you predicted in Exercise 2 necessarily be the exact value for the longevity of that type of animal? Could the actual longevity of that type of animal be longer than predicted? Could it be shorter?

We do not expect the longevity to be exactly 14.6 years. The actual longevity for this type of animal might be longer or shorter than 14.6 years.

You can investigate further by looking at the types of animals included in the original data set. Take the lion, for example. Its gestation time is 100 days. You also know that its longevity is 15 years, but what does the least squares line *predict* for the lion's longevity?

Substituting $x = 100$ days into the equation, you get $y = 6.642 + 0.03974(100)$ or approximately 10.6. The least squares line predicts the lion's longevity to be approximately 10.6 years.

4. How close is this to being correct? More precisely, how much do you have to add to 10.6 to get the lion's true longevity of 15?

We predicted 10.6 years for the longevity of the lion, and students are asked what needs to be added to this value in order to get the lion's actual longevity of 15 years. Students can do this calculation mentally by adding amounts to 10.6 until they get 15. It is important, then, to see the connection between this adding calculation and the subtraction $15 - 10.6$. The result of this calculation, 4.4, is a residual.

You can show the prediction error of 4.4 years on the graph like this:

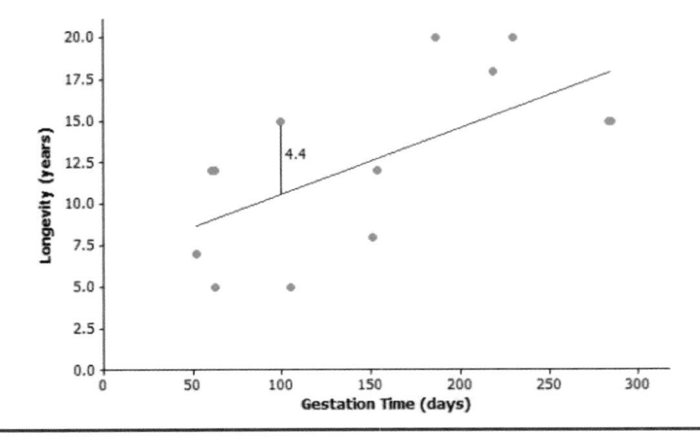

Exercises 5–6 (10 minutes)

Let students work in pairs on Exercises 5 and 6. Then discuss and confirm as a class.

Exercises 5–6

5. **Let's continue to think about the gestation times and longevities of animals. Let's specifically investigate how accurately the least squares line predicted the longevity of the black bear.**

   a. **What is the gestation time for the black bear?**

      219 *days*

   b. **Look at the graph. Roughly what does the least squares line predict for the longevity of the black bear?**

      Around 15 *years*

   c. **Use the gestation time from part (a) and the least squares line $y = 6.642 + 0.03974x$ to predict the black bear's longevity. Round your answer to the nearest tenth.**

      15.3 *years*

   d. **What is the actual longevity of the black bear?**

      18 *years*

   e. **How much do you have to add to the predicted value to get the actual longevity of the black bear?**

      2.7 *years*

   f. **Show your answer to part (e) on the graph as a vertical line segment.**

      Students should show a vertical line segment of length 2.7 *from the least squares line to the point representing the black bear.*

6. **Repeat this activity for the sheep.**

   a. **Substitute the sheep's gestation time for x into the equation to find the predicted value for the sheep's longevity. Round your answer to the nearest tenth.**

      $y = 6.642 + 0.03974(154) = 12.8$

      The predicted longevity for a sheep is 12.8 *years.*

   b. **What do you have to add to the predicted value in order to get the actual value of the sheep's longevity? (Hint: Your answer should be negative.)**

      $12 - 12.8 = -0.8$

      -0.8 *years would need to be added to the predicted value in order to get the actual value.*

   c. **Show your answer to part (b) on the graph as a vertical line segment. Write a sentence describing points in the graph for which a negative number would need to be added to the predicted value in order to get the actual value.**

      Students should show a vertical line segment of length 0.8 *from the least squares line to the point representing the sheep. For points that fall below the least squares line, you would need to add a negative number to the predicted value in order to get the actual value.*

Example 2 (5 minutes): Residuals as Prediction Errors

Explain the concept of residuals, and show students how the residuals in the table have been calculated.

To be sure students understand what the residual represents, ask the following:

- What do these residuals tell us?
  - *The residuals tell us how much needs to be added to the predicted longevity to get to the actual longevity.*
- Which type of animal has the largest positive residual? What does this tell us?
  - *Baboon; the actual longevity is* 5.9 *years more than the predicted value.*
- Which type of animal has the *biggest* negative residual? What does this tell us?
  - *Beaver; the actual longevity is* 5.8 *years less than the predicted value.*

MP.2

Discuss the scenario presented in the text; discuss how to find the predicted longevity of an animal not included in the data.

Example 2: Residuals as Prediction Errors

In previous exercises, you found out how much needs to be added to the predicted value to find the true value of an animal's longevity. In order to find this, you have been calculating

actual value − predicted value.

This quantity is referred to as a residual. It is summarized as

residual = actual y-value − predicted y-value.

You can now work out the residuals for all of the points in our animal longevity example. The values of the residuals are shown in the table below.

Animal	Gestation Time (days)	Longevity (years)	Residual (years)
Baboon	187	20	5.9
Black Bear	219	18	2.7
Beaver	105	5	-5.8
Bison	285	15	-3.0
Cat	63	12	2.9
Chimpanzee	230	20	4.2
Cow	284	15	-2.9
Dog	61	12	2.9
Fox (Red)	52	7	-1.7
Goat	151	8	-4.6
Lion	100	15	4.4
Sheep	154	12	-0.8
Wolf	63	5	-4.1

These residuals show that the actual longevity of an animal should be within six years of the longevity predicted by the least squares line.

Suppose you selected a type of animal that is not included in the original data set, and the gestation time for this type of animal is 270 days. Substituting $x = 270$ into the equation of the least squares line you get

$$y = 6.642 + 0.03974(270)$$
$$= 17.4.$$

The predicted longevity of this animal is 17.4 years.

Exercises 7–8 (5 minutes)

Let students work in pairs on Exercises 7–8. Then discuss and confirm as a class. Once students have completed these two questions, tell them that 270 days is the gestation time for humans, and ask whether this method produces an accurate predicted longevity for humans.

Exercises 7–8

Think about what the *actual* longevity of this type of animal might be.

7. **Could it be 30 years? How about 5 years?**

   It is unlikely that this type of animal would have a longevity as much as 30 years or as little as 5 years because these values are further from the predicted value (17.4 years) than the errors given by residuals in the table.

8. **Judging by the size of the residuals in our table, what kind of values do you think would be reasonable for the longevity of this type of animal?**

   A sensible range of possible values for the longevity is around 11–23 years.

Exercises 9–10 (5 minutes)

Let students work independently on Exercises 9 and 10. Then discuss and confirm as a class.

Exercises 9–10

Continue to think about the gestation times and longevities of animals. The gestation time for the type of animal called the ocelot is known to be 85 days.

The least squares line predicts the longevity of the ocelot to be 10.0 years.

$$y = 6.642 + 0.03974(85) = 10.0$$

9. **Based on the residuals in Example 3, would you be surprised to find that the longevity of the ocelot was 2 years? Why or why not? What might be a sensible range of values for the actual longevity of the ocelot?**

   It is unlikely that the actual longevity of the ocelot is as little as 2 years; this would have a residual of 8 years, which is greater than the ones in the table. A sensible range of possible values might be from 4 years to 16 years.

10. **We know that the actual longevity of the ocelot is 9 years. What is the residual for the ocelot?**

    Residual $= 9 - 10 = -1$

    The residual for the ocelot is -1 year.

Closing (2 minutes)

Review the term *residual* with students. Have students point out specific residuals found in the exercises and interpret their values. Ask students the following questions:

- If a residual is close to 0, what does that mean about the predicted value?
- If a residual is negative, what does that mean about the predicted value?

Lesson Summary

- When a least squares line is used to calculate a predicted value, the prediction error can be measured by

  residual = actual y-value − predicted y-value.
- On the graph, the residuals are the vertical distances of the points from the least squares line.
- The residuals give us an idea how close a prediction might be when the least squares line is used to make a prediction for a value that is not included in the data set.

Exit Ticket (5 minutes)

Name ______________________________ Date ______________

Lesson 15: Interpreting Residuals from a Line

Exit Ticket

Meerkats have a gestation time of 70 days.

a. Use the equation of the least squares line from today's class, $y = 6.643 + 0.03974x$, to predict the longevity of the meerkat. Remember x equals the gestation time in days, and y equals the longevity in years.

b. Approximately how close might your prediction be to the actual longevity of the meerkat? What was it (from class) that told you roughly how close a prediction might be to the true value?

c. According to your answers to parts (a) and (b), what is a reasonable range of possible values for the longevity of the meerkat?

d. The longevity of the meerkat is actually 10 years. Use this value and the predicted value that you calculated in part (a) to find the residual for the meerkat.

Exit Ticket Sample Solutions

Meerkats have a gestation time of 70 days.

a. Use the equation of the least squares line from today's class, $y = 6.643 + 0.03974x$, to predict the longevity of the meerkat. Remember x equals the gestation time in days, and y equals the longevity in years.

$y = 6.642 + 0.03974(70) = 9.4$

The predicted longevity of a meerkat is 9.4 *years.*

b. Approximately how close might your prediction be to the actual longevity of the meerkat? What was it (from class) that told you roughly how close a prediction might be to the true value?

The prediction would be within about 6 *years. We looked at the residuals for the original data set and saw that the largest residual was around* 6 *years.*

c. According to your answers to parts (a) and (b), what is a reasonable range of possible values for the longevity of the meerkat?

Between 3 *and* 15 *years would be sensible.*

d. The longevity of the meerkat is actually 10 years. Use this value and the predicted value that you calculated in part (a) to find the residual for the meerkat.

Residual $= 10 - 9.4 = 0.6$

The residual for the meerkat is 0.6 *years.*

Problem Set Sample Solutions

The time spent in surgery and the cost of surgery was recorded for six patients. The results and scatter plot are shown below.

Time (minutes)	Cost ($)
14	$1,510$
80	$6,178$
84	$5,912$
118	$9,184$
149	$8,855$
192	$11,023$

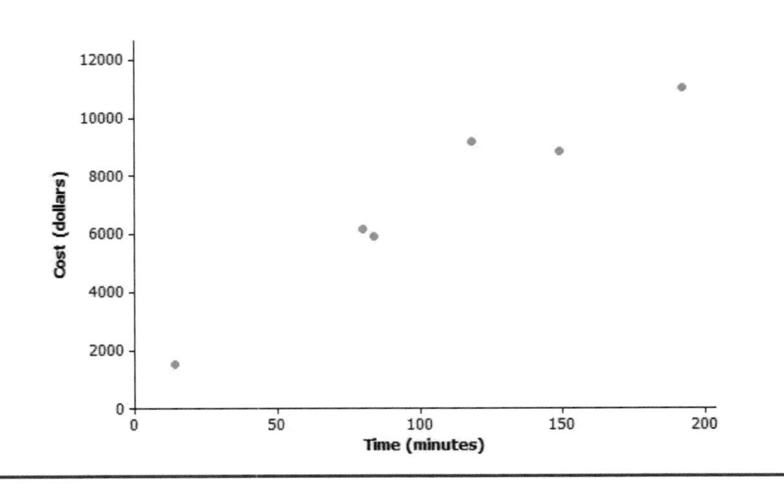

1. **Calculate the equation of the least squares line relating cost to time. (Indicate slope to the nearest tenth and y-intercept to the nearest whole number.)**

   $y = 1514 + 52.7x$, *where x represents time and y represents cost*

2. **Draw the least squares line on the graph above. (Hint: Substitute $x = 30$ into your equation to find the predicted y-value. Plot the point $(30$, your answer$)$ on the graph. Then substitute $x = 180$ into the equation, and plot the point. Join the two points with a straightedge.)**

   Plot the points $(30, 3095)$ and $(180, 11000)$ on the graph.

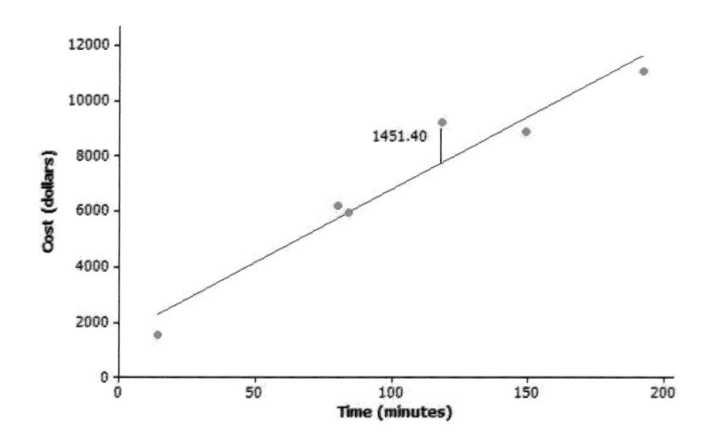

3. **What does the least squares line predict for the cost of a surgery that lasts 118 min.? (Calculate the cost to the nearest cent.)**

   $y = 1514 + 52.7(118) = 7732.60$

   The predicted cost for the surgery is $\$7,732.60$.

4. **How much do you have to add to your answer to Problem 3 to get the actual cost of surgery for a surgery lasting 118 min.? (This is the residual.)**

   $9184 - 7732.60 = 1451.40$

   $\$1,451.40$ *would need to be added.*

5. **Show your answer to Problem 4 as a vertical line between the point for that person in the scatter plot and the least squares line.**

   (Shown on the graph above.)

6. **Remember that the residual is the actual y-value minus the predicted y-value. Calculate the residual for the surgery that took 149 min. and cost $\$8,855$.**

   $x = 149$; $y = 1514 + 52.7(149) = 9366.30$

   Residual $= 8855 - 9366.3 = -511.30$

   The residual is -511.30 *dollars.*

7. Calculate the other residuals, and write all the residuals in the table below.

Time (minutes)	Cost ($)	Predicted Value ($)	Residual ($)
14	$1,510$	$2,251.8$	-741.8
80	$6,178$	$5,730$	448.0
84	$5,912$	$5,940.8$	-28.8
118	$9,184$	$7,732.6$	$1,451.4$
149	$8,855$	$9,366.3$	-511.3
192	$11,023$	$11,632.4$	-609.4

8. Suppose that a surgery took 100 min.

a. What does the least squares line predict for the cost of this surgery?

$x = 100; y = 1514 + 52.7(100) = 6784$

The predicted cost for the surgery is $\$6,784$.

b. Would you be surprised if the actual cost of this surgery were $\$9,000$? Why or why not?

$9000 - 6784 = 2216$. *This is much larger than any of the residuals in the table, so it would be surprising to find that the surgery was this expensive.*

c. Interpret the slope of the least squares line.

The slope is 52.7 *dollars per minute. Interpret this slope in the following way: For each additional minute in surgery, the cost of the surgery increases by* $\$52.70$.

Lesson 16: More on Modeling Relationships with a Line

Student Outcomes

- Students use the least squares line to predict values for a given data set.
- Students use residuals to evaluate the accuracy of predictions based on the least squares line.

Lesson Notes

Students continue their exploration of residuals. In this lesson, students build on their knowledge of calculating residuals and expand their practice by creating residual plots. Additionally, students reason abstractly by thinking about how a particular pattern in a scatter plot is represented in the residual plot. Students do not use residual plots as an indication of the appropriateness of fit for a model until Lesson 17.

Classwork

Example 1 (3 minutes): Calculating Residuals

Introduce the data and model for this example. Ask students to examine the scatter plot.

Example 1: Calculating Residuals

The curb weight of a car is the weight of the car without luggage or passengers. The table below shows the curb weights (in hundreds of pounds) and fuel efficiencies (in miles per gallon) of five compact cars.

Curb Weight (hundreds of pounds)	Fuel Efficiency (mpg)
25.33	43
26.94	38
27.79	30
30.12	34
32.47	30

Using a calculator, the least squares line for this data set was found to have the equation:

$$y = 78.62 - 1.5290x,$$

where x is the curb weight (in hundreds of pounds), and y is the predicted fuel efficiency (in miles per gallon).

The scatter plot of this data set is shown below, and the least squares line is shown on the graph.

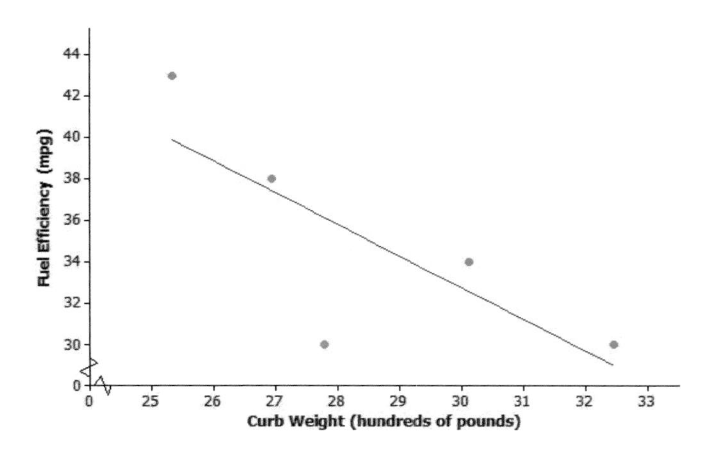

You will calculate the residuals for the five points in the scatter plot. Before calculating the residuals, look at the scatter plot.

Exercises 1–2 (8 minutes)

Ask students to examine the plot, and answer Exercises 1–2 as a class.

Exercises 1–2

1. **Will the residual for the car whose curb weight is 25.33 hundred pounds be positive or negative? Roughly what is the value of the residual for this point?**

   Positive residual of 3 mpg***; the actual value is approximately*** 3 ***units above the line.***

2. **Will the residual for the car whose curb weight is 27.79 hundred pounds be positive or negative? Roughly what is the value of the residual for this point?**

   Negative residual of -6 mpg***; the actual value is*** 6 ***units below the line.***

Now confirm the estimated residuals by calculating the exact residuals using the least squares line as shown in the text.

MP.4

The residuals for both of these curb weights are calculated as follows:

Substitute $x = 25.33$ into the equation of the least squares line to find the predicted fuel efficiency.	Substitute $x = 27.79$ into the equation of the least squares line to find the predicted fuel efficiency.
$y = 78.62 - 1.5290(25.33)$ $= 39.9$	$y = 78.62 - 1.5290(27.79)$ $= 36.1$
Now calculate the residual.	Now calculate the residual.
residual $=$ actual y-value $-$ predicted y-value $= 43$ mpg $- 39.9$ mpg $= 3.1$ mpg	residual $=$ actual y-value $-$ predicted y-value $= 30$ mpg $- 36.1$ mpg $= -6.1$ mpg

These two residuals have been written in the table below.

Curb Weight (hundreds of pounds)	Fuel Efficiency (mpg)	Residual (mpg)
25.33	43	3.1
26.94	38	
27.79	30	-6.1
30.12	34	
32.47	30	

Exercises 3–4 (12 minutes)

Let students work in small groups on Exercises 3–4. Then, discuss Exercise 4(b) as a class.

Exercises 3–4

Continue to think about the car weights and fuel efficiencies from Example 1.

3. **Calculate the remaining three residuals, and write them in the table.**

   The residuals are shown in the table below.

Curb weight (hundreds of pounds)	Fuel Efficiency (mpg)	Residual (mpg)
25.33	43	3.1
26.94	38	0.6
27.79	30	-6.1
30.12	34	1.4
32.47	30	1.0

4. **Suppose that a car has a curb weight of 31 hundred pounds.**

   a. **What does the least squares line predict for the fuel efficiency of this car?**

      $y = 78.62 - 1.5290(31) = 31.2$

      The predicted fuel efficiency is 31.2 **mpg.**

   b. **Would you be surprised if the actual fuel efficiency of this car was 29 miles per gallon? Explain your answer.**

      No. The residual for this point would be 29 **mpg** $- 31.2$ **mpg*, or*** -2.2 **mpg.** ***This is within the range of the residuals for the table above.***

Example 2 (6 minutes): Making a Residual Plot to Evaluate a Line

Explain that a residual plot is made by plotting the x-values on the horizontal axis and the corresponding residuals on the vertical axis.

MP.6 Graph the residual in the first row of the table $(25.33, 3.1)$.

Then ask students:

- What is the next ordered pair that you would graph?
  - *It should be* $(26.94, 0.6)$.

If students are unclear, remind them they are plotting the x-values with the corresponding *residuals*.

Example 2: Making a Residual Plot to Evaluate a Line

It is often useful to make a graph of the residuals, called a residual plot. You will make the residual plot for the compact car data set.

Plot the original x-variable (curb weight in this case) on the horizontal axis and the residuals on the vertical axis. For this example, you need to draw a horizontal axis that goes from 25 to 32 and a vertical axis with a scale that includes the values of the residuals that you calculated. Next, plot the point for the first car. The curb weight of the first car is 25.33 hundred pounds and the residual is 3.1 mpg. Plot the point $(25.33, 3.1)$.

The axes and this first point are shown below.

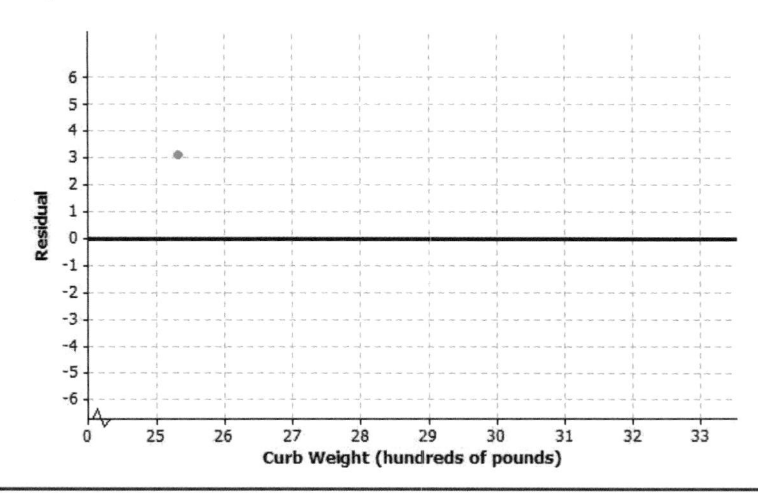

Exercises 5–6 (8 minutes)

Let students work in small groups on Exercises 5–6. Then compare answers for Exercise 6 as a class.

Exercises 5–6

5. **Plot the other four residuals in the residual plot started in Example 3.**

   The completed residual plot is shown below.

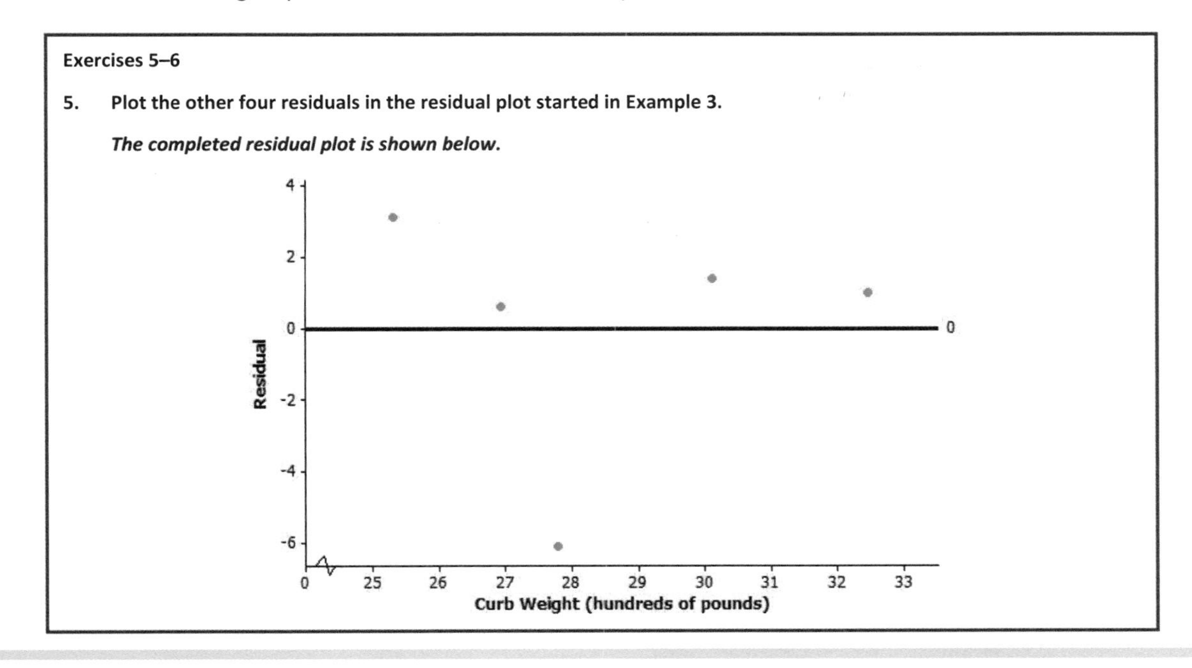

6. **How does the pattern of the points in the residual plot relate to the pattern in the original scatter plot? Looking at the original scatter plot, could you have known what the pattern in the residual plot would be?**

   The first point in the scatter plot is quite a long way above the least squares line (compared to the distances above or below the line of most of the other points), so it has a relatively large positive residual. The second point is a relatively small distance above the line, so it has a small positive residual. The third point is a long way below the line, so it has a large negative residual. The fourth point is a somewhat small distance above the line, so it has a somewhat small positive residual. Likewise, the fifth point has a relatively small positive residual. Looking at the original scatter plot, there were four points above the least squares line and only one point below, so I would have expected to have four points above the zero line in the residual plot and only one point below. Since the points above the line in the original scatter plot were closer to the line than the one point below it, I would have expected the points above the zero line in the residual plot to be closer to the zero line than the one point below.

Closing (3 minutes)

Review the Lesson Summary with students.

Lesson Summary

- **The predicted y-value is calculated using the equation of the least squares line.**
- **The residual is calculated using**

  residual $=$ actual y-value $-$ predicted y-value.
- **The sum of the residuals provides an idea of the degree of accuracy when using the least squares line to make predictions.**
- **To make a residual plot, plot the x-values on the horizontal axis and the residuals on the vertical axis.**

Exit Ticket (5 minutes)

Name ______________________________ Date ______________

Lesson 16: More on Modeling Relationships with a Line

Exit Ticket

1. Suppose you are given a scatter plot (with least squares line) that looks like this:

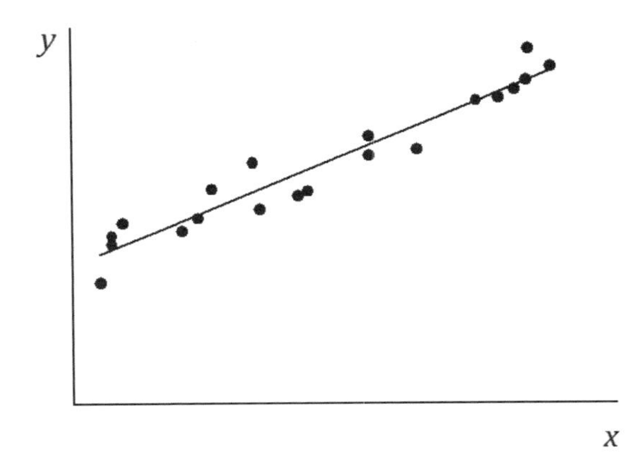

What would the residual plot look like? Make a quick sketch on the axes given below. (There is no need to plot the points exactly.)

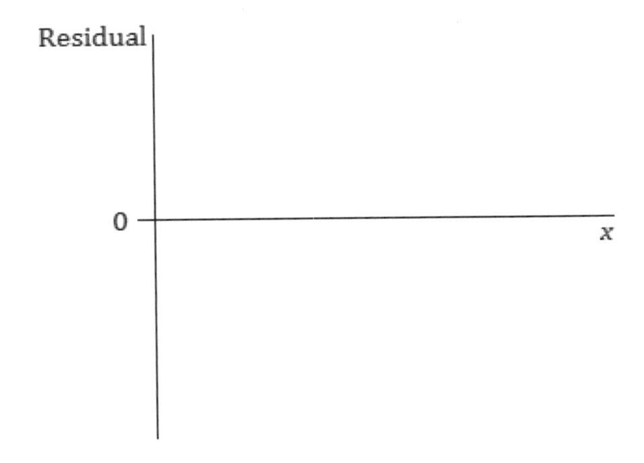

2. Suppose the scatter plot looked like this:

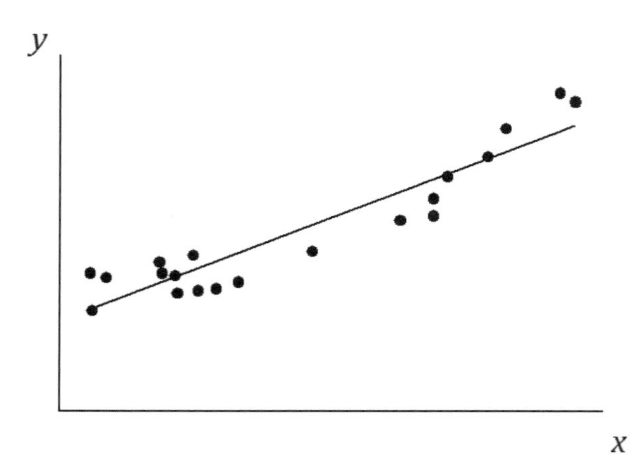

Make a quick sketch on the axes below of how the residual plot would look.

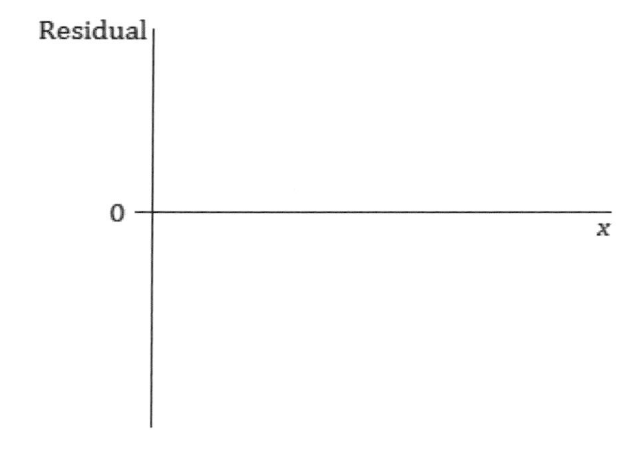

Exit Ticket Sample Solutions

1. **Suppose you are given a scatter plot (with least squares line) that looks like this:**

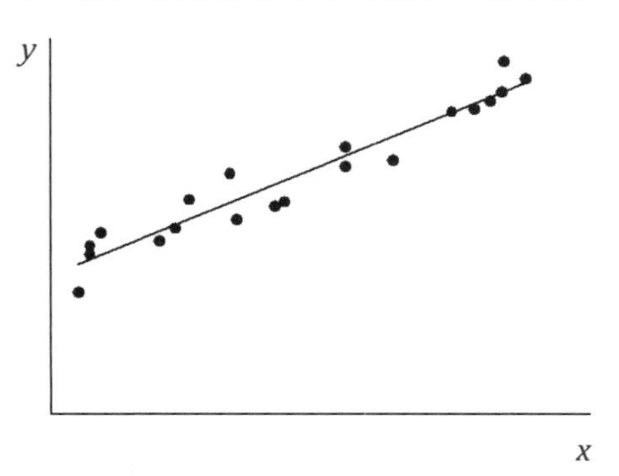

What would the residual plot look like? Make a quick sketch on the axes given below. (There is no need to plot the points exactly.)

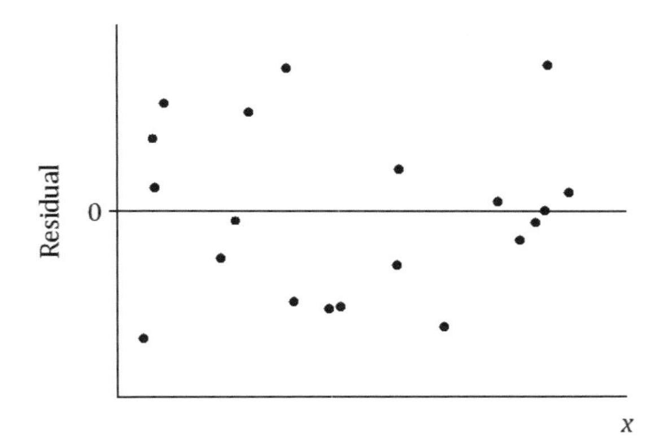

2. **Suppose the scatter plot looked like this:**

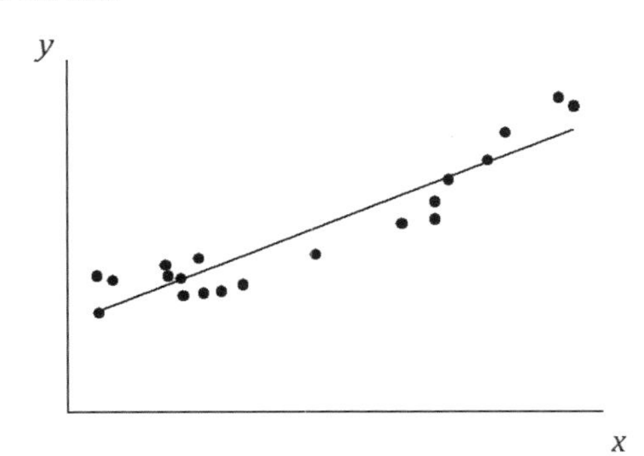

Make a quick sketch on the axes below of how the residual plot would look.

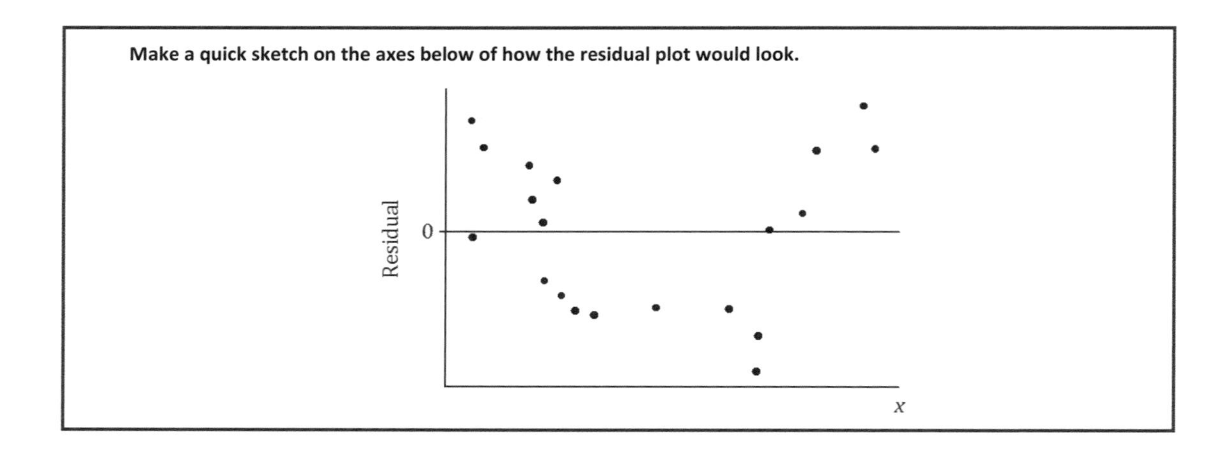

Note: It is important that students begin to see the general shape of the pattern in the residual plot, a random scatter of points in Problem 1, and a U-shape in Problem 2. Beyond that, the details of the residual plots are not of concern at this point in the study of residuals.

Problem Set Sample Solutions

Four athletes on a track team are comparing their personal bests in the 100 meter and 200 meter events. A table of their best times is shown below.

Athlete	100 m time (seconds)	200 m time (seconds)
1	12.95	26.68
2	13.81	29.48
3	14.66	28.11
4	14.88	30.93

A scatter plot of these results (including the least squares line) is shown below.

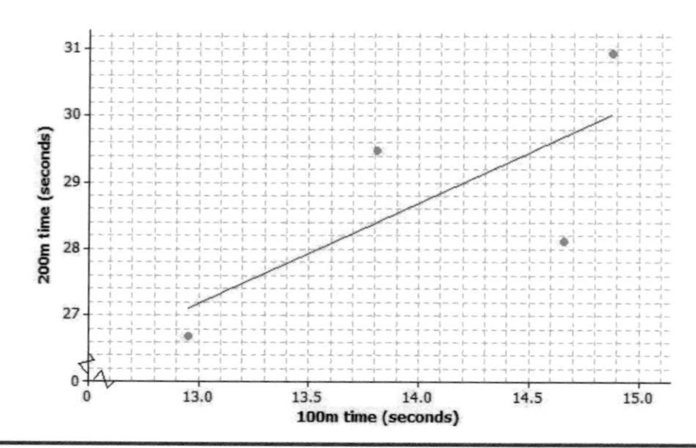

1. **Use your calculator or computer to find the equation of the least squares line.**

   $y = 7.526 + 1.5115x$, *where x represents 100-meter time and y represents 200-meter time.*

2. **Use your equation to find the predicted 200-meter time for the runner whose 100-meter time is 12.95 seconds. What is the residual for this athlete?**

   $y = 7.526 + 1.5115(12.95) \approx 27.10$

   Residual $= 26.68 - 27.10 = -0.42$

   The predicted 200 m time for the runner is 27.10 seconds. The residual is -0.42 seconds.

3. **Calculate the residuals for the other three athletes. Write all the residuals in the table given below.**

Athlete	100 m time (seconds)	200 m time (seconds)	Residual (seconds)
1	12.95	26.68	-0.42
2	13.81	29.48	1.08
3	14.66	28.11	-1.57
4	14.88	30.93	0.91

4. **Using the axes provided below, construct a residual plot for this data set.**

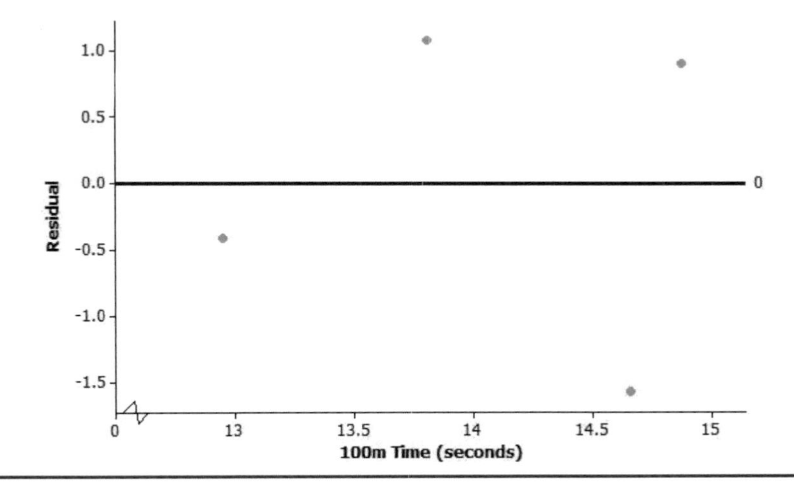

Lesson 17: Analyzing Residuals

Student Outcomes

- Students use a graphing calculator to construct the residual plot for a given data set.
- Students use a residual plot as an indication of whether the model used to describe the relationship between two numerical variables is an appropriate choice.

Lesson Notes

In this lesson, students use technology to generate residual plots. Students build on their knowledge of using technology to determine the least squares line for a data set. The steps for using TI-83/84 graphing calculators to create residual plots are provided in the teacher notes, which can be printed and distributed for students to follow during the lesson as a guide. Similar summaries may be needed for any graphing software or other graphing calculators that students may use. Residual plots are also analyzed to determine the appropriateness of informally fitting the linear models to the data set.

Classwork

Example 1 (10 minutes): Predicting the Pattern in the Residual Plot

Students learn how to use the pattern in the scatter plot to predict what the residual plot will look like. Vertical distances from the least squares line in the scatter plot are plotted as the y-values in the residual plot, with the x-coordinates remaining the same. Note that the scales on the vertical axes of the two graphs are different, and as a result, the sizes of the displacements are greatly exaggerated in the residual plot.

Ask students:

- What will the residual plot look like?

If students have trouble with this, explain each point in the scatter plot one by one. For each point, look at whether it has a positive or negative residual and whether the residual is large or small relative to the other residuals. Once they have seen two or three points in the scatter plot and how they translate to points in the residual plot, students should see how the pattern translates as a whole. Students look at the residual plot as an indication of the fit of the points to the line.

Example 1: Predicting the Pattern in the Residual Plot

Suppose you are given a scatter plot and least squares line that looks like this:

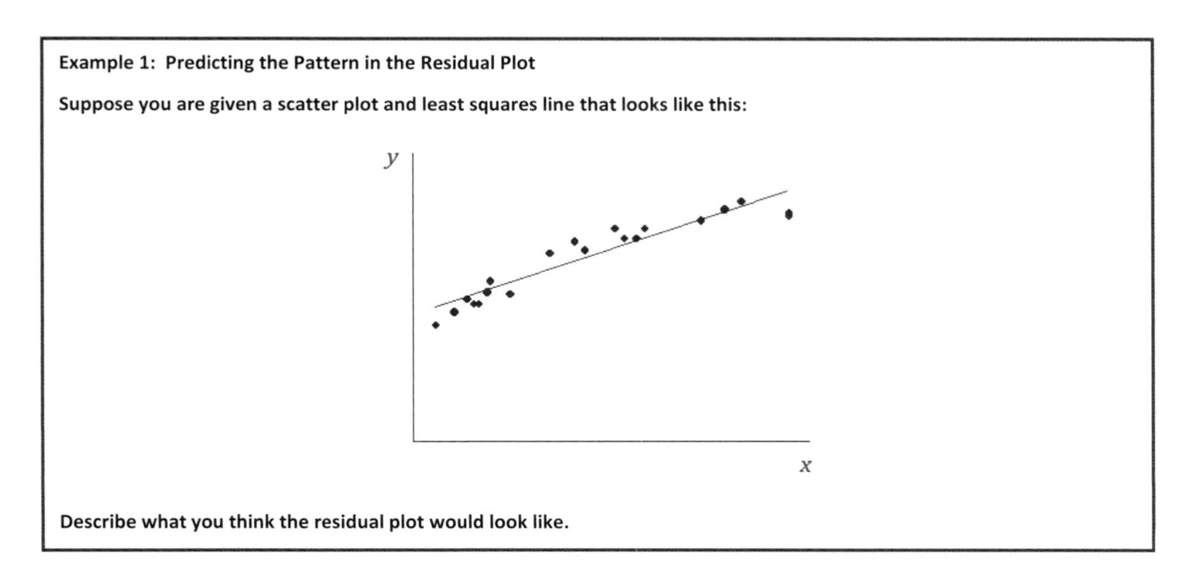

Describe what you think the residual plot would look like.

If students struggle, have them look carefully at the scatter plot. Point out that moving from left to right, the points initially tend to be below the least squares line, then move above it, and then below it. The residuals are negative, then positive, and then negative again. This means that the points in the residual plot will be below the horizontal axis, then above it, and then below it again.

The residual plot has an arch shape like this:

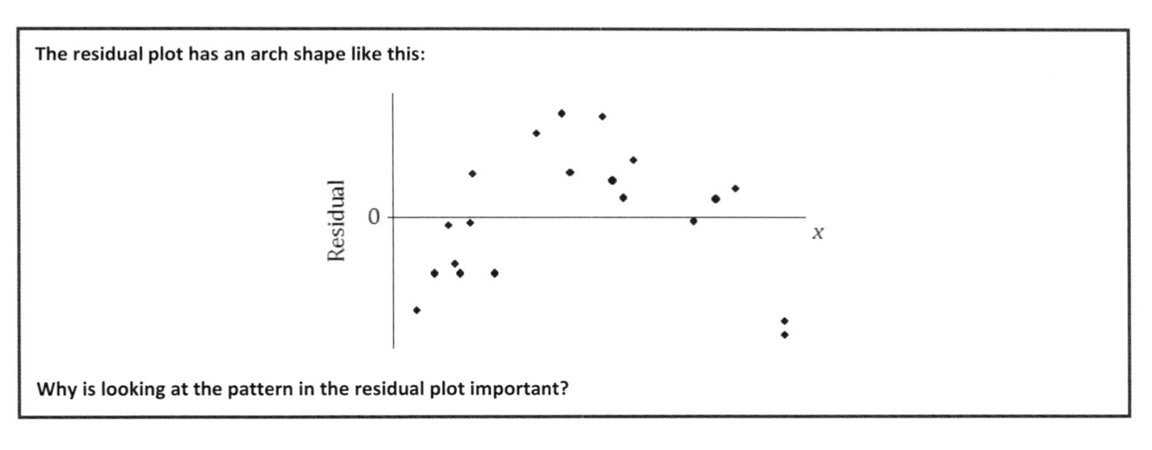

Why is looking at the pattern in the residual plot important?

Discuss with students that the residual plot provides another indication of the type of relationship between two variables.

Example 2 (10 minutes): The Meaning of Residuals

The purpose of this example is to remind students of what a residual plot is before they construct one using a calculator. If students seem comfortable with the concept of a residual plot following the previous lesson and Problem Set, this example can be covered quickly. If students need some review, this is a good opportunity to do that.

Example 2: The Meaning of Residuals

Suppose that you have a scatter plot and that you have drawn the least squares line on your plot. Remember that the residual for a point in the scatter plot is the vertical distance of that point from the least squares line.

In the previous lesson, you looked at a scatter plot showing how fuel efficiency was related to curb weight for five compact cars. The scatter plot and least squares line are shown below.

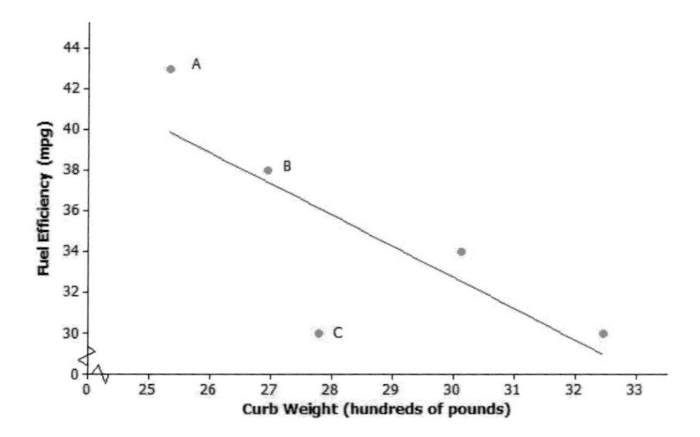

Consider the following questions:

- **What kind of residual does Point A have?**

  Point A has a large positive residual.

- **What kind of residual does Point B have?**

  Point B has a small positive residual.

- **What kind of residual does Point C have?**

  Point C has a very large negative residual.

You also looked at the residual plot for this data set:

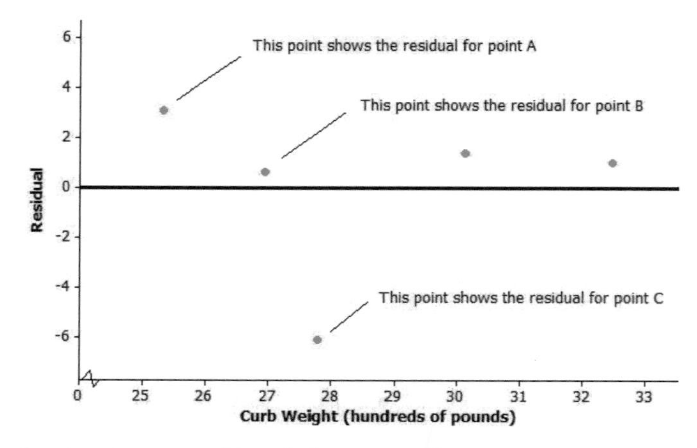

Your teacher will now show how to use a graphing calculator or graphing program to construct a scatter plot and a residual plot. Consider the following example.

Example 3 (15 minutes): Using a Graphing Calculator to Construct a Residual Plot

Even though students have already learned how to calculate the equation of the least squares line using a graphing calculator, the instructions are repeated here for completeness. In this example, students construct a scatter plot with the least squares line and construct a residual plot using technology.

The instructions shown here are for the TI-83 and TI-84 calculators and are intended as a guide only. Alternate graphing software may also be used. Most graphing programs have similar directions to those listed for the TI-83 or TI-84.

Note: Students using the TI-83 or TI-84 should clear out any equations under $Y =$ before beginning this example.

Example 3: Using a Graphing Calculator to Construct a Residual Plot

In an earlier lesson, you looked at a data set giving the shoe lengths and heights of 12 adult women. This data set is shown in the table below.

x (Shoe Length)	y (Height)
inches	inches
8.9	61
9.6	61
9.8	66
10.0	64
10.2	64
10.4	65
10.6	65
10.6	67
10.5	66
10.8	67
11.0	67
11.8	70

Use a calculator to construct the scatter plot (with least squares line) and the residual plot for this data set.

Calculation of the equation of the least squares line:

1. From the home screen, go to the statistics editor by pressing STAT, ENTER.
2. Enter the x-values into L_1 and the y-values into L_2.
3. Press 2nd, QUIT to return to the home screen.
4. Press STAT, select CALC, select LinReg($a + bx$), and press ENTER.
5. Type L_1, L_2, Y_1 so that your entry reads *LinReg(*$a + bx$*)* L_1, L_2, Y_1. (Y_1 is accessed by pressing VARS and selecting Y-VARS, Function, 1.) Press ENTER.
6. The y-intercept, a, and the slope, b, of the least squares line are displayed on the screen. (Also, the calculator stores in its memory a list called RESID, which is used in constructing the residual plot. Furthermore, since Y_1 was included in the entry, the equation of the least squares line is entered as the Y_1 equation in the Y = menu.)

Construction of scatter plot:

1. From the home screen press 2nd, STAT PLOT.
2. Select Plot1, and press ENTER.
3. Select *On*. Under *Type* choose the first (scatter plot) icon, for Xlist enter L_1, for Ylist enter L_2, and under *Mark* choose the first (square) symbol.
4. Press 2nd, QUIT to return to the home screen.
5. Press Y =.
6. Go to any unwanted graph equations and press CLEAR. Make sure that only Plot1 is selected (not Plot2 or Plot3).
7. Press Zoom, select ZoomStat (option 9), and press ENTER.
8. The scatter plot and the least squares line are displayed.

Construction of residual plot:

1. From the home screen, press 2nd, STATPLOT.
2. Select Plot2, and press ENTER.
3. Select *On*. Under *Type,* choose the first (scatter plot) icon, for Xlist enter L_1, for Ylist enter RESID, and under *Mark* choose the first (square) symbol. (RESID is accessed by pressing 2nd, LIST, selecting NAMES, scrolling down to RESID and pressing ENTER.)
4. Press 2nd, QUIT to return to the home screen.
5. Press Y =.
6. First, deselect the equation of the least squares line in Y_1 by going to the $=$ sign for Y_1 and pressing ENTER. Then deselect Plot1, and make sure that Plot2 is selected.
7. Press Zoom, select ZoomStat (option 9), and press ENTER.
8. The residual plot is displayed.

Note that when constructing a residual plot, you need the correct set of residuals to form the list called *RESID*. This is only the case if you have run the LinReg($a + bx$) or LinReg($ax + b$) command for the data set on which you are working.

Students often ask why we use LinReg($a + bx$) rather than LinReg($ax + b$). Explain how the two forms offer different representations of a linear equation. The more common convention in statistics is that a is the y-intercept and b is the slope, not vice-versa.

To save time and help students do the problem set, it might be worthwhile to give each student a copy of the calculator instructions.

The equation of the least squares line for this example is $y = 32.679 + 3.1469x$, where x is the shoe length (in inches), and y is the height (in inches). The scatter plot and residual plot are shown below.

Scatter plot:

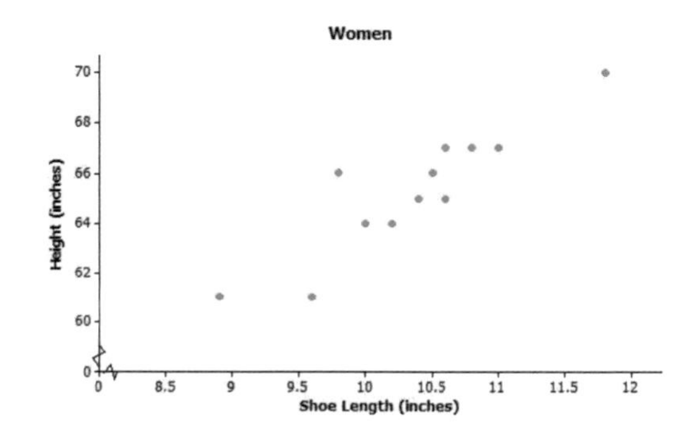

Residual plot:

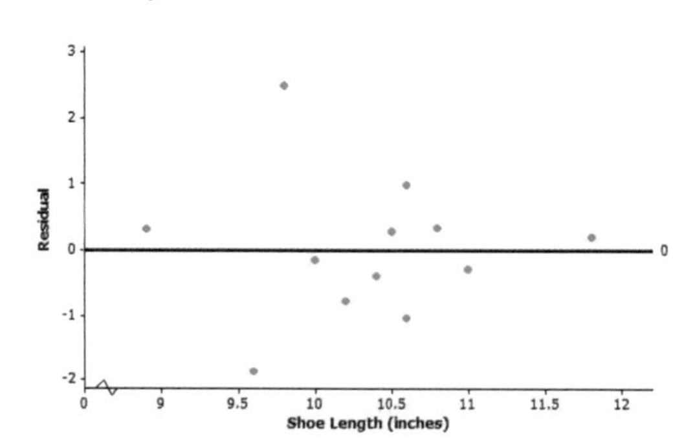

Closing (5 minutes)

Discuss the Lesson Summary with students.

> **Lesson Summary**
>
> - **After fitting a line, the residual plot can be constructed using a graphing calculator.**
> - **A pattern in the residual plot indicates that the relationship in the original data set is not linear.**

Exit Ticket (5 minutes)

Name ____ Date ____________________

Lesson 17: Analyzing Residuals

Exit Ticket

1. If you see a random scatter of points in the residual plot, what does this say about the original data set?

2. Suppose a scatter plot of bivariate numerical data shows a linear pattern. Describe what you think the residual plot would look like. Explain why you think this.

Exit Ticket Sample Solutions

1. **If you see a random scatter of points in the residual plot, what does this say about the original data set?**

   A random scatter of points in the residual plot tells us that a linear function is an appropriate model for the relationship between the two variables in the original data set.

2. **Suppose a scatter plot of bivariate numerical data shows a linear pattern. Describe what you think the residual plot would look like. Explain why you think this.**

   Because the relationship between the two variables is linear, the residual plot would have a random pattern.

Problem Set Sample Solutions

Assist those students still needing help with the calculator or statistical program. If students are using a TI graphing calculator (e.g., a TI-83 or TI-84), tell them to turn off the STAT plot for 2. The first question asks only about the least squares line and the scatter plot.

Consider again a data set giving the shoe lengths and heights of 10 adult men. This data set is shown in the table below.

x (Shoe Length)	y (Height)
inches	inches
12.6	74
11.8	65
12.2	71
11.6	67
12.2	69
11.4	68
12.8	70
12.2	69
12.6	72
11.8	71

1. **Use your calculator or graphing program to construct the scatter plot of this data set. Include the least squares line on your graph. Explain what the slope of the least squares line indicates about shoe length and height.**

   The slope indicates that as the shoe length increases, so does the height. The following illustrates the scatter plot and residual plot from a calculator. (Note: If it is not possible for you to observe your students' work on their calculators, have them show you a sketch of each graph.)

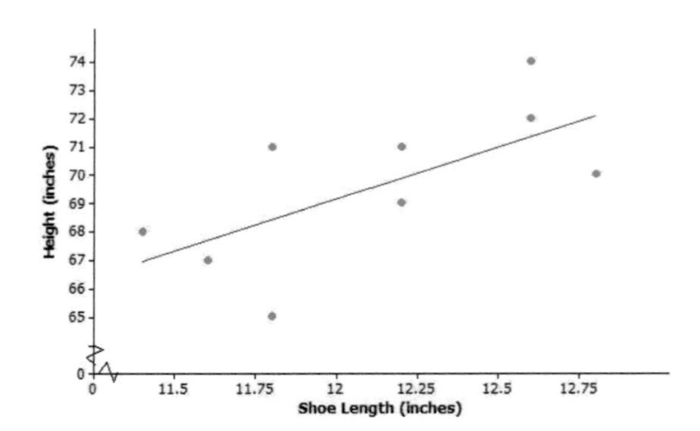

2. **Use your calculator to construct the residual plot for this data set.**

   See plot below.

3. **Make a sketch of the residual plot on the axes given below. Does the scatter of points in the residual plot indicate a linear relationship in the original data set? Explain your answer.**

   There is no curved pattern in the residual plot, and the points in the residual plot appear to be scattered at random around the zero line. This indicates that the relationship in the original data set is linear.

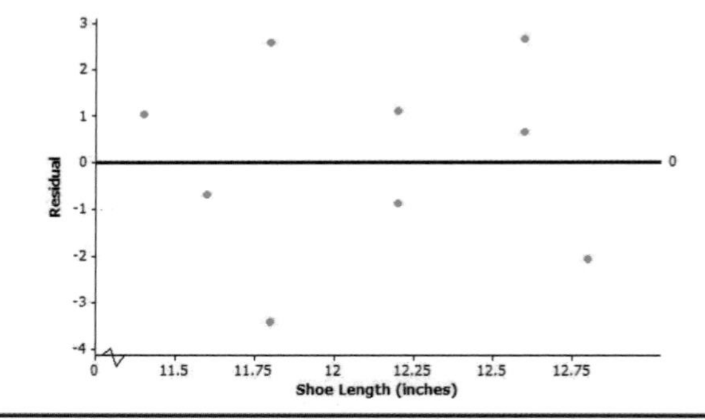

Lesson 18: Analyzing Residuals

Student Outcomes

- Students use a graphing calculator to construct the residual plot for a given data set.
- Students use a residual plot as an indication of whether the model used to describe the relationship between two numerical variables is an appropriate choice.

Lesson Notes

In this lesson, students continue to construct residual plots. Residual plots are analyzed to determine if the points are scattered at random around the horizontal line (indicating a linear relationship) or if the points have a pattern (indicating a nonlinear relationship).

Classwork

The previous lesson shows that when data is fitted to a line, a scatter plot with a curved pattern produces a residual plot that shows a clear pattern. You also saw that when a line is fit, a scatter plot where the points show a straight-line pattern results in a residual plot where the points are randomly scattered.

Example 1 (10 minutes): The Relevance of the Pattern in the Residual Plot

This is another opportunity to reinforce *why* the particular patterns in the scatter plots result in the corresponding patterns in the residual plots. Pose these questions:

- Why does the first scatter plot result in an *arch* shape in the residual plot?
  - *The points in the scatter plot are not in a straight line.*
- Why does the second scatter plot result in a *U* shape in the residual plot?
  - *The points in the scatter plot are not in a straight line.*
- Why does the third scatter plot result in a random scatter of points in the residual plot?
  - *The points seem to be linear.*

Explain how the patterns in the residual plot show us whether a linear model is a good fit for the data.

- If the points in a residual plot are random, a linear model is the best fit.
- If the points have a pattern, a line is not the best fit.

Pose the following question to students to connect back to previous lessons:

- If a linear model is not the best fit for the first and second scatter plots, what type of model might be more appropriate?
  - *Exponential or (possibly) quadratic*

Example 1: The Relevance of the Pattern in the Residual Plot

Our previous findings are summarized in the plots below:

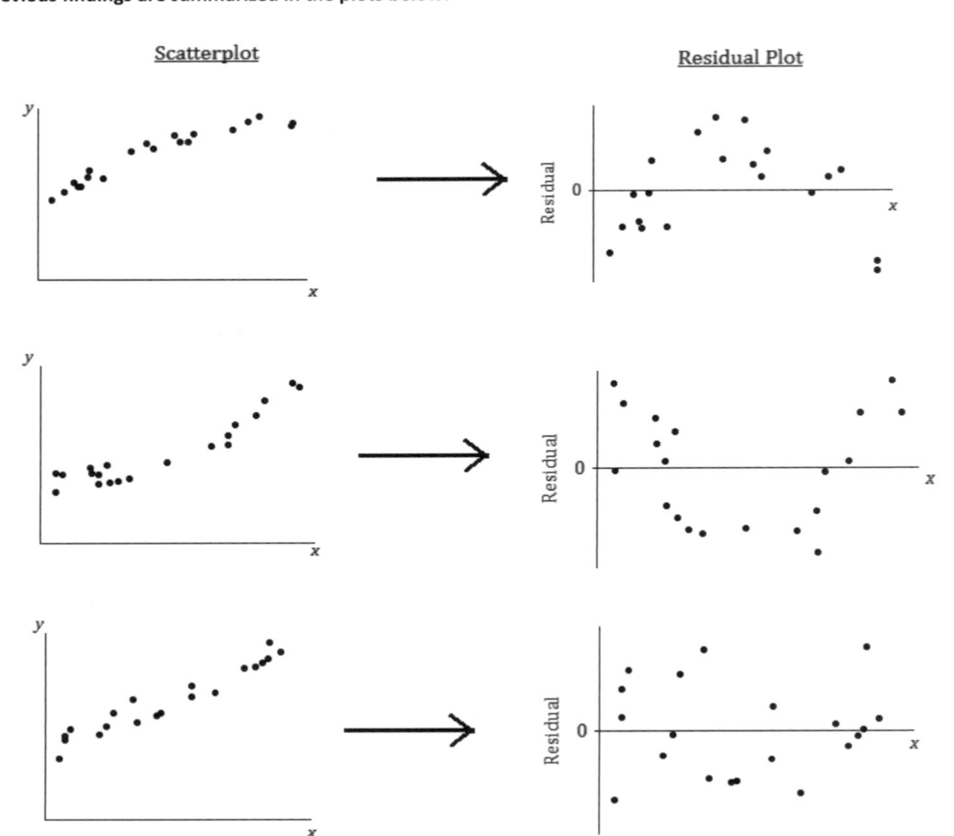

What does it mean when there is a curved pattern in the residual plot?

Allow students to answer this question. Discuss with students that a curved pattern in the residual plot indicates that the relationship would be better described by a nonlinear function. When you see a curved pattern in the residual plot, you should investigate nonlinear models rather than using a line or model to describe the relationship. (See the first two scatter plots and residual plots in the figure above, which show a curved pattern in both the scatter plot and the residual plot.)

What does it mean when the points in the residual plot appear to be scattered at random with no visible pattern?

Again, allow students to answer this question. Discuss with students that when the relationship is approximately linear, the points in the residual plot are scattered at random around the horizontal line at zero. This indicates that a linear model is an appropriate way to describe the relationship. (See the third scatter plot and residual plot in the figure above, which shows a linear pattern in the scatter plot and no pattern in the residual plot.)

Why not just look at the scatter plot of the original data set? Why was the residual plot necessary? The next example answers these questions.

Example 2 (10 minutes): Why Do You Need the Residual Plot?

Ask students the following:

- What does the residual plot for Example 2 indicate about using a linear model?
  - *It is not a good fit. There is a nonlinear relationship.*

The point is that because the scale on the vertical axis of the residual plot exaggerates the vertical deviations, the residual plot shows detail of the pattern in the residuals that is not easily seen in the scatter plot.

Example 2: Why Do You Need the Residual Plot?

The temperature (in degrees Fahrenheit) was measured at various altitudes (in thousands of feet) above Los Angeles. The scatter plot (below) seems to show a linear (straight-line) relationship between these two quantities.

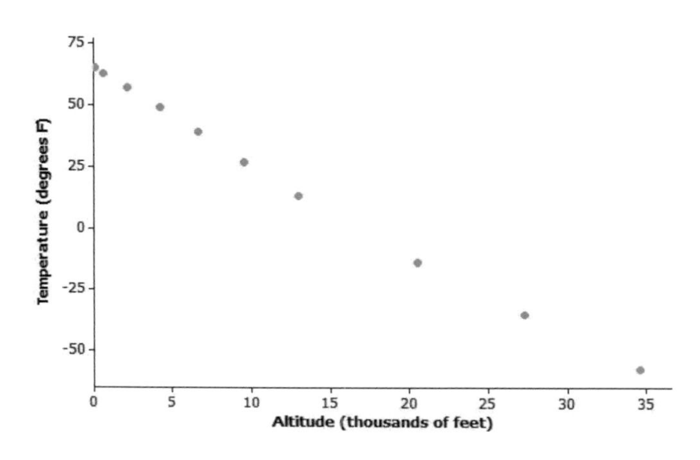

Data source: *Core Math Tools*, http://nctm.org

However, look at the residual plot:

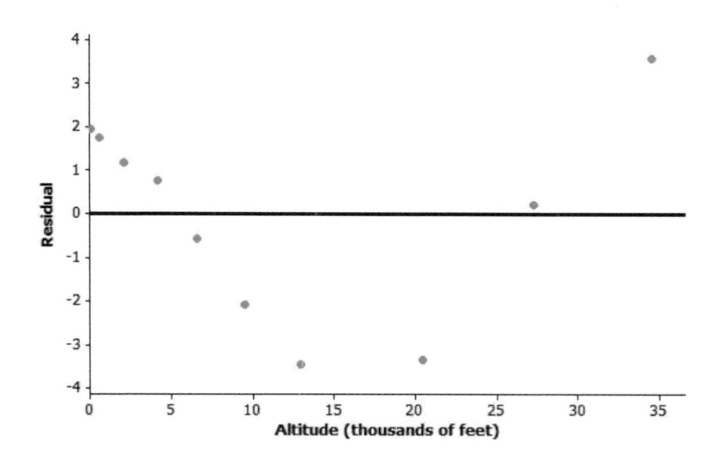

There is a clear curve in the residual plot. So what appeared to be a linear relationship in the original scatter plot was, in fact, a nonlinear relationship.

> **How did this residual plot result from the original scatter plot?**
>
> ***The residuals are the vertical deviations from the least squares line in the original scatter plot. Because of the change of scale, tiny vertical deviations can be shown as much larger distances from the zero line in the residual plot. Therefore, a very subtle curvature in the original relationship can be seen more clearly in the residual plot. This is why you draw residual plots.***

Exercises 1–3 (15 minutes): Volume and Temperature

Let students work with a partner on Exercises 1–3. Then discuss and confirm answers as a class.

> **Exercises 1–3: Volume and Temperature**
>
> **Water expands as it heats. Researchers measured the volume (in milliliters) of water at various temperatures. The results are shown below.**

Temperature (°C)	Volume (ml)
20	100.125
21	100.145
22	100.170
23	100.191
24	100.215
25	100.239
26	100.266
27	100.290
28	100.319
29	100.345
30	100.374

1. **Using a graphing calculator, construct the scatter plot of this data set. Include the least squares line on your graph. Make a sketch of the scatter plot including the least squares line on the axes below.**

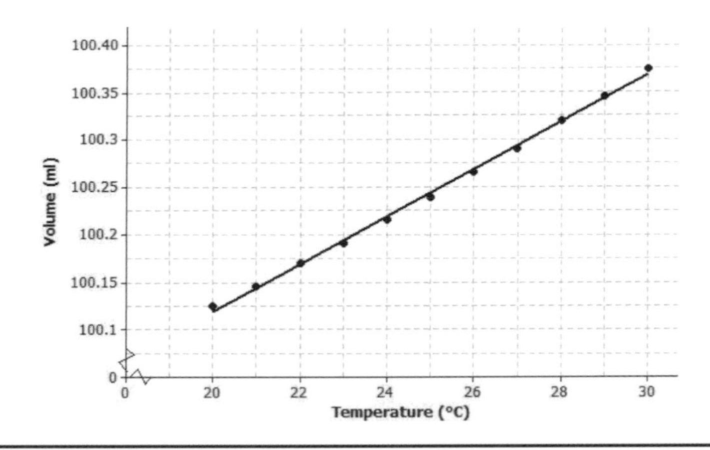

Although it might be clear from the scatter plot given here that there is a curved relationship between the two variables, this detail cannot, however, be seen in the low-resolution graph produced by a calculator.

2. **Using the calculator, construct a residual plot for this data set. Make a sketch of the residual plot on the axes given below.**

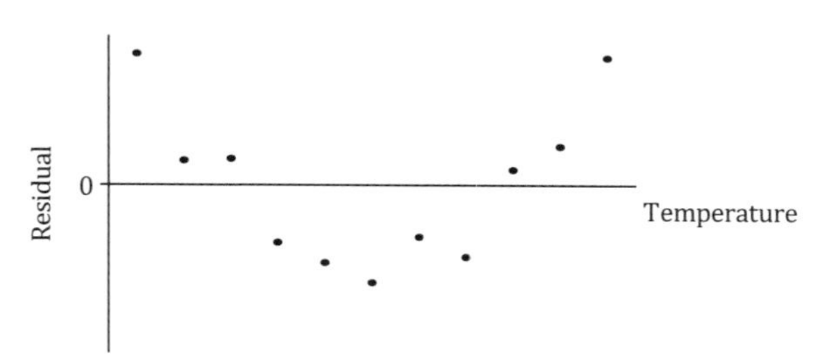

3. **Do you see a clear curve in the residual plot? What does this say about the original data set?**

Yes, there is a clear curve in the residual plot. This indicates a nonlinear (curved) relationship between volume and temperature.

Closing (5 minutes)

Discuss the Lesson Summary with students.

Lesson Summary

- After fitting a line, the residual plot can be constructed using a graphing calculator.
- A curve or pattern in the residual plot indicates a nonlinear relationship in the original data set.
- A random scatter of points in the residual plot indicates a linear relationship in the original data set.

Exit Ticket (5 minutes)

Name ____ Date ____________________

Lesson 18: Analyzing Residuals

Exit Ticket

1. If you see a clear curve in the residual plot, what does this say about the original data set?

2. If you see a random scatter of points in the residual plot, what does this say about the original data set?

Exit Ticket Sample Solutions

1. **If you see a clear curve in the residual plot, what does this say about the original data set?**

   A clear curve in the residual plot shows that the variables in the original data set have a nonlinear relationship.

2. **If you see a random scatter of points in the residual plot, what does this say about the original data set?**

   A random scatter of points in the residual plot shows that a straight line is an appropriate model for the relationship between the two variables in the original data set.

Problem Set Sample Solutions

1. **For each of the following residual plots, what conclusion would you reach about the relationship between the variables in the original data set? Indicate whether the values would be better represented by a linear or a nonlinear relationship.**

   a.

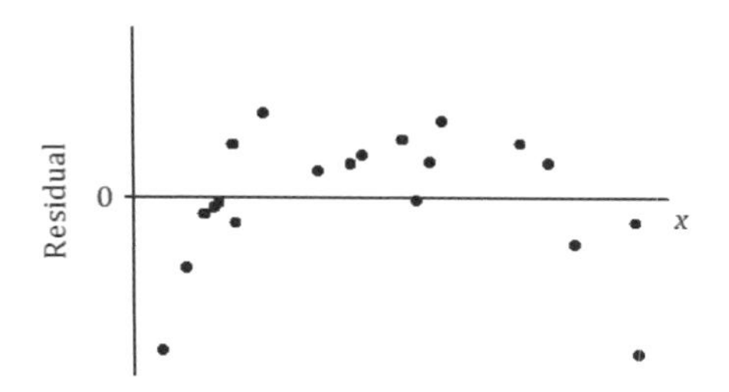

   There is a nonlinear relationship between the variables in the original data set.

   b.

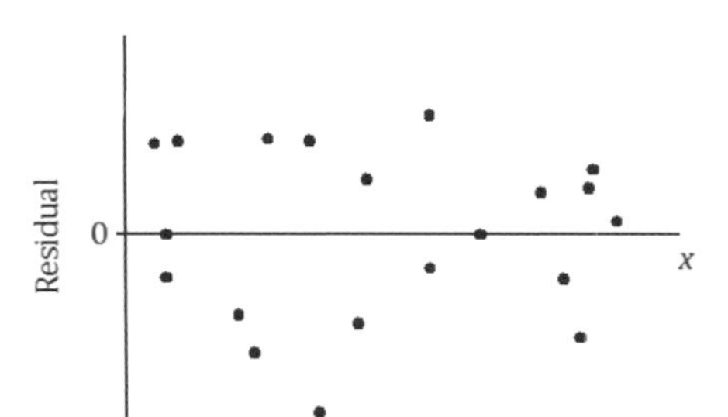

   There is a linear relationship between the variables in the original data set.

   c.

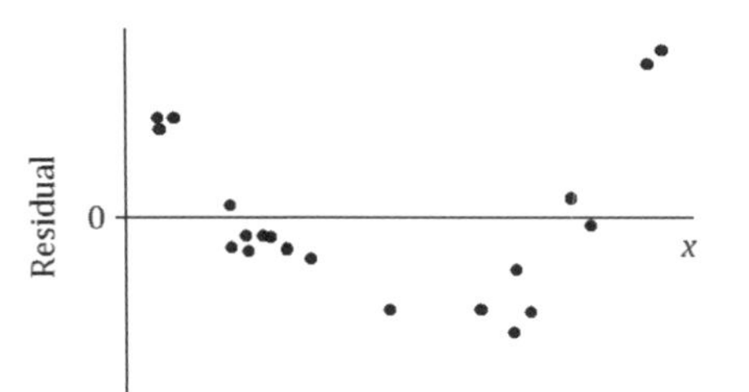

   There is a nonlinear relationship between the variables in the original data set.

2. **Suppose that after fitting a line, a data set produces the residual plot shown below.**

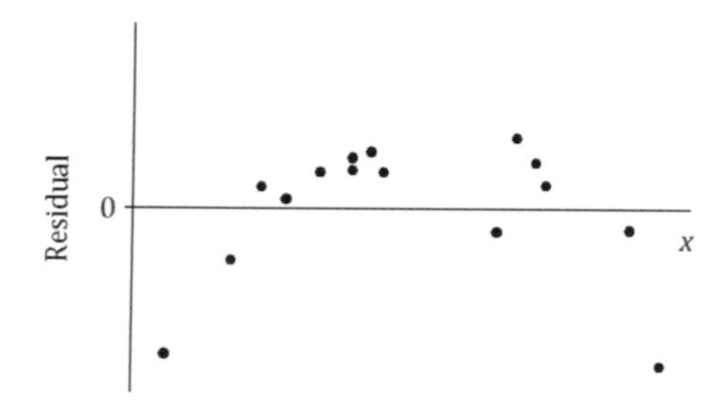

An incomplete scatter plot of the original data set is shown below. The least squares line is shown, but the points in the scatter plot have been erased. Estimate the locations of the original points, and create an approximation of the scatter plot below.

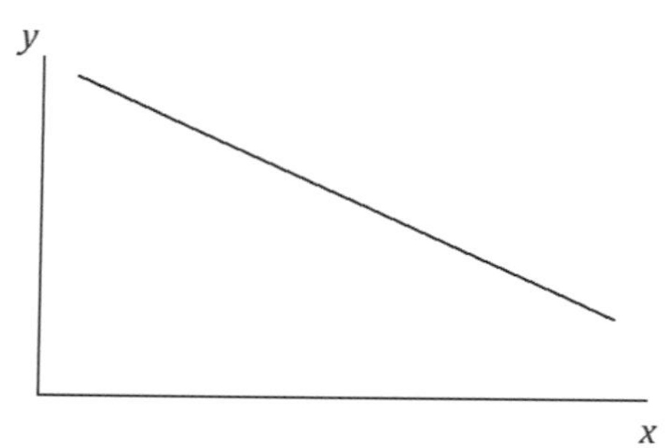

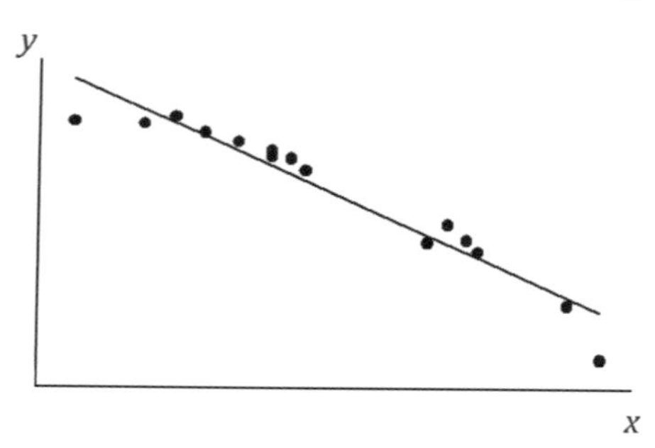

This problem should challenge students. There are many correct answers. Students should show points in the scatter plot whose vertical deviations from the given least squares line are in proportion to the values of the residuals in the residual plot. A student's answer is only acceptable if it shows a general pattern like the one shown above. Confirm that each student's points could result in (approximately) the given least squares line.

Lesson 19: Interpreting Correlation

Student Outcomes

- Students use technology to determine the value of the correlation coefficient for a given data set.
- Students interpret the value of the correlation coefficient as a measure of strength and direction of a linear relationship.
- Students explain why correlation does not imply causation.

Lesson Notes

This lesson introduces students to the correlation coefficient, a measure of the strength of a linear relationship between two numerical values. The focus of this lesson is on what the correlation coefficient (generally identified as r) tells us about the relationship between two numerical variables. Students use technology to determine the value of the correlation coefficient, or r. Instructions are provided in the teacher notes for using TI-83/84 graphing calculators. The instructions can be printed and distributed to students during the lesson.

It is important that whenever students evaluate whether or not two variables have a linear relationship, they do not interpret the correlation as causation. This lesson addresses several examples in which a correlation is noted, but the correlation does not indicate causation.

This lesson concludes the new content for the Algebra I statistics module. In the last lesson, students are expected to summarize at least one of the examples or exercises developed in this module in a poster or a class presentation. Students complete their current study of the fit of a linear model by using technology to interpret the correlation coefficient as an indication of the strength and direction of a linear relationship.

This is an extensive lesson. Several examples are provided to address varying strengths of linearity, along with positive and negative linear relationships. Students use technology, summary tables, and graphs to answer the questions. If it is a challenge to address the entire lesson in one class period, teachers should select problems that cover varying examples of the linear relationship between two variables. It may be necessary to spend more than one class period on this lesson.

It is not necessary for students to compute the correlation coefficient by hand, but if they want to know how this is done, you can share the formula for the correlation coefficient given below.

$$r = \frac{\sum(x - \bar{x})}{\sqrt{\sum(x - \bar{x})^2}\,\sqrt{\sum(y - \bar{y})^2}}$$

Classwork

Example 1 (2 minutes): Positive and Negative Linear Relationships

Read through Example 1 with students.

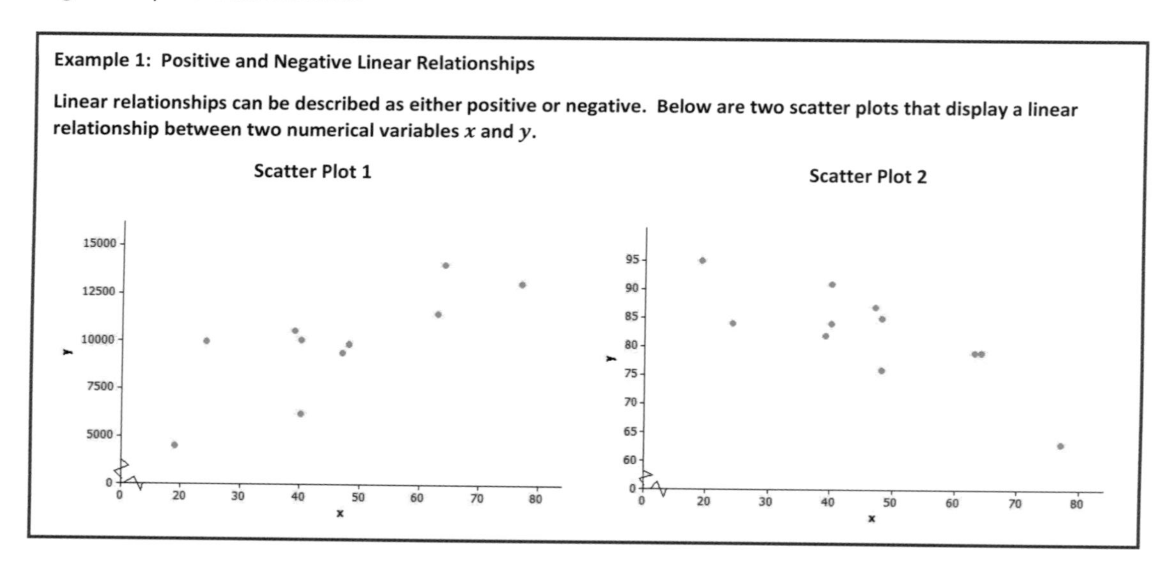

Example 1: Positive and Negative Linear Relationships

Linear relationships can be described as either positive or negative. Below are two scatter plots that display a linear relationship between two numerical variables x and y.

Exercises 1–4 (4 minutes)

Discuss and confirm Exercises 1–4 as a class.

Exercises 1–4

1. **The relationship displayed in Scatter Plot 1 is a positive linear relationship. Does the value of the y-variable tend to increase or decrease as the value of x increases? If you were to describe this relationship using a line, would the line have a positive or negative slope?**

   Increase; positive slope

2. **The relationship displayed in Scatter Plot 2 is a negative linear relationship. As the value of one of the variables increases, what happens to the value of the other variable? If you were to describe this relationship using a line, would the line have a positive or negative slope?**

   The other variable decreases; negative slope

3. **What does it mean to say that there is a positive linear relationship between two variables?**

   A positive linear relationship indicates that as the values of one variable increase, the values of the other variable also tend to increase.

4. **What does it mean to say that there is a negative linear relationship between two variables?**

   A negative linear relationship indicates that as the values of one variable increase, the values of the other variable tend to decrease.

Example 2 (2 minutes): Some Linear Relationships Are Stronger than Others

Introduce the scatter plots in the example. Ask students:

- In your opinion, which plot has a stronger linear relationship?

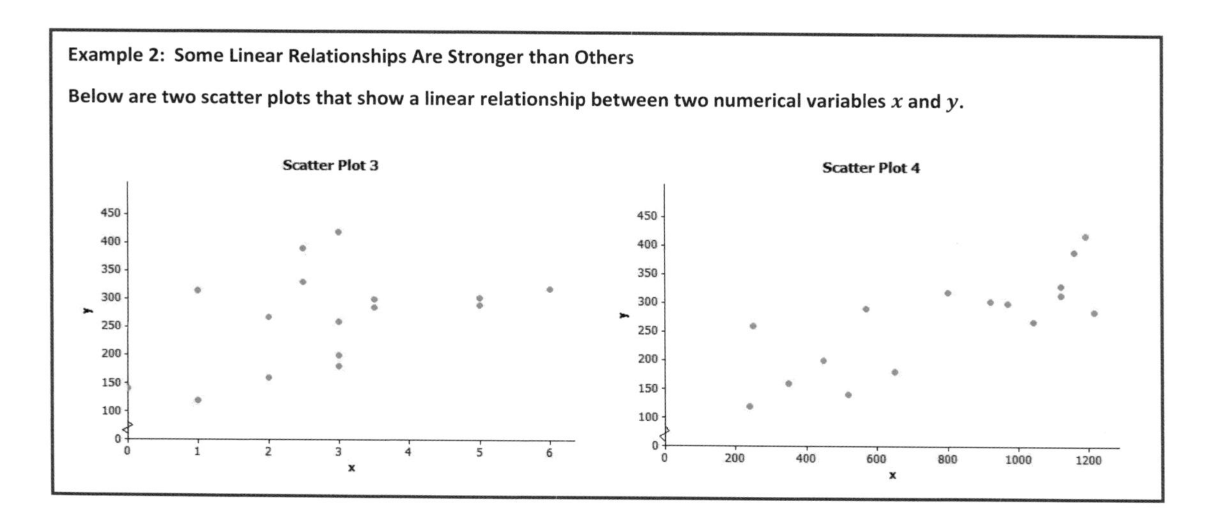

Exercises 5–9 (4 minutes)

Let students work independently on Exercises 5–9. Then confirm as a class.

Exercises 5–9

5. **Is the linear relationship in Scatter Plot 3 positive or negative?**

   Expect students to comment that this scatter plot is not as clear-cut as the previous examples. In general, there are more points in the scatter plot that describe a positive relationship.

6. **Is the linear relationship in Scatter Plot 4 positive or negative?**

   This scatter plot also indicates a positive relationship. For most of the points, students note that as the x-values increase, the y-values also tend to increase.

Discuss Exercises 7–9 as a class. Allow for multiple responses.

It is also common to describe the strength of a linear relationship. We would say that the linear relationship in Scatter Plot 3 is weaker than the linear relationship in Scatter Plot 4.

7. **Why do you think the linear relationship in Scatter Plot 3 is considered weaker than the linear relationship in Scatter Plot 4?**

   Students should comment on the general scatter of the points. The points in Scatter Plot 3 are more scattered and do not cluster tightly around a line, while in Scatter Plot 4, the points conform more closely to a line.

8. **What do you think a scatter plot with the strongest possible linear relationship might look like if it is a positive relationship? Draw a scatter plot with five points that illustrates this.**

   A scatter plot that has all of the points on a line with a positive slope indicates the strongest possible positive linear relationship. Students should draw points that form a line with a positive slope. See example below.

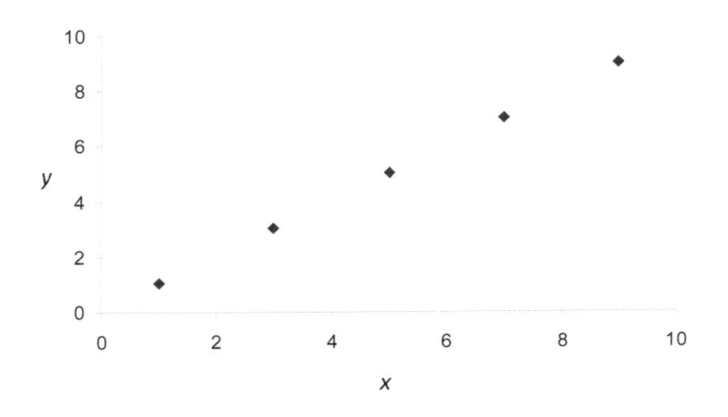

9. **How would a scatter plot that shows the strongest possible linear relationship that is negative look different from the scatter plot that you drew in the previous question?**

   A scatter plot with the strongest possible negative linear relationship would be one in which all of the points are on a line with a negative slope. This line has a negative slope, while the line drawn in Exercise 8 would have a positive slope.

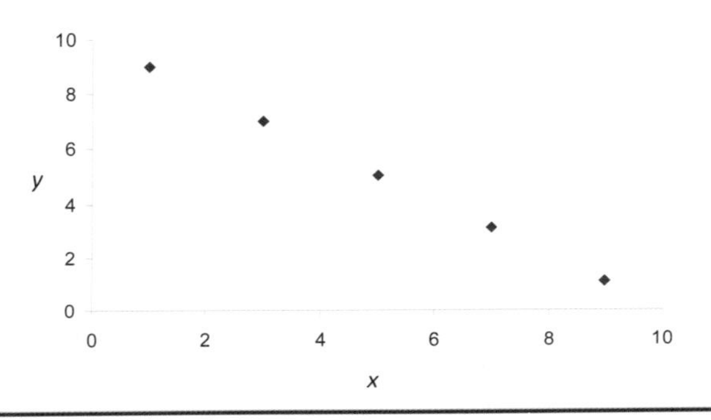

Exercises 10–12 (4 minutes): Strength of Linear Relationships

Let students work on Exercises 10–12 in small groups.

Exercises 10–12: Strength of Linear Relationships

10. **Consider the three scatter plots below. Place them in order from the one that shows the strongest linear relationship to the one that shows the weakest linear relationship.**

Strongest	→	Weakest
Scatter Plot 7	***Scatter Plot 6***	***Scatter Plot 5***

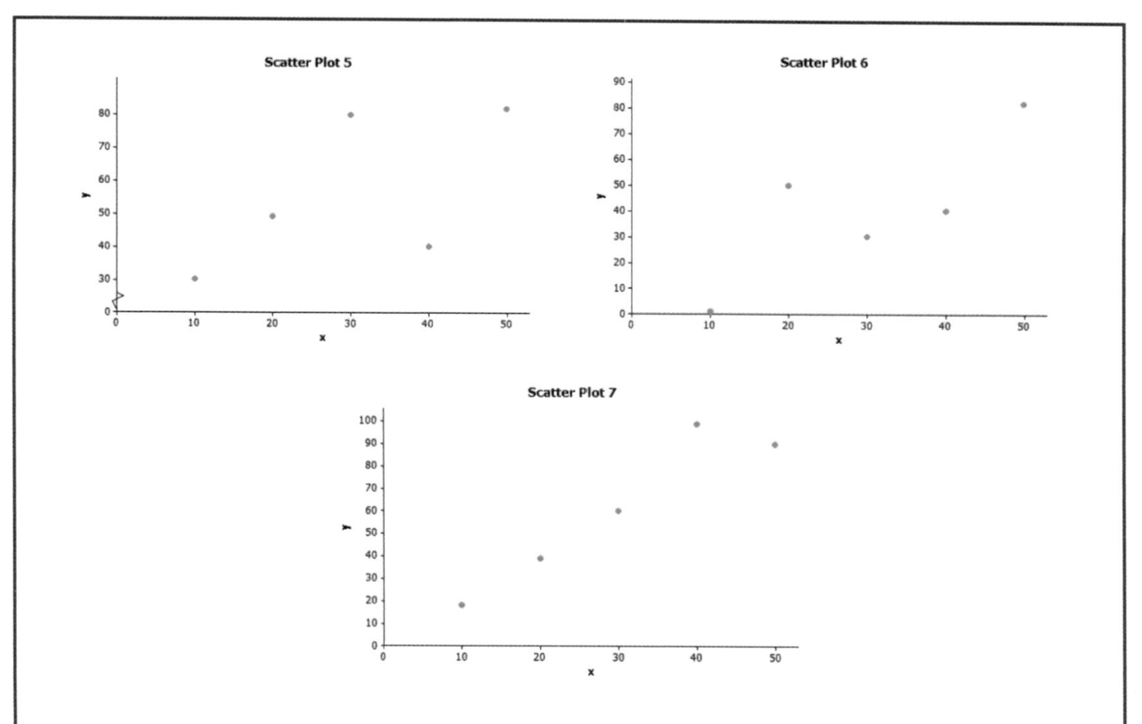

11. Explain your reasoning for choosing the order in Exercise 10.

Students should imagine there is a least squares line in each plot. The strongest linear relationship has the smallest sum of the squares of the residuals while the weakest linear relationship has the largest sum of the squares of the residuals.

12. Which of the following two scatter plots shows the stronger linear relationship? (Think carefully about this one!)

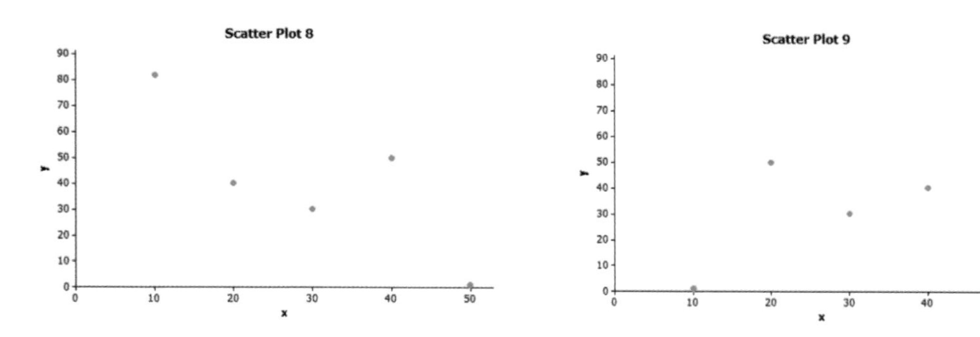

The strength of the linear relationship is actually the same for each of these examples. The difference in the scatter plots, however, is that Scatter Plot 8 indicates a negative linear relationship, and Scatter Plot 9 indicates a positive relationship. (Note that it is important to discuss this response with students if the question is not answered correctly.)

Example 3 (4 minutes): The Correlation Coefficient

MP.1 Analyze the scatter plots and *correlation coefficients* as a class. Ask the following as students view the plots:

- Is there a positive or negative relationship?
- Is the relationship strong or weak?

Example 3: The Correlation Coefficient

The *correlation coefficient* is a number between -1 and $+1$ (including -1 and $+1$) that measures the strength and direction of a linear relationship. The correlation coefficient is denoted by the letter r.

Several scatter plots are shown below. The value of the correlation coefficient for the data displayed in each plot is also given.

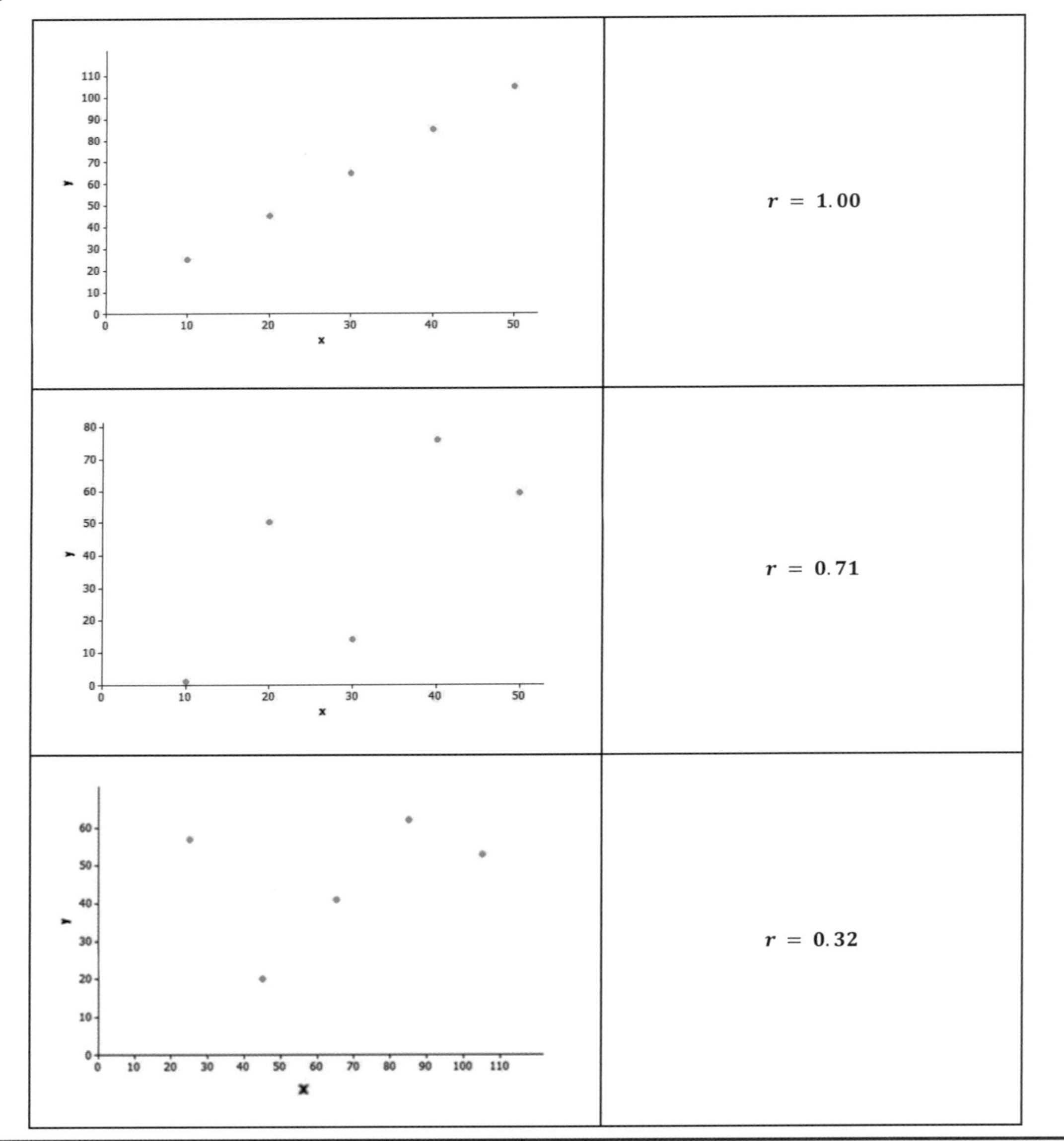

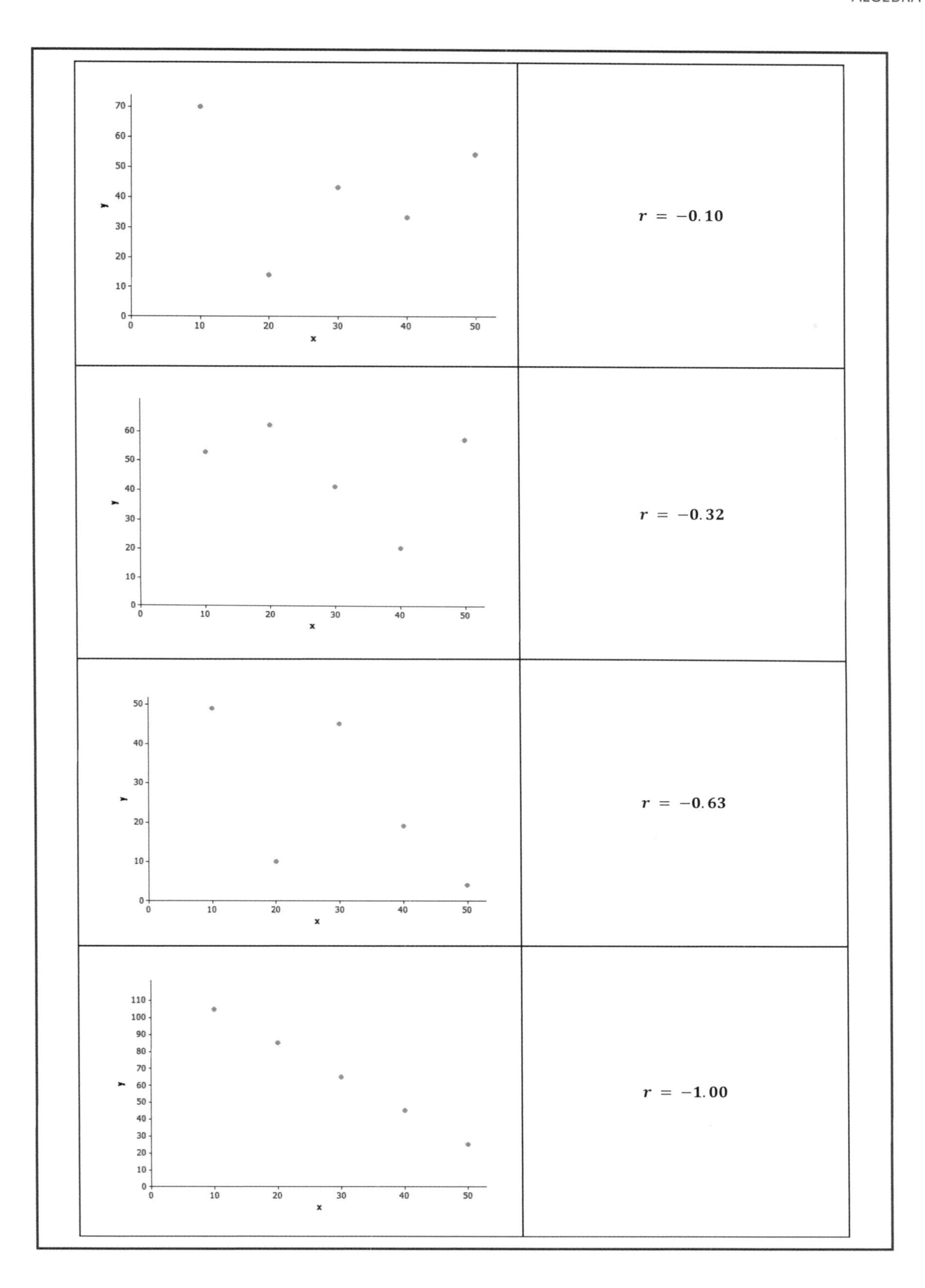

x
y
$r = -0.10$
$r = -0.32$
$r = -0.63$
$r = -1.00$

Exercises 13–15 (4 minutes)

Discuss Exercises 13–15 as a class.

Exercises 13–15

13. **When is the value of the correlation coefficient positive?**

    The correlation coefficient is positive when as the x-values increase, the y-values also tend to increase.

14. **When is the value of the correlation coefficient negative?**

    The correlation coefficient is negative when as the x-values increase, the y-values tend to decrease.

15. **Is the linear relationship stronger when the correlation coefficient is closer to 0 or to 1 (or -1)?**

    As the points form a stronger negative or positive linear relationship, the correlation coefficient gets farther from 0. Students note that when all of the points are on a line with a positive slope, the correlation coefficient is $+1$. The correlation coefficient is -1 if all of the points are on a line with a negative slope.

Discuss the properties of the correlation coefficient with students. Find connections between the questions in this example and those properties.

Looking at the scatter plots in Example 4, you should have discovered the following properties of the correlation coefficient:

Property 1: **The sign of r (positive or negative) corresponds to the direction of the linear relationship.**

Property 2: **A value of $r = +1$ indicates a perfect positive linear relationship, with all points in the scatter plot falling exactly on a straight line.**

Property 3: **A value of $r = -1$ indicates a perfect negative linear relationship, with all points in the scatter plot falling exactly on a straight line.**

Property 4: **The closer the value of r is to $+1$ or -1, the stronger the linear relationship.**

Example 4 (4 minutes): Calculating the Value of the Correlation Coefficient

Explain to students that they will be using technology to calculate the correlation coefficient. Show students the steps for finding the correlation coefficient (r) by using whatever graphing calculator or statistical software is available to them. The following steps are included for a TI-84 Plus calculator. (These steps should be similar for other graphing calculators or statistics software, as well.) For this type of calculator, the diagnostics must be turned on. The value of r^2 displayed may be unfamiliar to students. At this point, indicate to students that the role of r^2 will be addressed in future statistics modules when they study the actual calculation of r and r^2.

Steps for calculating the correlation coefficient using a TI-84 Plus:

1. Determine which variable represents x and which variable represents y based on x- and y-variable designations.
2. From the home screen, select STAT.
3. Click ENTER from the Edit option of the menu.
4. Enter the values of x in L1 and the values of y in L2.
5. When complete, enter 2ND QUIT.
6. Select STAT.
7. With the arrows, move the top cursor over to the option CALC and move the down cursor to 8: LinReg($a + bx$), and then click ENTER.
8. With LinReg($a + bx$) on the screen, enter L1, L2 and then ENTER.
9. The value of r, the correlation coefficient, should appear on the screen.

Example 4: Calculating the Value of the Correlation Coefficient

There is an equation that can be used to calculate the value of the correlation coefficient given data on two numerical variables. Using this formula requires a lot of tedious calculations that are discussed in later grades. Fortunately, a graphing calculator can be used to find the value of the correlation coefficient once you have entered the data.

Your teacher will show you how to enter data and how to use a graphing calculator to obtain the value of the correlation coefficient.

Here is the data from a previous lesson on shoe length in inches and height in inches for 10 men.

x (Shoe Length) inches	y (Height) inches
12.6	74
11.8	65
12.2	71
11.6	67
12.2	69
11.4	68
12.8	70
12.2	69
12.6	72
11.8	71

Exercises 16–17 (3 minutes)

Let students work independently on Exercises 16–17 and confirm answers with a neighbor. Assist students having difficulty with their calculators.

Exercises 16–17

16. **Enter the shoe length and height data in your calculator. Find the value of the correlation coefficient between shoe length and height. Round to the nearest tenth.**

Although it is not required to answer this question, you could encourage students to also examine the scatter plot of the data. The correlation coefficient is $r \approx 0.6$.

The table below shows how you can informally interpret the value of a correlation coefficient.

If the value of the correlation coefficient is between ...	You can say that ...
$r = 1.0$	There is a perfect positive linear relationship.
$0.7 \leq r < 1.0$	There is a strong positive linear relationship.
$0.3 \leq r < 0.7$	There is a moderate positive linear relationship.
$0 < r < 0.3$	There is a weak positive linear relationship.
$r = 0$	There is no linear relationship.
$-0.3 < r < 0$	There is a weak negative linear relationship.
$-0.7 < r \leq -0.3$	There is a moderate negative linear relationship.
$-1.0 < r \leq -0.7$	There is a strong negative linear relationship.
$r = -1.0$	There is a perfect negative linear relationship.

17. **Interpret the value of the correlation coefficient between shoe length and height for the data given above.**

Based on the table, there is a moderate positive linear relationship. Connecting this to the scatter plot provides an example of a moderate positive linear relationship.

Exercises 18–24 (6 minutes): Practice Calculating and Interpreting Correlation Coefficients

Let students work in small groups on Exercises 18–24.

Exercises 18–24: Practice Calculating and Interpreting Correlation Coefficients

Consumer Reports **published a study of fast-food items. The table and scatter plot below display the fat content (in grams) and number of calories per serving for 16 fast-food items.**

Fat (g)	Calories (kcal)
2	268
5	303
3	260
3.5	300
1	315
2	160
3	200
6	320
3	420
5	290
3.5	285
2.5	390
0	140
2.5	330
1	120
3	180

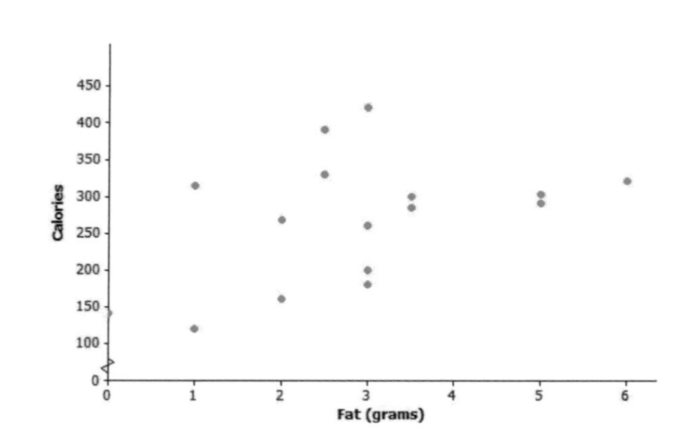

Data Source: ***Consumer Reports***

18. Based on the scatter plot, do you think that the value of the correlation coefficient between fat content and calories per serving will be positive or negative? Explain why you made this choice.

Positive; the general pattern is that as the fat content increases, the number of calories tends to increase.

19. Based on the scatter plot, estimate the value of the correlation coefficient between fat content and calories.

The scatter plot appears to have a positive correlation coefficient, but it also does not appear to be a strong relationship. As a result, students would indicate a moderate positive linear relationship and might predict a value between 0.3 *and* 0.7*.*

20. Calculate the value of the correlation coefficient between fat content and calories per serving. Round to the nearest hundredth. Interpret this value.

The correlation coefficient is $r \approx 0.44$*. It indicates a moderate positive linear relationship.*

The *Consumer Reports* study also collected data on sodium content (in mg) and number of calories per serving for the same 16 fast food items. The data is represented in the table and scatter plot below.

Sodium (mg)	Calories (kcal)
$1,042$	268
921	303
250	260
970	300
$1,120$	315
350	160
450	200
800	320
$1,190$	420
570	290
$1,215$	285
$1,160$	390
520	140
$1,120$	330
240	120
650	180

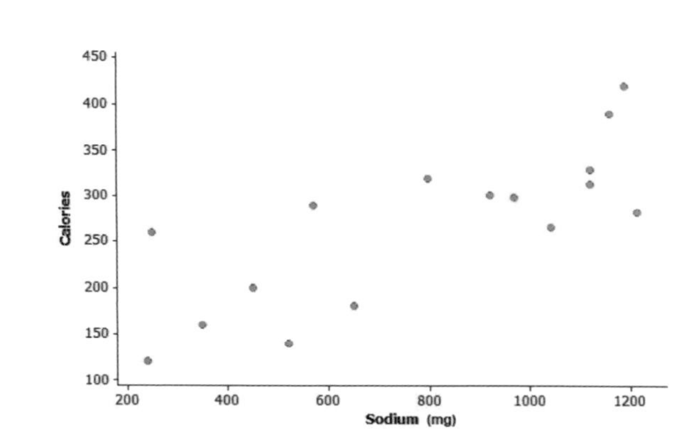

Data Source: *Consumer Reports*

21. Based on the scatter plot, do you think that the value of the correlation coefficient between sodium content and calories per serving will be positive or negative? Explain why you made this choice.

Positive; as the sodium content increases, the number of calories tends to increase.

22. Based on the scatter plot, estimate the value of the correlation coefficient between sodium content and calories per serving.

This relationship appears to be stronger than the previous example. An estimate of the correlation coefficient is between 0.7 *and* 1.0*.*

23. Calculate the value of the correlation coefficient between sodium content and calories per serving. Round to the nearest hundredth. Interpret this value.

The correlation coefficient is $r \approx 0.79$*. By the table, this indicates a strong positive linear relationship between sodium content and calories.*

> **24. For these 16 fast-food items, is the linear relationship between fat content and number of calories stronger or weaker than the linear relationship between sodium content and number of calories? Does this surprise you? Explain why or why not.**
>
> ***The linear relationship is stronger for the sodium content and calories. Answers will vary as to whether or not this would surprise a student. It is anticipated that many students would think the fat was more strongly correlated to the number of calories. A summary to help explain this is provided in the next example.***

If there is enough time, ask students:

- Is there a connection between the slope of the least squares line and the value of the correlation coefficient, or r? If yes, what is the connection?
  - *There is a connection regarding the sign of r (the correlation coefficient) and the sign of the slope if there is a linear relationship. If the least squares line is increasing, the slope is positive, and the value of the correlation coefficient, or r, is positive. If the least squares line is decreasing, then the slope is negative, and the value of the correlation coefficient is negative.*
- Why is it important to know if a relationship is strong or weak?
  - *If a relationship is strong, then the data are close to the line, and the equation of the line can be used to predict values. If the relationship is weak, then the equation cannot be used as easily to predict values.*

Example 5 (4 minutes): Correlation Does Not Mean There is a Cause-and-Effect Relationship Between Variables

Students have a difficult time separating the concepts of correlation and causation. It is important to develop clear examples of causation for students to understand the difference.

Discuss the example provided in the text. This example shows the distinction between correlation and causation. Some students may see correlation as indicating a cause-and-effect relationship; therefore, it is important to teach them how to distinguish between the two (**S-ID.C.9**).

> **Example 5: Correlation Does Not Mean There is a Cause-and-Effect Relationship Between Variables**
>
> **It is sometimes tempting to conclude that if there is a strong linear relationship between two variables that one variable is causing the value of the other variable to increase or decrease. But you should avoid making this mistake. When there is a strong linear relationship, it means that the two variables tend to vary together in a predictable way, which might be due to something other than a cause-and-effect relationship.**
>
> **For example, the value of the correlation coefficient between sodium content and number of calories for the fast food items in the previous example was $r = 0.79$, indicating a strong positive relationship. This means that the items with higher sodium content tend to have a higher number of calories. But the high number of calories is not caused by the high sodium content. In fact, sodium does not have any calories. What may be happening is that food items with high sodium content also may be the items that are high in sugar or fat, and this is the reason for the higher number of calories in these items.**
>
> **Similarly, there is a strong positive correlation between shoe size and reading ability in children. But it would be silly to think that having big feet causes children to read better. It just means that the two variables vary together in a predictable way. Can you think of a reason that might explain why children with larger feet also tend to score higher on reading tests?**

Read through the last paragraph in the example and pose the question to students:

- Can you think of a reason that might explain why children with larger feet also tend to score higher on reading tests?
  - *As children get older, reading ability also tends to increase.*

If students need more examples, discuss whether or not the following display a cause-and-effect relationship:

- As the amount of time spent studying increases, so do SAT scores.
  - *This is an example that is not a cause-and-effect relationship. Although the time of study might be associated to the SAT scores, the data are not collected from a statistical study that would investigate cause-and-effect. This should provoke an interesting discussion. While it could be argued that studying causes scores to increase, undoubtedly some do well without studying, and some may study a lot and still score poorly.*
- As the temperature increases in Florida, so do the number of shark attacks.
  - *This may not be a cause-and-effect relationship because the temperature is not* causing *the sharks to attack people.*

Closing (1 minute)

> Lesson Summary
>
> - **Linear relationships are often described in terms of strength and direction.**
> - **The correlation coefficient is a measure of the strength and direction of a linear relationship.**
> - **The closer the value of the correlation coefficient is to $+1$ or -1, the stronger the linear relationship.**
> - **Just because there is a strong correlation between the two variables does not mean there is a cause-and-effect relationship.**

Exit Ticket (3 minutes)

Name ______________________________ Date ______________

Lesson 19: Interpreting Correlation

Exit Ticket

The scatter plot below displays data on the number of defects per 100 cars and a measure of customer satisfaction (on a scale from 1 to 1,000, with higher scores indicating greater satisfaction) for the 33 brands of cars sold in the United States in 2009.

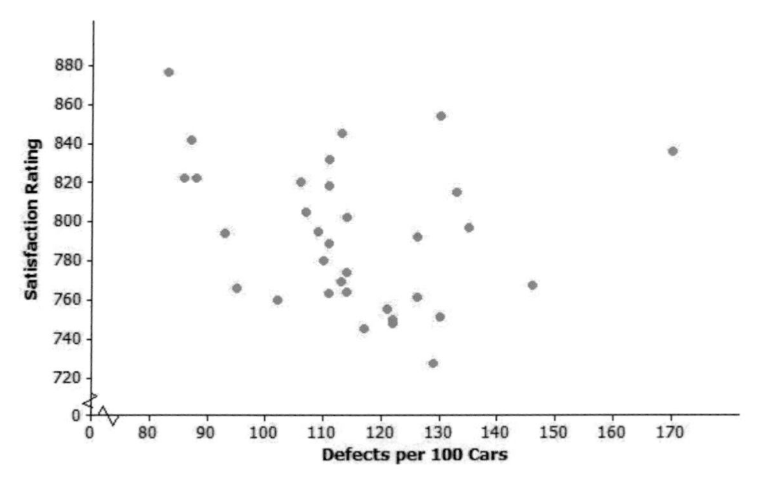

Data Source: *USA Today*, June 16, 2010 and July 17, 2010

a. Which of the following is the value of the correlation coefficient for this data set: $r = -0.95$, $r = -0.24$, $r = 0.83$, or $r = 1.00$?

b. Explain why you selected this value.

Exit Ticket Sample Solutions

The scatter plot below displays data on the number of defects per 100 cars and a measure of customer satisfaction (on a scale from 1 to $1,000$, with higher scores indicating greater satisfaction) for the 33 brands of cars sold in the United States in 2009.

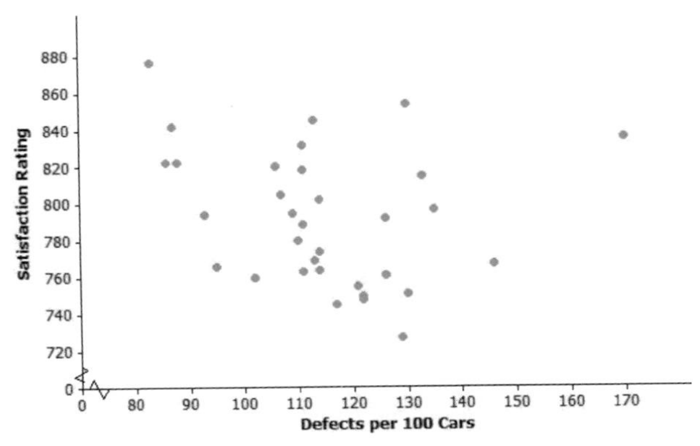

Data Source: *USA Today*, June 16, 2010 and July 17, 2010

a. Which of the following is the value of the correlation coefficient for this data set: $r = -0.95$, $r = -0.24$, $r = 0.83$, or $r = 1.00$?

$r = -0.24$

b. Explain why you selected this value.

Students' answers should indicate that there is not a strong pattern of a linear relationship with this scatter plot. Students may struggle with an explanation based on weak relationship; however, there is a general pattern that as the number of defects increase, the satisfaction rating tends to decrease. As a result, students would estimate a weak negative association or a negative value of r close to zero. Based on the values provided, students would estimate $r = -0.24$.

Problem Set Sample Solutions

1. Which of the three scatter plots below shows the strongest linear relationship? Which shows the weakest linear relationship?

The strongest linear relationship would be Scatter Plot 3. The weakest linear relationship would be Scatter Plot 2.

Scatter Plot 1 | Scatter Plot 2 | Scatter Plot 3

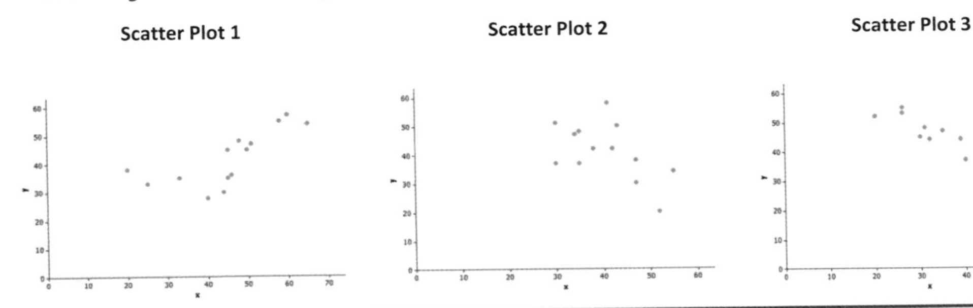

2. *Consumer Reports* published data on the price (in dollars) and quality rating (on a scale of 0 to 100) for 10 different brands of men's athletic shoes.

Price (\$)	Quality Rating
65	71
45	70
45	62
80	59
110	58
110	57
30	56
80	52
110	51
70	51

a. Construct a scatter plot of these data using the grid provided.

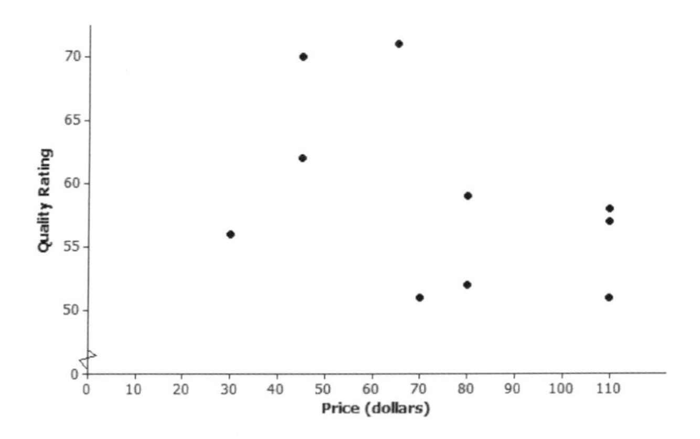

b. Calculate the value of the correlation coefficient between price and quality rating, and interpret this value. Round to the nearest hundredth.

The correlation coefficient is $r \approx -0.42$, using a TI-84. This indicates a moderate negative relationship between price and quality rating. It indicates that as the price increases, quality rating tends to decrease.

c. Does it surprise you that the value of the correlation coefficient is negative? Explain why or why not.

It is anticipated that students will be surprised by this relationship. Students might think that as the price increases, the quality rating increases.

d. Is it reasonable to conclude that higher-priced shoes are higher quality? Explain.

Based on this data, you would not necessarily assume that as the price increases, the quality tends to increase.

e. The correlation between price and quality rating is negative. Is it reasonable to conclude that increasing the price causes a decrease in quality rating? Explain.

No, just because there is a correlation between two variables does not mean that there is a cause-and-effect relationship between the two.

3. *The Princeton Review* publishes information about colleges and universities. The data below are for six public 4-year colleges in New York. Graduation rate is the percentage of students who graduate within six years. Student-to-faculty ratio is the number of students per full-time faculty member.

School	Number of Full-Time Students	Student-to-Faculty Ratio	Graduation Rate
CUNY Bernard M. Baruch College	$11,477$	17	63
CUNY Brooklyn College	$9,876$	15.3	48
CUNY City College	$10,047$	13.1	40
SUNY at Albany	$14,013$	19.5	64
SUNY at Binghamton	$13,031$	20	77
SUNY College at Buffalo	$9,398$	14.1	47

a. Calculate the value of the correlation coefficient between the number of full-time students and graduation rate. Round to the nearest hundredth.

Let x represent the number of full-time students and y represent the graduation rate. The correlation coefficient is $r \approx 0.83$, using a TI-84.

b. Is the linear relationship between graduation rate and number of full-time students weak, moderate, or strong? On what did you base your decision?

Based on the table presented in the lesson, the linear relationship between graduation rate and the number of full-time students is strong.

c. Is the following statement true or false? Based on the value of the correlation coefficient, it is reasonable to conclude that having a larger number of students at a school is the cause of a higher graduation rate.

False; it is not reasonable to assume a cause-and-effect. There are other factors that might also contribute to higher graduation rates, including the student-to-faculty ratio and admission standards of the school.

d. Calculate the value of the correlation coefficient between the student-to-faculty ratio and the graduation rate. Round to the nearest hundredth.

Let x represent the student-to-faculty ratio and y represent the graduation rate. The correlation coefficient is $r \approx 0.95$, using a TI-84.

e. Which linear relationship is stronger: graduation rate and number of full-time students or graduation rate and student-to-faculty ratio? Justify your choice.

The stronger relationship is between graduation rate and student-to-faculty ratio. The correlation coefficient is greater in this case.

Lesson 20: Analyzing Data Collected on Two Variables

Student Outcomes

- Students use data to develop a poster that involves the focus standards.
- Students construct a scatter plot of the data.
- Students analyze their data, examine the residual plot, and interpret the correlation coefficient.

Lesson Notes

This lesson provides an opportunity to integrate the methods presented in Lessons 12–19. In this lesson, students develop a poster to explore the relationship between two numerical variables. This lesson directs students to select one of the data sets introduced in Lessons 12–19 and to summarize how well the data fit a specific model. Encourage students who may have struggled with this process to select of one of the linear relationships because understanding linearity provides the basis for understanding other models.

Teachers must decide the following prior to the lesson:

- What is the format of the poster or presentation?
  - Creating posters may require supplies, such as poster board and markers. Large sticky notes could also work for the posters. Teachers may prefer to have students create a short presentation using presentation software. Or, teachers may want students to develop the posters in small groups or individually.
- How will the presentation be evaluated?
  - A well-defined rubric is recommended; an example is available at the following location: www.amstat.org/education/posterprojects/index.cfm.
- As rubric designs are highly dependent on the process used to complete this type of presentation, the final rubric design is the teacher's decision. To assess the poster or presentation, teachers should look at how well students addressed the following: the statistical question of how the variables presented are related, the scatter plot and the fit of a possible function to the data, an explanation of the selected model, and an answer to the statistical question.

Classwork

Read through the introductory paragraph with students. The poster or presentation addresses numerical variables.

Lessons 12–19 included several data sets to learn about how two numerical variables might be related. Recall the data on elevation above sea level and the number of clear days per year for 14 cities in the United States. Could a city's elevation above sea level be used to predict the number of clear days per year a city experiences? After observing a scatter plot of the data, a linear model (or the least squares linear model obtained from a calculator or computer software) provided a reasonable description of the relationship between these two variables. This linear model was evaluated by considering how close the data points were to the corresponding graph of the line. The equation of the linear model was used to answer the statistical question about elevation and the number of clear days.

Several data sets were also provided to illustrate other possible models, specifically quadratic and exponential models. Finding a model that describes the relationship between two variables allows you to answer statistical questions about how the two numerical variables vary. For example, the following statistical question was posed in Lesson 13 regarding latitude and the mean number of flycatcher chicks in a nest: What latitude is best for hatching flycatcher chicks? A quadratic model of the latitude and the mean number of flycatcher chicks in a nest was used to answer this statistical question.

In Lessons 12–19, you worked with several data sets and models used to answer statistical questions. Select one of the data sets presented in Lessons 12–19, and develop a poster that summarizes how a statistical question is answered that involves two numerical variables. Your poster should include the following: a brief summary of the data, the statistical question asking the relationship between two numerical variables, a scatter plot of the data, and a brief summary to indicate how well the data fit a specific model.

After you identify one of the problems to summarize with a poster, consider the following questions to plan your poster:

1. What two variables were involved in this problem?

2. What was the statistical question? Remember, a statistical question involves data. The question also anticipates that the data will vary.

3. What model was used to describe the relationship between the two variables?

4. Based on the scatter plot of the data, was the model a good one?

5. Was the residual plot used to evaluate the model? What did the residual plot indicate about the model?

6. How would you use the model to predict values not included in the data set?

7. Does the model answer the statistical question posed?

Examples of posters involving two numerical variables can be found at the website of the American Statistical Association (www.amstat.org/education/posterprojects/index.cfm).

Ask students:

- What is the difference between categorical and numerical variables? (This question reminds students that they are not selecting a data set that was summarized by a two-way frequency table.)

Recall with students some of the examples of models from Lessons 12–19 that would be excellent problems to summarize in a poster. The opening paragraphs in the student lesson refer to elevation of a city and the mean number of clear days, as well as latitude and the number of chicks in a nest from Lesson 13. Additional examples:

- Shoe length and height (Lesson 14 Example)
- Animal gestation time and longevity (Lesson 15 Example)
- Time and cost of surgery (Lesson 15 Problem Set)
- Curb weight and fuel efficiency (Lesson 16 Example)
- Athlete track times (Lesson 16 Problem Set)
- Temperature and volume (Lesson 18 Exercise)

Organize students in small groups to select one of the models from Lessons 12–19 for their presentation. Explain the chosen format for the presentation (poster, presentation software). Also explain whether students should develop their posters in small groups or if they are expected to develop the posters individually. The poster or presentation should include a statistical question, a scatter plot, and an evaluation that indicates how well the data fits the model. Use the seven questions in the lesson as a guide for helping students organize their presentations.

As students are working, walk around and ask the following:

- (1) What two variables are you studying? Why do you think the model connects the two variables?
  - *Students should define their variables based on the data set they selected.*
- (2) What is the statistical question you would like to answer?
  - *Again, have students reflect on the data. Ask them to describe the context that is connected to the data, possibly indicating how it might have been collected. Also ask them to indicate why the data may vary.*
- (3) How does the model describe the relationship between the two variables?
  - *Encourage students to talk about the trend: linear, quadratic, or exponential. If linear, what is the meaning of the slope and y-intercept within the context of the problem?*

- (4) Is the model appropriate based on a scatter plot of the data?
  - *Encourage students to talk about the trend: linear, quadratic, or exponential. Students should also discuss estimates of residuals and how close the points are to the graph of the least squares line.*
- (5) How are you evaluating the model selected for the data?
  - *Students can use residual plots or correlation coefficients to justify the strength and appropriateness of the model.*
- (6) What predictions could you make from the model of the relationship between the two variables?
  - *Examples from the lessons include:*

    What is the estimated age of a lobster with an exterior shell length of 75 mm *or less?*

    What elevations above sea level are predicted to have at least 100 *clear days per year?*

If time permits, organize a display of the posters. Encourage students to explain their posters to other students or to the entire class.

Name ______________________________ Date ______________

1. A recent social survey asked 654 men and 813 women to indicate how many close friends they have to talk about important issues in their lives. Below are frequency tables of the responses.

Number of Close Friends	0	1	2	3	4	5	6	Total
Males	196	135	108	100	42	40	33	654
Females	201	146	155	132	86	56	37	813

a. The shape of the distribution of the number of close friends for the males is best characterized as

A. Skewed to the higher values (i.e., right or positively skewed).
B. Skewed to the lower values (i.e., left or negatively skewed).
C. Symmetric.

b. Calculate the median number of close friends for the females. Show your work.

c. Do you expect the mean number of close friends for the females to be larger or smaller than the median you found in part (b), or do you expect them to be the same? Explain your choice.

d. Do you expect the mean number of close friends for the males to be larger or smaller than the mean number of close friends for the females, or do you expect them to be the same? Explain your choice.

2. The physician's health study examined whether physicians who took aspirin were less likely to have heart attacks than those who took a placebo (fake) treatment. The table below shows their findings.

	Placebo	Aspirin	Total
Heart Attack	189	104	293
No Heart Attack	10,845	10,933	21,778
Total	11,034	11,037	22,071

Based on the data in the table, what conclusions can be drawn about the association between taking aspirin and whether or not a heart attack occurred? Justify your conclusion using the given data.

3. Suppose 500 high school students are asked the following two questions:

- What is the highest degree you plan to obtain? (check one)
  ☐ High school degree ☐ College (Bachelor's degree)
  ☐ Graduate school (e.g., Master's degree or higher)

- How many credit cards do you currently own? (check one)
  ☐ None ☐ One ☐ More than one

Consider the data shown in the following frequency table.

	No Credit Cards	One Credit Card	More Than One Credit Card	Total
High School	?		6	59
College	120	240	40	394
Graduate School				47
Total		297		500

Fill in the missing value in the cell in the table that is marked with a "?" so that the data would be consistent with no association between education aspiration and current number of credit cards for these students. Explain how you determined this value.

4. Weather data were recorded for a sample of 25 American cities in one year. Variables measured included January high temperature (in degrees Fahrenheit), January low temperature (in degrees Fahrenheit), annual precipitation (in inches), and annual snow accumulation. The relationships for three pairs of variables are shown in the graphs below (January Low Temperature—Graph A; Precipitation—Graph B; Annual Snow Accumulation—Graph C).

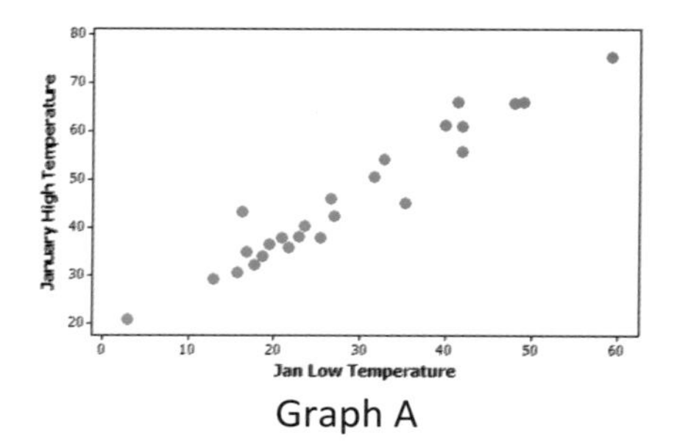

Graph A

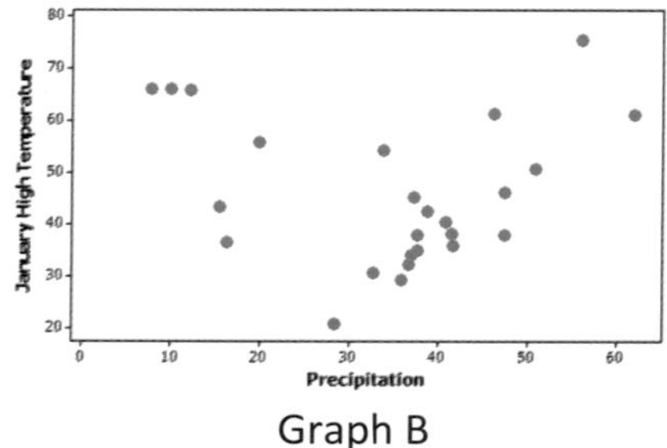

Graph B

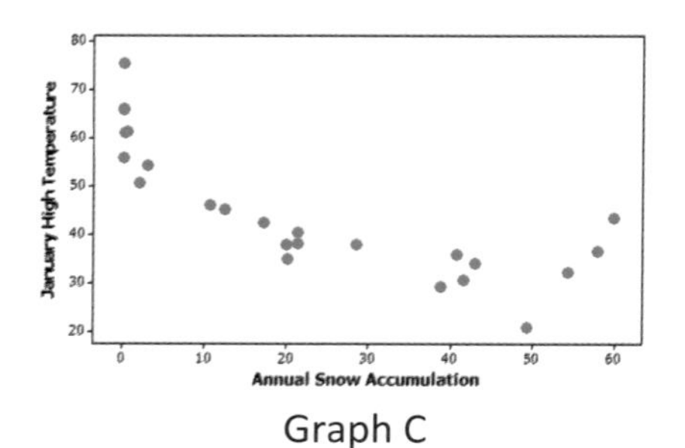

Graph C

a. Which pair of variables will have a correlation coefficient closest to 0?

A. January high temperature and January low temperature
B. January high temperature and precipitation
C. January high temperature and annual snow accumulation

Explain your choice:

b. Which of the above scatter plots would be best described as a strong nonlinear relationship? Explain your choice.

c. Suppose we fit a least squares regression line to Graph A. Circle one word choice for each blank that best completes this sentence based on the equation:

If I compare a city with a January low temperature of $30°\text{F}$ *to a city with a higher January low temperature, then the ___(1)___ January high temperature of the second city will ___(2)___ be ___(3)___.*

(1) actual, predicted

(2) probably, definitely

(3) lower, higher, the same, equally likely to be higher or lower

d. For the city with a January low temperature of $30°\text{F}$, what do you predict for the annual snow accumulation? Explain how you are estimating this based on the three graphs above.

5. Suppose times (in minutes) to run one mile were recorded for a sample of 100 runners ages 16–66 years, and the following least squares regression line was found.

   Predicted time in minutes to run one mile $= 5.35 + 0.25 \times (age)$

   a. Provide an interpretation in context for this slope coefficient.

   b. Explain what it would mean in the context of this study for a runner to have a negative residual.

c. Suppose, instead, that someone suggests using the following curve to predict time to run one mile. Explain what this model implies about the relationship between running time and age and why that relationship might make sense in this context.

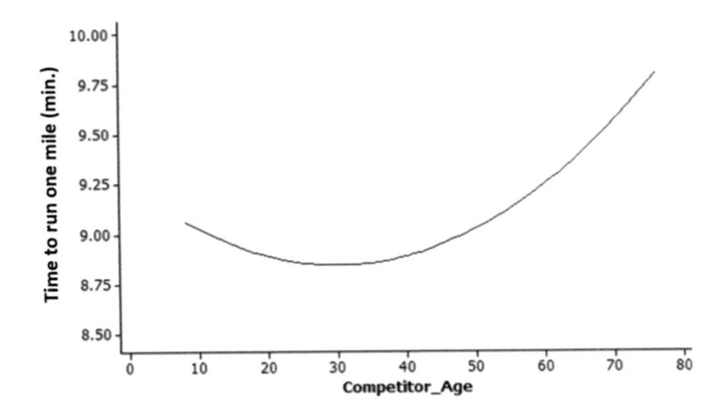

d. Based on the results for these 100 runners, explain how you could decide whether the first model or the second model provides a better fit to the data.

e. The sum of the residuals is always equal to zero for the least squares regression line. Which of the following must also always be equal to zero?

A. The mean of the residuals
B. The median of the residuals
C. Both the mean and the median of the residuals
D. Neither the mean nor the median of the residuals

A Progression Toward Mastery					
Assessment Task Item		STEP 1 Missing or incorrect answer and little evidence of reasoning or application of mathematics to solve the problem	STEP 2 Missing or incorrect answer but evidence of some reasoning or application of mathematics to solve the problem	STEP 3 A correct answer with some evidence of reasoning or application of mathematics to solve the problem, OR an incorrect answer with substantial evidence of solid reasoning or application of mathematics to solve the problem	STEP 4 A correct answer supported by substantial evidence of solid reasoning or application of mathematics to solve the problem
1	a S-ID.A.3	Student selects B or C.	N/A	N/A	Student selects A.
	b S-ID.A.2	Student focuses on the counts and not on the number of siblings.	Student calculates the correct location (407) but fails to convert that to a value. OR Student only finds the median of 0–6, ignoring the tally information.	Student provides a reasonable value (2) but does not clearly explain how it was found.	Student calculates the correct location (407) and then uses the tally information to find that number (2).
	c S-ID.A.3	Student does not make a clear choice or justification.	Student does not make a choice based on skewedness of the distribution.	Student makes a choice based on skewedness but fails to explain how the table provides information indicating that the female distribution is skewed to the right.	Student selects the mean to be larger based on the skewedness apparent in the distribution from the initial large counts, which decrease with number of friends.

	d **S-ID.A.3**	Student fails to compare the two distributions based on the table.	Student fails to use the frequency information in comparing the two distributions.	Student selects the females to have the higher mean based on the higher counts but does not consider the higher number of females (all frequencies are higher).	Student selects the females to have the higher mean based on the higher relative frequencies at the higher values (e.g., $\frac{86+56+37}{813} \approx 22\%$ vs. $\frac{42+40+33}{654} \approx 18\%$).
2	**S-ID.B.5**	Student does not address the association between the two variables.	Student focuses only on frequencies and not proportions.	Student appears to use appropriate conditional proportions but does not fully justify his or her approach.	Student uses appropriate conditional proportions (e.g., $\frac{189}{11034}$ vs. $\frac{104}{11037}$) to compare the two groups.
3	**S-ID.B.5**	Student does not complete the table.	Student fills in some values without enough justification to allow completion of the table.	Student understands the need to equalize the conditional distributions but is not able to perform the algebra to do so.	Student equates the conditional proportions across the columns or equates conditional proportions across rows.
4	**a** **S-ID.B.6** **S-ID.C.8**	Student does not make a consistent choice or give an explanation.	Student chooses C because of the clear nonlinear association.	Student chooses B and gives an explanation consistent with looking for the strongest association.	Student chooses B and gives an explanation focusing on the lack of an apparent linear association.
	b **S-ID.B.6** **S-ID.C.8**	Student does not make a consistent choice or give an explanation.	Student chooses B based on a lack of association.	Student chooses A and justifies the choice based on a strong linear association.	Student chooses C based on the dots following a clear curve.
	c **S-ID.B.6** **S-ID.C.8**	Student gets none of the answers correct (see Step 4 answer).	Student answers one of the three correctly (see Step 4 answer).	Student answers two of the three correctly (see Step 4 answer).	Student circles (1) predicted; (2) definitely; (3) higher.
	d **S-ID.B.6** **S-ID.C.8**	Student does not provide an estimate.	Student only uses Graph C with a January high of about 30°.	Student attempts to integrate information across two or more graphs but fails to provide a reasonable estimate.	Student finds a January high temperature from Graph A and then uses that with Graph C to estimate an annual snow accumulation amount.

5	a S-ID.C.7	Student focuses on the intercept.	Student reverses the role of the explanatory and response variables.	Student does not use context and/or does not interpret in terms of *predicted* time.	Student correctly addresses predicted change in time with a (one-unit) change in age (in context).
	b S-ID.B.6	Student does not define residual in terms of predicted vs. actual.	Student reverses positive and negative residuals.	Student compares predicted and actual value correctly but not in context.	Student places the actual value below the predicted value and relates it to context.
	c S-ID.B.6	Student does not interpret the model.	Student does not address the curved nature of the model.	Student discusses times decreasing and then increasing but fails to provide a justification or does not relate the justification to the graph.	Student interprets the decrease and then increase in context and discusses this in terms of the age of the runners.
	d S-ID.B.6	Student response does not address seeing how well the model fits the data.	Student does not focus on residuals.	Student focuses on residuals but does not explain how they would be used.	Student focuses on examination of residuals as a way to measure model fit and addresses whether there is a pattern to the residuals or the overall sizes of the residuals.
	e S-ID.A.2 S-ID.B.6	Student selects B, C, or D.	N/A	N/A	Student selects A and offers a response that indicates if the sum is zero, the mean must be zero, but median may not necessarily equal zero.

Name ______________________________ Date ______________

1. A recent social survey asked 654 men and 813 women to indicate how many close friends they have to talk about important issues in their lives. Below are frequency tables of the responses.

Number of Close Friends	0	1	2	3	4	5	6	Total
Males	196	135	108	100	42	40	33	654
Females	201	146	155	132	86	56	37	813

a. The shape of the distribution of the number of close friends for the males is best characterized as

(A.) Skewed to the higher values (i.e., right or positively skewed).
B. Skewed to the lower values (i.e., left or negatively skewed).
C. Symmetric.

b. Calculate the median number of close friends for the females. Show your work.

$$\frac{(813+1)}{2} = 407$$

$201 + 146 = 347 + 155 = 502$

407th observation falls in 2 columns

2 close friends

c. Do you expect the mean number of close friends for the females to be larger or smaller than the median you found in part (b), or do you expect them to be the same? Explain your choice.

Mean should be larger than median because of skewedness.

d. Do you expect the mean number of close friends for the males to be larger or smaller than the mean number of close friends for the females, or do you expect them to be the same? Explain your choice.

From 2 on, females have higher counts than males in every column. This shows that females tend to have more close friends. So, the male average is probably smaller than the female average.

2. The physician's health study examined whether physicians who took aspirin were less likely to have heart attacks than those who took a placebo (fake) treatment. The table below shows their findings.

	Placebo	Aspirin	Total
Heart Attack	189	104	293
No Heart Attack	10,845	10,933	21,778
Total	11,034	11,037	22,071

Based on the data in the table, what conclusions can be drawn about the association between taking aspirin and whether or not a heart attack occurred? Justify your conclusion using the given data.

$\frac{189}{11034} = 0.017$ $\quad$ $\frac{104}{11037} = 0.0094$

The placebo group had higher proportion of heart attacks, although both numbers are pretty small.

3. Suppose 500 high school students are asked the following two questions:

   - What is the highest degree you plan to obtain? (check one)

     ☐ High school degree ☐ College (Bachelor's degree)
     ☐ Graduate school (e.g., Master's degree or higher)

   - How many credit cards do you currently own? (check one)

     ☐ None ☐ One ☐ More than one

   Consider the data shown in the following frequency table.

	No Credit Cards	**One Credit Card**	**More Than One Credit Card**	**Total**
High School	?	y	6	59
College	120	240	40	394
Graduate School				47
Total	x	297	z	500

   Fill in the missing value in the cell in the table that is marked with a "?" so that the data would be consistent with no association between education aspiration and current number of credit cards for these students. Explain how you determined this value.

$$\frac{?}{x} = \frac{y}{297} = \frac{6}{z} = \frac{59}{500}$$

$$z = \frac{500 \times 6}{59} = 50.8 \approx 51$$

$$500 - 51 - 297 = 152$$

$$\frac{?}{152} = \frac{59}{500}$$

$$\text{So, } ? = 17.936 \approx 18$$

4. Weather data were recorded for a sample of 25 American cities in one year. Variables measured included January high temperature (in degrees Fahrenheit), January low temperature (in degrees Fahrenheit), annual precipitation (in inches), and annual snow accumulation. The relationships for three pairs of variables are shown in the graphs below (January Low Temperature—Graph A; Precipitation—Graph B; Annual Snow Accumulation—Graph C).

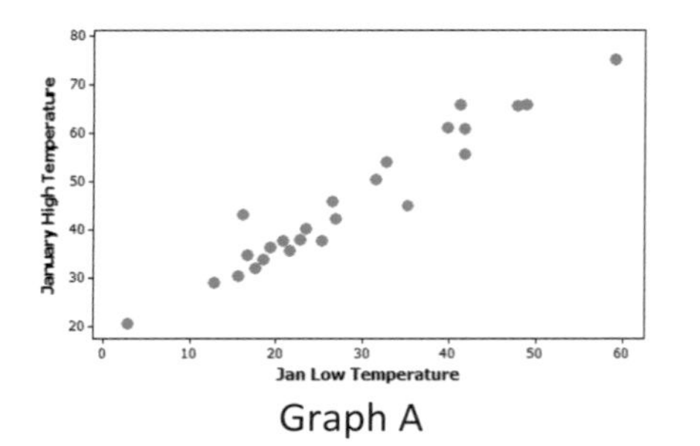

Graph A

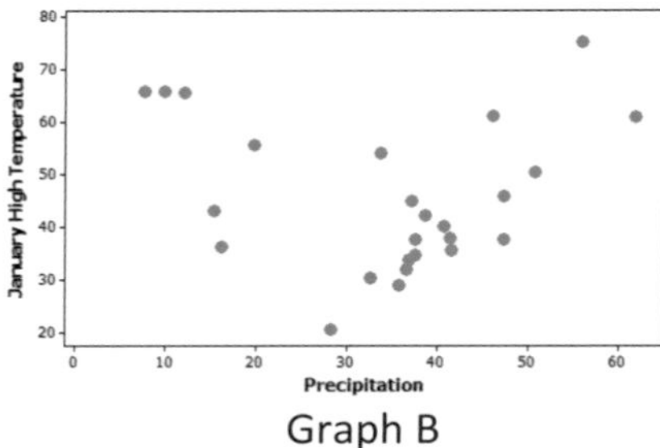

Graph B

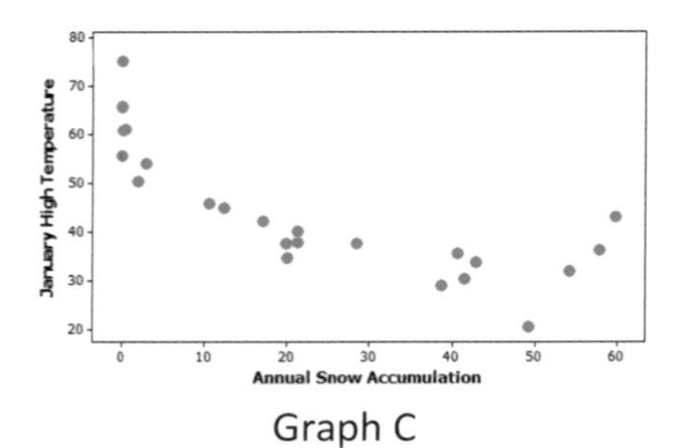

Graph C

a. Which pair of variables will have a correlation coefficient closest to 0?

A. January high temperature and January low temperature
(B.) January high temperature and precipitation
C. January high temperature and annual snow accumulation

Explain your choice: *There is not much of a linear association but lots of scatter.*

b. Which of the above scatter plots would be best described as a strong nonlinear relationship? Explain your choice.

Graph C has a strong nonlinear relationship because it has a curved pattern, and the dots follow the pattern pretty closely.

c. Suppose we fit a least squares regression line to Graph A. Circle one word choice for each blank that best completes this sentence based on the equation:

If I compare a city with a January low temperature of $30°\text{F}$ *and a city with a higher January low temperature, then the ___(1)___ January high temperature of the second city will ___(2)___ be ___(3)___.*

(1) actual, predicted — (circled: predicted) *From the equation*

(2) probably, definitely — (circled: definitely)

(3) lower, higher, the same, equally likely to be higher or lower — (circled: higher)

d. For the city with a January low temperature of $30°\text{F}$, what do you predict for the annual snow accumulation? Explain how you are estimating this based on the three graphs above.

The annual snow accumulation will be about 10 inches because January's low of 30°F corresponds to a January high of about 50°F in Graph A, which matches with 10 inches in Graph C.

5. Suppose times (in minutes) to run one mile were recorded for a sample of 100 runners ages 16–66, and the following least squares regression line was found.

Predicted time in minutes to run one mile $= 5.35 + 0.25 \times (age)$

a. Provide an interpretation in context for this slope coefficient.

For every year older that a runner is, we predict the time to run one mile to increase by 0.25 seconds.

b. Explain what it would mean in the context of this study for a runner to have a negative residual.

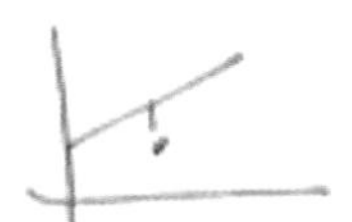

The runner was even faster (lower time) than we could have predicted for that age.

c. Suppose, instead, that someone suggests using the following curve to predict time to run one mile. Explain what this model implies about the relationship between running time and age and why that relationship might make sense in this context.

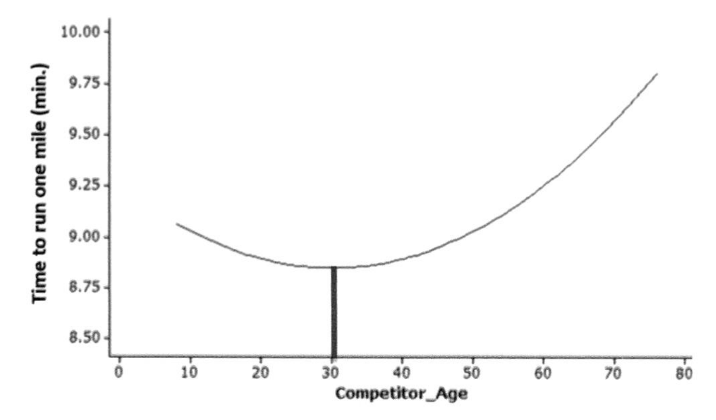

This model implies that runners get faster (lower mile times) until around age 30, when they start to slow down. In this context, the relationship might indicate that the younger runners had not trained as long as runners in their thirties, which would explain the decrease in times from age 10 to age 30. Then, as runners' ages continue to increase, their mile times also increase due to the decrease in muscle strength that comes with age.

d. Based on the results for these 100 runners, explain how you could decide whether the first model or the second model provides a better fit to the data.

Look at the residuals and see which model (straight line or curve) provides a better match to the data.

e. The sum of the residuals is always equal to zero for the least squares regression line. Which of the following must also always be equal to zero?

(A.) The mean of the residuals
B. The median of the residuals
C. Both the mean and the median of the residuals
D. Neither the mean nor the median of the residuals